W. H. Thorpe.

Jesus College.

Cambridge.
2

GROUNDWORK OF BIOPHYSICS

GROUNDWORK OF
BIOPHYSICS

BY

G. M. WISHART, B.Sc., M.D.

GRIEVE LECTURER IN PHYSIOLOGICAL CHEMISTRY AND
LECTURER IN BIOPHYSICS THE UNIVERSITY OF GLASGOW

LONDON
G. BELL AND SONS LTD
1931

Printed in Great Britain by
NEILL & CO., LTD., EDINBURGH.

PREFACE

IT often appears to the teacher of modern physiology that the student's difficulties are due to an inadequate foundation of physics and chemistry, and, more especially, of physical chemistry. The student takes these subjects in the very earliest stages of his university career, when mind and temperament are only beginning to adjust themselves to new modes of instruction. Possibly, too, he deludes himself into the belief that these are only preliminary exercises to be got up for examination purposes and forthwith forgotten. If so, his second year undeceives him.

This book does not pretend to compete with the several excellent elementary text-books on physical chemistry now available, neither can it pretend to be a manual of Biophysics. It is an attempt to aid the student by bringing within small compass those aspects of physical chemistry and of physics which he will find most necessary in his physiological studies. In such a book a selection has to be made, and no selection will meet with universal approval. Some will probably think that space has been wasted in a superfluity of detail, in, for example, the derivation of the relation between electrical potential and hydrogen-ion concentration. This detail has been given with intention, for the writer believes that the ordinary student is mentally dissatisfied with being told that certain mathematical relations exist, without being given at least some inkling why.

The first part of the book is confined to physical chemistry. In the second part the writer has attempted to deal briefly with certain sections of physiology which especially demand familiarity with physics and physical chemistry, and with which the average student experiences greatest difficulty. This section includes chapters on the cell and cell-membrane, on the action of nerves and excitability in general, on the more physical aspects of muscular action, on blood, on energy exchanges, and on the estimation of various forms of biological

v

work and efficiency.   Chapters on vision and hearing are also included, with short introductions on optics and sound.

The material has been drawn from many sources, all of which it is impossible to acknowledge.   In the physical chemistry section use has been made of the various elementary physical chemistry manuals written specially for students of biology.   In the physiological section much is, of course, derived from the standard book, Bayliss's *Principles of General Physiology*.   I must also acknowledge my indebtedness to Lovatt Evans's universally useful *Recent Advances in Physiology*, and to Hartridge's section on the eye in Starling's *Principles of Physiology*.

It is a great pleasure to express my thanks to Professor E. P. Cathcart, without whose inspiration, constant encouragement, and help this book could never have been written; and to Professor Andrew Hunter, who also very generously found time to read the manuscript closely, and made many valuable criticisms and suggestions.   The criticisms of my colleagues, Dr N. Morris, Dr R. C. Garry, and Mr J. D. Stirling, have, too, been very helpful.

To the publishers I owe much for their courteous patience and helpful advice.   They have generously allowed an abundance of diagrams.   The sources of those drawn from other publications are, I hope, all duly acknowledged both here and in their places.   A few I have modified slightly to fit the text.

G. M. W.

GLASGOW, *December* 1930.

The following authors and publishers have kindly allowed me to make use of their figures: Professor J. Barcroft, F.R.S. (figs. 25 and 26); Professor J. S. Haldane, F.R.S. (fig. 30); Professor H. H. Hartridge, F.R.S. (figs. 57 and 64); Professor A. V. Hill, F.R.S. (figs. 34, 42, 43, 44, 46, and 47); Professor Lovatt Evans, F.R.S. (figs. 10, 28, 31, 45, and 50); and Mrs. P. T. Kerridge (fig. 18). Messrs. P. Blakiston's (fig. 20); The Cambridge University Press (figs. 25 and 26); Messrs. J. & A. Churchill (figs. 10, 28, 31, 45, 57, and 64); Messrs. Longmans, Green & Co. (figs. 21 and 22); The Oxford University Press (fig. 18); Messrs. Shaw & Son (fig. 39); The University of London Press (fig. 32); The Williams & Wilkins Co. (fig. 14).

CONTENTS

CHAPTER I

THE STRUCTURE OF MATTER

ALL sciences in their infancy investigate and describe the qualitative relations of the phenomena with which they deal, and progress by becoming more and more quantitative in method. A moment's consideration of the relative precision of the laws and theories of psychology, physiology, and chemistry at the present time will bring home the working efficiency of the quantitative method. The qualitative science of chemistry is as old as ancient Egypt, if not prehistoric, but for many centuries it made little real progress because chemists developed neither technique for exact measurement nor mental avidity for numerical statement. It was the investigation of the quantitative relations of chemical combination during the latter part of the eighteenth century that ultimately led Dalton, in 1808, to bring forward his atomic hypothesis as an interpretation. The 'Law of Fixed Proportions' and the 'Law of Reciprocal Proportions' had been established. Dalton's atomic hypothesis afforded an explanation of these, and led to the deduction of a third, the 'Law of Multiple Proportions.'

While Dalton's theory provided a sound basis for the elucidation of the laws of chemical combination, and led to the useful conceptions of atomic and molecular weight, it did not go very far towards a solution of the problem of the structure of matter. There were undoubtedly feelings among the more philosophically minded that there must be some underlying similarity in the structure of the elements. It was quite unsatisfactory to suppose that the great differences in the physical and chemical properties of the elements were due in the last analysis only to differences in the *weight* of their atoms. If the differences could be correlated with variations in actual atomic structure, then a much more satisfactory position would be reached. This is what the modern electronic theory has achieved, and the amplification of Dalton's simple atomic theory by modern conceptions of the internal structure of the atom has given us a much more comprehensive picture of chemical phenomena.

Modern ideas of material structure have been developed along two lines—first, by the investigation of the relation between matter and electricity, and secondly, by the study of radio-activity.

The study of the relation of electricity to matter may be said to have begun with the classical work of Faraday on electrolysis. From his work on the decomposition of substances dissolved in water, he formulated the two following laws:—

(1) *The mass of the substance liberated at an electrode is proportional to the quantity of electricity that passes.*

(2) *The mass of a substance liberated by a current per unit time is proportional to the chemical equivalent weight of the substance.*

This second law tells us that if the same current flows through a series of solutions, say H_2SO_4, $AgNO_3$, and $CuSO_4$, there will be liberated at the anode 8 parts by weight of O_2 and at the cathode 1·008 parts of H_2, 107·9 parts of Ag and 31·8 parts of Cu. Expressed in another way, this means that if a certain quantity of electricity will liberate from a compound one gram-atom of a monovalent element, double that quantity of electricity will be necessary to liberate one gram-atom of a divalent element; that is, the quantity of electricity necessary to rupture one chemical bond is the same for all compounds. The importance of this unit quantity of electricity was realised by Johnston Stoney, who gave it the name of 'electron.' This 'electron,' which originally signified a quantity of electricity, has now taken on a new significance as a structural component of the atom.

More direct evidence that electricity is involved in material structure has been obtained from the study of the discharge produced by passing an electrical current through an evacuated tube. If a glass tube is evacuated to a pressure of about $\frac{1}{100}$ mm. Hg, and a current of sufficiently high potential is applied to two electrodes fused within the tube, the walls of the tube will become phosphorescent. Crookes came to the conclusion (1886) that this phosphorescence was due to the discharge of negatively electrified particles projected at very high speed in a direction normal to the cathode (cathode rays). In 1897 Sir J. J. Thomson made the momentous discovery that the negatively charged particles constituting the cathode rays were formed by the disintegration of the atoms of the small amount of gas that still remained in the tube. The phenomenon was the same regardless of the nature of the gas, which was conclusive evidence that the negative particles were common constituents of all atoms. These negative particles were called electrons, the name originally used by Stoney to designate a quantity of electricity.

If the tube is arranged as shown in the diagram (fig. 1), with the cathode A concave in section so as to bring the streams

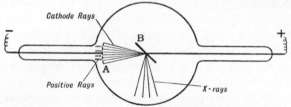

FIG. 1—Diagram to show relation of cathode rays, X-rays, and positive rays

of cathode particles to a focus at a platinum plate B set at an angle of 45° to the axis of A, it is found that the sudden stoppage of the cathode particles at B gives rise to a second kind of radiation which is projected from the plate B out through the side of the tube.

The existence of this radiation was first discovered by Röntgen in 1895. These Röntgen or X-rays consist of series of regular pulsations in the ether, similar to light-waves, but of very much shorter wave-length.

The discharge in an evacuated tube is also attended by the production of 'positive rays.' These are streams of positively charged particles, which are strongly attracted to the cathode. They also are products of atomic disruption. If the cathode plate is perforated, they pass through the holes and become evident as a violet phosphorescence behind the plate. Unlike the cathode particles, the nature of these positive particles varies with the nature of the gas in the tube.

Not only has the existence in the atom of negative and positive particles been demonstrated in this way, but (by methods which need not be gone into here) both the mass of positive and negative particles, and the electric charges on them, have been determined. The electric charge on the negative particle is found to be exactly the same as the charge on the hydrogen ion, so that the application of Stoney's term 'electrons' to such particles is justified. The ratio of the charge to mass in the electron is found to be 1845 times as great as in the hydrogen ion; so that since the charges on electron and hydrogen ion are of equal magnitude, the mass of the former must be only $\frac{1}{1845}$ of the latter. Similar determinations on the positive rays have shown that, while the particles of which they are composed all carry a positive charge equal to, or some multiple of, the negative electron charge, the mass of these positive particles differs with the nature of the gas in the tube, and, in fact, their mass is practically identical with the mass of the *atoms* of the gas. These positive particles are, indeed, atoms which have lost one or more of their electrons.

While these investigations were going on, information of a confirmatory nature was being acquired through a closer study of radio-active substances. The phosphorescence that occurs in an X-ray tube had caused Becquerel to interest himself in naturally phosphorescent substances, with the resulting discovery (1896) that uranium salts give off a radiation which affects a photographic plate, even after penetrating substances which are opaque to ordinary light. A few years later Mme. Curie found that thorium gives off a similar radiation, and that uranium minerals are much more radio-active than can be accounted for by their uranium content. She was thus led to the isolation of radium and polonium, the former of which has much the greatest radio-activity of the forty or so radio-active elements now known.

The nature of the radiations from such substances was studied in detail by Rutherford, who made the important discovery that the radiations are complex and consist of one or more of the following three components:

(1) The α-rays, which have properties similar to those of the positive rays of the vacuum tube, but have a mass approxi-

mately four times that of the hydrogen atom. Such a mass would correspond with that of the helium atom, and the identity of these α-rays with helium was subsequently proved.

(2) The β-rays, which were found to be similar to the cathode rays in almost all respects, except that they travel with a much higher velocity. Their mass was found to be about $\frac{1}{1800}$ that of hydrogen, and therefore these β-rays are apparently electrons moving at high velocity.

(3) The γ-rays, which were found to be so similar to the X-rays of the vacuum tube that they are generally regarded as identical with them. Moreover, they are only emitted where β-rays are also given off, so that they are probably a product of the latter, just as the X-rays are produced by the cathode rays in the vacuum tube.

In addition to the rays, some of the radio-active elements give off what is called an emanation, which is really a radio-active substance in gaseous form. The radio-active elements thorium, radium, and actinium all give off such emanations, but that from radium has been most studied, since it is quantitatively greatest. Many of its physical constants have been determined, that of most interest in the present discussion being its molecular weight, which is found to be 222, *i.e.* 4 less than the radium from which it is derived. Further, this radium emanation, or radon, is found to decompose spontaneously with liberation of α-rays into a radio-active solid known as radium A, and this radium A is changed by expulsion of further α-rays into a radium B, which then expels β-particles with the production of a radium C. Similar changes are undergone by thorium and actinium.

To account for these changes among the radio-active elements, the disintegration theory propounded by Rutherford and Soddy (1903) is now generally accepted. According to this theory, the radio-active elements are constantly undergoing a spontaneous transmutation into other elements, all ultimately reaching a stable end-product in lead. If the transmutation is accompanied by the expulsion of α-rays, *i.e.* helium atoms with an atomic weight of four, then the newly formed element will have an atomic weight four less than that of its parent element. If, on the other hand, the change is

RADIO-ACTIVE DISINTEGRATION

Element	Atomic weight	'Half-period'	Radiation emitted
Uranium = Radium Series			
Uranium I . . .	238	$4 \cdot 5 \times 10^9$ years	α
Uranium X_1 . .	234	23·8 days	$\beta \cdot \gamma$
Uranium X_2 . .	234	1·15 minutes	$\beta \cdot \gamma$
Uranium Z . . .	234	6·7 hours	β
Uranium II . .	234	$2 \cdot 0 \times 10^6$ years	α
Uranium Y . . .	230	24·6 hours	β
Ionium . . .	230	$9 \cdot 0 \times 10^4$ years	α
Radium . . .	226	1580 years	α
Radon . . . (Radium emanation)	222	3·82 days	α
Radium A . . .	218	3·05 minutes	α
Radium B . . .	214	26·8 ,,	$\beta \cdot \gamma$
Radium C . . .	214	19·7 ,,	$\alpha . \beta . \gamma$
Radium D . . .	210	16·0 years	$\beta \cdot \gamma$
Radium E . . .	210	5·0 days	$\beta \cdot \gamma$
Radium F . . . (Polonium)	210	136·5 days	α
Radium G . . . (end-product uranium-lead)	206	infinite	..
Thorium Series			
Thorium . . .	232	$2 \cdot 2 \times 10^{10}$ years	α
Mesothorium I . .	228	6·7 years	$\beta \cdot \gamma$
Mesothorium II . .	228	6·2 hours	$\beta \cdot \gamma$
Radiothorium . .	228	1·90 years	α
Thorium X . .	224	3·64 days	α
Thoron . . . (Thorium emanation)	220	54 seconds	α
Thorium A . .	216	0·14 second	α
Thorium B . .	212	10·6 hours	$\beta \cdot \gamma$
Thorium C . .	212	60 minutes	α
Thorium C" . .	208	3·2 ,,	$\beta \cdot \gamma$
Thorium D . . (end-product thorium-lead)	208	infinite	..

Element	Atomic weight	'Half-period'	Radiation emitted
Actinium Series			
Protoactinium . .	230	10^4 years	α
Actinium . . .	226	20 ,,	β
Radioactinium . .	226	19 days	α
Actinium X . .	222	11·2 days	α
Actinon . . .	218	3·9 seconds	α
(Actinium emanation)			
Actinium A . .	214	0·002 second	α
Actinium B . .	210	36 minutes	$\beta.\gamma$
Actinium C . .	210	2·16 ,,	α
Actinium C″ . .	206	4·76 ,,	$\beta.\gamma$
Actinium D . .	206	infinite	..
(end-product actinium-lead)			

(Rutherford)

accompanied by the expulsion of only β-particles, *i.e.* electrons, which are of negligible mass, the atomic weight of the new element will be the same as that of the parent element. The γ-rays, being non-material and only a product of the expulsion of β-particles, will not of themselves have any influence in changing the characteristics of the element.

The time involved in these radio-activity changes varies very greatly with the different elements. Moreover, if we consider any one radio-active transformation, the velocity of change is proportional to the amount of substance undergoing that change. Therefore, if one starts with a definite quantity of radium emanation, the rapidity of change of the emanation into radium A will be very great at first, but will diminish as the amount of unchanged emanation becomes smaller. As such a change would theoretically never reach absolute completion, it is usual to state the duration of any particular radio-active transformation in 'half-periods,' *i.e.* the length of time required for half of the original quantity of the parent element to decompose. The above table shows the radio-active transmutations undergone by the various radio-active elements, their relation to one another, their atomic weights, their 'half-periods,' and the character of the radiation given off at each step.

Mainly from these two lines of investigation, the study of the artificial disruption of atoms by electrical discharges, and of the natural atomic disruptions that are going on in radio-active substances, physicists have been led to the following conception of atomic structure.

The atoms of all elements are essentially electrical in structure. Each consists of a positively charged nucleus whose mass is practically that of the whole atom. Surrounding this nucleus are one or more negatively charged particles—electrons—whose mass relative to that of the nucleus is negligible. Since the atoms, unless disturbed in some way, are electrically neutral, the positive charge on the nucleus must be balanced by the total negative charges of its surrounding electrons. In the investigation of atoms disrupted by the electric discharge, no positively charged particle has been so far discovered with a mass less than that of the hydrogen ion, so that the assumption is made that, in hydrogen, the lightest atom, we have a nucleus composed only of the unit positive charge of electricity (proton), this positive charge being balanced by one external electron. The atoms of all the other elements are constructed on a similar plan, but are constituted by more than one proton and more than one extranuclear electron. (As we shall presently see, in all atoms except hydrogen there are a number of intranuclear electrons in addition to the extranuclear ones.)

Now, when the elements are arranged in order of increasing atomic weight and numbered according to their position in the series, this 'atomic number' is found among the lower members of the series to be approximately half the atomic weight. The atomic number thus appeared to have some structural significance, and experiments by Rutherford on the deflection of the positively charged α-rays by certain metals indicated that the atomic number of an element was identical with its nuclear charge. This identity was confirmed by Moseley's important discovery, that the square root of the frequency of the main lines in the X-ray spectra of the different elements increased by regular steps with each unit increase of atomic number.

Since the protons are almost entirely responsible for the mass of the atom, it is obvious that there must be in the nucleus a number of protons at least approximately equal to the atomic weight. But this in all elements, with the exception of hydrogen, would give a nuclear positive charge in excess of that presumed to exist from their atomic number. Therefore, associated with the nuclei of all atoms, except that of hydrogen, there are believed to be a number of *nuclear* electrons sufficient to reduce the nuclear charge to the value demanded by the atomic number, without essentially altering its mass. These electrons are component parts of the nuclei and are to be distinguished from the surrounding 'planetary' electrons, which determine the chemical characters of the particular atom. The atom being electrically neutral, the number of extranuclear electrons must be equivalent to the atomic number.

Thus, as we pass up the series of atoms of progressively increasing weight, the nuclei are composed of more and more protons associated with a number of nuclear electrons which, however, only partially balance the aggregate positive charge on all the protons. The net positive charges still left on the nucleus are annulled by the negative charges on the extranuclear electrons.

Now the periodic recurrence of similar properties with increasing atomic weight suggests that there must be some recurring similarity in the grouping of the planetary electrons. We may get a rudimentary idea of this electronic grouping from the following outline of the 'octet' theory of Lewis and Langmuir, which, though it is now superseded, serves very well as a simple introduction.

With increasing atomic number, the increasing numbers of planetary electrons are arranged in a series of concentric shells. The first shell contains as a maximum 2 electrons, the second shell is formed in its completed condition by two groups of 8, the third shell when complete contains two groups of 18, and the fourth shell, two groups of 32 electrons. Thus hydrogen has one electron occupying a position in the first shell;

in helium this shell is completed by the addition of a second electron. With the next element, lithium, begins the formation of the first group of the second shell, which is completed when we reach the element neon. The second group of this shell begins with sodium, and is completed in the element argon, and so on, until in uranium, the heaviest atom, we have all these inner shells and the first group of 32 in the fourth shell complete, and, in addition, 6 electrons in the second group of the fourth shell. The table on opposite page will perhaps make these points clearer. Only the first three and part of the fourth periods of the periodic table have been included, but the reader can readily imagine its extension.

The value of such theories may be indicated by a few considerations and examples:

(1) The atoms with completed shells of electrons, being in a comparatively stable condition, should be chemically inert, and, as may be seen from the table, the elements with this structure are the inert gases of the atmosphere, and fall into the zero group.

(2) The valency of an element is determined by the number of electrons by which it is either short of, or in excess of, the stable condition of a completed shell. For example, sodium and chlorine are each monovalent—sodium because it has one electron in excess of the stable condition, and chlorine because it has one electron less than the number required to make a stable atomic structure.

(3) Sodium and chlorine are both highly reactive elements— that is, their electronic pattern is unstable; by their combination a stable molecule, NaCl, is produced, the extra sodium electron filling the place of the electron lacking in the chlorine atom. Combination of such atoms, therefore, occurs very readily. A point may be noted here in passing for the light that it throws upon electrolytic dissociation. In the molecule of such a compound as NaCl, the sodium as a component of the molecule has an excess of positive electricity, having lost an electron, while the chlorine component has an excess of negative electricity, having gained an electron.

(4) While many atomic combinations are explicable by a direct transference of electrons, as in our sodium and chlorine

	Group 0	Group 1	Group 2	Group 3	Group 4	Group 5	Group 6	Group 7
Name	⋮	Hydrogen						
Constitution of nucleus	⋮	$1p$						
Atomic No.	⋮	1						
No. and arrangement of electrons	⋮	$(1)^1$						
Atomic weight		1·008						
Name	Helium	Lithium	Beryllium	Boron	Carbon	Nitrogen	Oxygen	Fluorine
Constitution of nucleus	$4p+2e$	$7p+4e$	$9p+5e$	$11p+6e$	$12p+6e$	$14p+7e$	$16p+8e$	$19p+10e$
Atomic No.	2	3	4	5	6	7	8	9
No. and arrangement of electrons	$(2)^1$	$(2)^1+(1)^{2a}$	$(2)^1+(2)^{2a}$	$(2)^1+(3)^{2a}$	$(2)^1+(4)^{2a}$	$(2)^1+(5)^{2a}$	$(2)^1+(6)^{2a}$	$(2)^1+(7)^{2a}$
Atomic weight	4·00	6·94	9·02	10·82	12·00	14·01	16·00	19·00
Name	Neon	Sodium	Magnesium	Aluminium	Silicon	Phosphorus	Sulphur	Chlorine
Constitution of nucleus	$20p+10e$	$23p+12e$	$24p+12e$	$27p+14e$	$28p+14e$	$31p+16e$	$32p+16e$	$35p+18e$
Atomic No.	10	11	12	13	14	15	16	17
No. and arrangement of electrons	$(2)^1+(8)^{2a}$	$(2)^1+(8)^{2a}+(1)^{2b}$	$(2)^1+(8)^{2a}+(2)^{2b}$	$(2)^1+(8)^{2a}+(3)^{2b}$	$(2)^1+(8)^{2a}+(4)^{2b}$	$(2)^1+(8)^{2a}+(5)^{2b}$	$(2)^1+(8)^{2a}+(6)^{2b}$	$(2)^1+(8)^{2a}+(7)^{2b}$
Atomic weight	20·2	23·00	24·32	27·00	28·3	31·04	32·07	35·46
Name	Argon	Potassium	Calcium	Scandium	Titanium	Vanadium	Chromium	Manganese
Constitution of nucleus	$39p+21e$	$39p+20e$	$40p+20e$	$45p+24e$	$48p+26e$	$51p+28e$	$52p+28e$	$55p+30e$
Atomic No.	18	19	20	21	22	23	24	25
No. and arrangement of electrons	$(2)^1+(8)^{2a}+(8)^{2b}$	$(2)^1+(8)^{2a}+(8)^{2b}+(1)^{3a}$	$(2)^1+(8)^{2a}+(8)^{2b}+(2)^{3a}$	$(2)^1+(8)^{2a}+(8)^{2b}+(3)^{3a}$	$(2)^1+(8)^{2a}+(8)^{2b}+(4)^{3a}$	$(2)^1+(8)^{2a}+(8)^{2b}+(5)^{3a}$	$(2)^1+(8)^{2a}+(8)^{2b}+(6)^{3a}$	$(2)^1+(8)^{2a}+(8)^{2b}+(7)^{3a}$
Atomic weight	39·88	39·10	40·07	45·1	48·1	51·0	52·0	54·93

p = proton.
e = electron.
$(\ )^1$ = first shell of planetary electrons.

$(\ )^{2a}$ = first group of second shell.
$(\ )^{2b}$ = second group of second shell.
$(\ )^{3a}$ = first group of third shell.

example, others may be explained on the basis of a sharing of electrons. As an example of this we may take the combination of two atoms of oxygen to form an oxygen molecule. Each oxygen atom has six electrons in the second shell (see table). If we assume, for the purpose of pictorial representation, that the completed shell of electrons would have its component electrons placed at the corners of a cube surrounding the nucleus, then two oxygen atoms could combine together, forming two such cubes, by sharing two of their electrons with each other. In this way each atom, as a component of the molecule, has now a complete shell of eight electrons. Note that, in molecules formed by the sharing of electrons, the electrical balance of the component atoms is not disturbed.

CHAPTER II
ENERGY

WORK, in the mechanical sense, is the product of the force and the distance through which it acts in the direction of the force, e.g. the work of lifting a weight is equal to the force of gravity acting on the weight, multiplied by the distance through which it is raised. In this case the work is the direct result of the expenditure of a certain amount of energy of motion, or kinetic energy. There are other familiar forms of energy, such as heat and electrical energy, which by suitable machines can be converted into mechanical work, and this is also true of less familiar types, such as the energy of gas under pressure, surface energy, chemical and radiant energy.

These other types of energy are not at first sight energy of motion, but require some sort of conversion machine to transform their energy into an obviously kinetic form; yet, in the ultimate analysis, all forms of energy are energy of motion. In the previous chapter we have seen how the component atoms of the molecules are centres of electronic motion. According to the universally accepted kinetic theory, the molecules of all matter are also in a state of ceaseless movement, the energy of this movement varying directly with the temperature of the substance, and becoming theoretically nil at absolute zero ($-273°$ C.). Matter, though it may appear inert, particularly in the solid state, would present the liveliest whirl of electronic and molecular activity if it were within our power to see its infinitesimally small components. Now heat is nothing but the external manifestation of random molecular motion; electrical energy is the external manifestation of an orderly movement of electrons; chemical energy is possessed by certain substances in virtue of a comparatively unstable arrangement of electrons within their molecules, and is liberated when these electrons move to take up more stable positions; radiant energy is a recurrent ethereal disturbance produced by

13

intra-atomic transposition of electrons; in short, all forms of energy are motion.

Energy is the capacity for work, and no change can occur in our universe without the performance of work. When we observe a change taking place, what we are observing is the liberation, and often the change of form, of some energy. Moreover, since the molecular activity of matter is zero only at a temperature of $-273°$ C., and the temperature of our environment is much above this, the energy changes that we commonly observe are changes above a base-line at which all materials still possess a very large quantity of energy. We have no knowledge of the total energy content of substances, our observations being limited to the changes that occur above the energy level of our surroundings. This is a most important point, as will subsequently emerge.

First and Second Laws of Thermodynamics –There are two great statements which are found to be universally true of changes of energy from one form to another. These statements of fact are called the First and Second Laws of Thermodynamics, since they were first evolved mainly from observations of heat energy.

The first law was formulated by Mayer in 1842 as follows: " When a quantity of energy disappears in any form, a precisely equivalent quantity simultaneously appears in some other form or forms"; or, as Clausius stated it: "The energy content of the universe is a constant quantity." To take a practical example, an electric motor is supplied with a certain amount of electrical energy; this energy is transformed partly into energy of motion in the rotating pulley, and partly into heat energy in the field and armature coils, owing to their electrical resistance, and in the bearings, owing to the friction of the rotating shaft. If the output of energy from the motor in these various forms is accurately measured, the total amount is found to balance exactly the input of energy in electrical form. The disappearance of the electrical energy has been accompanied by the appearance of an equal amount of energy in the form of motion and heat, exactly as the first law states.

Not all the input of energy, however, is available for the

performance of useful work, but only that part which is converted into motion at the pulley. The remainder, the heat quota, is lost by conduction to the surroundings, and is of no value as far as work is concerned. It serves only to raise slightly the temperature of the immediate environment, this in turn raising the temperature of a wider environment by a smaller amount, until ultimately the heat is distributed over such a wide area that its effect in raising the temperature is unrecognisable. Helmholtz introduced the words 'free' and 'bound' to distinguish between energy at a high potential, and therefore capable of performing work, and energy which, already dissipated to heat, is incapable of further work.

The *efficiency* of any energy-transforming machine is the ratio of output of useful energy to total input of energy:

$$\text{Efficiency} = \frac{\text{Energy available for useful work}}{\text{Energy input}}.$$

In the electric motor, in addition to the loss of energy by friction and heating of the field and armature, the energy of motion developed could also be converted to heat by the friction of a brake applied to the pulley. In these circumstances, all the input of electrical energy would be transformed to heat. This complete conversion to heat is possible not only with electrical energy but with all forms of energy. On the other hand, it is impossible to convert heat entirely into other types of energy. The reason for this lies in a difference in the intrinsic nature of the energy in the two cases. In heat energy we are dealing with a chaotic and inco-ordinate motion of the molecules of matter, while in the other forms of energy we are dealing with a motion wholly or partially co-ordinated. For example, in the kinetic energy of a rotating pulley, the molecules of the metal of the pulley are, as a whole, moving in a definite direction—the direction of the rotation. In the passage of an electric current along a wire, we are dealing with a stream of electrons which are all moving in one direction, or at least the resultant of the motions of the electrons is in this direction. Again, in the expansion of a compressed gas, while each molecule of gas considered by itself is moving in an apparently random manner, there is a predominant tendency to move in the direction in which expansion is being allowed.

But in the conversion of heat to work the problem is that of converting unordered molecular kinetic energy into ordered kinetic energy. To do this we have to slow down the kinetic energy of the molecules as a whole, that is, to reduce their average kinetic energy, and in so doing we perforce lower the temperature of the body from which the heat energy is to be derived. While such lowering of temperature spontaneously occurs in a body above the temperature of its environment, its cooling below the environmental temperature can only be brought about by doing work upon it. To derive work from a substance already at the temperature of its surroundings would thus require the performance of an equal amount of work upon it.

This is the principle formulated in the Second Law of Thermodynamics, which deals with the restrictions under which transformations of heat to mechanical work can occur. It has been stated in various ways, each of which emphasises a particular aspect of the restriction of the heat-work trans-formation, but we may confine our attention to the state-ment of Clausius that "the entropy of the universe is always striving towards a maximum." This statement is rather a deduction from, than a direct expression of, the second law. In it 'entropy' is practically synonymous with the 'bound' energy of Helmholtz, and therefore the statement of Clausius could equally well be rendered as "the free energy of the universe is always tending towards a minimum." This 'principle of Carnot and Clausius' is a most important one. The tendency of energy at a higher potential to run down to a dead level of heat is one of the most striking phenomena of our universe. It is the constant principle which underlies the innumerable empirical judgments of craftsmen in all ages, and justifies the most deliberate prediction of the modern physical chemist, when he declares that any process which would result in diminution of free energy will certainly be found to take place. In its application to surface-tension phenomena, this is known as the Gibbs-Thomson principle (p. 38).

A brief word may be said of the quantitative aspect of the

transformation of heat energy. To obtain the whole of the heat energy resident in a substance, it is obvious that its temperature would have to be reduced to absolute zero. But except under specially devised conditions, the cooling of a hot substance ceases when it has reached the temperature of our environment, say 15° C. During this cooling only a portion of its heat energy has been evolved, a portion which will be represented by the ratio between the range of temperature through which it actually did cool, to the range through which it would cool if the process went on to the absolute zero. For example, a substance originally at 100° C. and cooling to an environmental temperature of 15° C. would liberate only $\frac{373-288}{373}$ of its total heat energy. The thermal efficiency of a heat engine is thus in general $\frac{T_1-T_2}{T_1}$, where T_1 is the absolute temperature of the steam or other material used as the 'working-substance' of the engine, and T_2 the absolute temperature to which it is cooled, *i.e.*, in the steam-engine, the temperature of the condenser. It is plain, since T_2 must always have a very considerable magnitude, that the pure thermal efficiency of a heat engine can never be very high.

Measurement of Energy – Since we know of energy only through its performance of work, measurements of energy must obviously be in work units, and the performance of work on examination is found to be dependent on two factors—a *capacity* factor and an *intensity* factor. For example, the energy to be derived from a waterfall depends partly on the volume of water per unit time (the capacity factor) and partly on the height of the fall (the intensity factor). Similarly, the energy of a compressed gas depends on a capacity factor (volume) and an intensity factor (pressure). In electrical energy the capacity factor is quantity (coulomb) and the intensity factor, potential (volt). Heat energy depends on the heat capacity of a substance (=mass × specific heat), and its intensity factor is temperature; while the capacity and intensity factors of kinetic energy are obviously mass and velocity. When we seek the corresponding factors in chemical energy, it is apparent

2

that the capacity factor will be the mass of substance entering into chemical combination, that is, the *equivalent weight* of the substance, but the intensity factor is not at once so evident. However, if we consider the direct transformation of chemical energy into electrical energy in a voltaic cell, and remember that Faraday found that the amount of chemical change and the quantity of electrical energy generated are proportional, so that the capacity factors of these two types of energy are closely related to one another, it appears that there must be a chemical potential analogous to electrical potential. A difference in chemical potential between the reacting substances and their products will determine the occurrence of a chemical reaction, just as differences of electrical potential must exist before a flow of current takes place. The magnitude of the difference of chemical potential determines the reactivity of substances. Chemical potential is what used to be called 'chemical affinity,' a vague old metaphorical term which may well be dropped now that the electronic theory has given us a clearer concept of chemical reactivity.

Transformations of chemical energy are, of course, no exceptions to the First Law of Thermodynamics, and, in 1840, before Mayer's formulation of this general principle, Hess, from experiments on chemical combination, had come to the conclusion that "the amount of heat generated by a chemical reaction is the same whether it takes place all at once or in steps." This, which we now realise to be a particular case of the First Law of Thermodynamics, is called Hess's Law, and is of practical utility in physiology, for it justifies our estimation of the heat of combustion of substances within the body by burning them outside the body to the same end-products, though the intermediate substances formed in the two cases may be entirely different.

Since the disappearance of energy in any one form is accompanied by the appearance of an exactly equal quantity of energy in another, the various units in which energy is measured must be convertible one into another by using the appropriate numerical factor.

It may be well at this point to remind the reader of the derivation and interrelationship of the more important physical units. From the three fundamental units of mass, length, and time all the other units may be derived. When the derived units bear the simplest possible relationship to the fundamental units, the system is known as an *absolute* system. Thus there is an absolute system derived from the fundamental units of the gram, the centimetre, and the second (C.G.S. system), and another absolute system derived from the foot, pound, and second. In addition, in many branches of physics other units have been introduced which are specially suitable for technical and practical purposes. We shall briefly review some of the more important C.G.S. units and a few of the practical units that are in common use.

Work, in the mechanical sense, is the product of the force and the distance through which it acts.

Dyne – The unit of force is the dyne; it is the force required to give unit mass (1 grm.), unit acceleration (1 cm. per sec. per sec.).

Erg – The work which is done when 1 dyne acts through a distance of 1 cm. Since the erg is an extremely small unit of work, the

Joule, which is equivalent to 10^7 ergs, is often used.

Mechanical work is also frequently measured by the distance through which a weight is raised against the force of gravity, *e.g.* in kilogrammetres. The force of gravity being 981 dynes,

$$1 \; kilogrammetre = 981 \times 1000 \times 100 = 9 \cdot 81 \times 10^7 \text{ ergs}$$
$$= 9 \cdot 81 \text{ joules.}$$

For electrical measurements we have two sets of derived units, according as we are dealing with the forces of electrostatic repulsion and attraction, or with electric currents produced by the ordered motion of electrons in a conductor.

The C.G.S. Electrostatic Unit of Quantity or Unit Charge is that quantity of electricity which, at 1 cm. distance in air, exerts a force of 1 dyne over an equal quantity, and the

C.G.S. Electrostatic Unit Difference of Potential exists between two points when 1 erg of work is done in the movement of a C.G.S. electrostatic charge from the one point to the other point. Electrical energy measured as the product of these two units is therefore in ergs.

In dealing with electric currents, the

C.G.S. Electromagnetic Unit of Current is defined in terms of the force of the magnetic field produced by the current under certain prescribed conditions. More commonly used, however, as a practical unit of current is the

Ampere, which is one-tenth of the C.G.S. unit.

Neither of these units of current denotes a quantity of electricity, but a rate of flow of electricity. To express quantity either must be multiplied by the time during which the current is passing. The

C.G.S. Electromagnetic Unit of Quantity of electricity is that quantity which, in each second, passes through every cross-section of a linear conductor which carries a steady current of one C.G.S. electromagnetic unit strength. The common unit of quantity is the

Coulomb, which is the quantity of electricity passing any section of a conductor in 1 second when a current of 1 ampere is flowing; hence coulombs=amperes × seconds. The coulomb $=3 \times 10^9$ electrostatic units of quantity. Again, for practical purposes, differences of potential are measured in

Volts – The volt is $\frac{1}{300}$ of the electrostatic unit of potential difference. From these relations we have, therefore, that

$$\begin{array}{ccc} \text{Volts} & \times \quad \text{Coulombs} & = \quad \text{Joules} \\ (\frac{1}{300}\ \text{E.S.U.}) & (3 \times 10^9\ \text{E.S.U.}) & (10^7\ \text{ergs}). \end{array}$$

In heat units, the

Small calorie and the Large Calorie (Kilocalorie) are the amounts of heat required to raise the temperature of respectively 1 grm. or 1 kg. of water by 1° C., or, to be more precise, from 14·5° C. to 15·5° C.

The relation between mechanical work and heat was first investigated by Joule, and the symbol J is used to denote the mechanical equivalent of heat—that is, the number of work units equivalent to one heat unit. When expressed as kilogrammetres per large Calorie,

J=426·6. From this we have that

1 Calorie$=426\cdot6$ kg.-mt. $=4184\cdot9 \times 10^7$ ergs$=4184\cdot9$ joules.

In dealing with gases, energy is measured by the product of an intensity factor (pressure) and a capacity factor (volume). Since these are usually measured in atmospheres and litres, we have another unit of energy and of work in the

Litre-Atmosphere – The relation of this unit to ergs is shown by the following:

$$1 \text{ atmosphere} = \text{pressure of 76 cm. column of mercury.}$$
$$= 1033 \text{ grm. per sq. cm.}$$
$$1 \text{ litre-atmosphere} = 1000 \text{ c.cm.} \times 1033 \frac{\text{grm.}}{\text{sq. cm.}}$$
$$= 1033 \times 10^3 \text{ grm. cm.}$$
$$= 1033 \times 10^3 \times 981 \text{ ergs.}$$
$$= 101\cdot34 \times 10^7 \text{ ergs.}$$
$$= 101\cdot34 \text{ joules.}$$
$$= 0\cdot024 \text{ Calories.}$$

Power measures the rate at which work is done. In the foot-pound-second system the unit of power is the horse-power. The C.G.S. unit is the

Watt – The watt is equivalent to 1 joule per second. Since joules$=$coulombs $\times$ volts, and coulombs$=$amperes $\times$ seconds, it is evident that joules per second, or watts, will be given directly by amperes $\times$ volts.

CHAPTER III

GASES

EVERYBODY knows that matter may appear in three different forms, or states of aggregation, solid, liquid, and gaseous, and that a particular substance may change its state of aggregation with changing temperatures, as when ice passes through water to steam when the temperature (at atmospheric pressure) rises from 0° C. to 100° C. When a solid passes into a liquid the change in volume is relatively small, but when a liquid changes into a gas the increase in volume is very great and the resulting gas is very compressible. This compressibility makes it obvious that matter in gaseous form cannot be continuous, but must be dispersed throughout the occupied space in extremely small particles, separated from one another by spaces very large in proportion to the particles themselves. That liquids and solids are also particulate in structure is a less obvious but equally well-grounded induction.

A gas rapidly escapes from an open vessel containing it— that is, it tends to occupy any space offered to it. The particles must therefore be in constant motion in all directions. As a result of their constant chaotic motion they must be continually colliding with one another and with the walls of the containing vessel, and, as the motion continues in spite of these constant collisions, we must suppose that the particles are perfectly elastic, since otherwise their motion would soon be diminished to zero and they would settle. The pressure exerted by a gas on the walls of the containing vessel is simply the resultant of the constant bombardment of these walls by the rapidly moving particles of which the gas is composed. This theory of the discontinuous particulate structure of matter, having all its particles in rapid motion, is known as the 'kinetic theory,' and was first propounded for gases by Bernouilli in 1738, and subsequently developed and extended by Waterston, Clausius, Clerk Maxwell, and others. Since the kinetic theory has accounted satisfactorily for the observed facts not only of gases but also of liquids and solids, it is of such importance that we must look into its implications in greater detail.

Consider a definite volume of a gas. This volume of gas will contain a certain number of particles (usually molecules) in random motion, colliding with one another and with the walls of the containing vessel, thus producing a pressure on the vessel walls. At ordinary pressures and temperatures the molecules are widely separated from one another, because by their continual energetic collision and jostling they push each other apart. Now the random character of the motion means that the distance of any one molecule from its neighbour will be constantly varying from moment to moment, and the interval of time and the distance travelled between any two successive collisions will also vary. However, under fixed conditions of pressure and temperature, and over a period of time involving many collisions, the average distance travelled between one collision and the next will be the same for all the molecules of the gas. This average distance is called the 'mean free path' of the molecules. Again, since every mass of matter attracts every other mass of matter, there must be a mutual attraction between the molecules. In a gas at ordinary pressures and temperatures, however, this mutual attraction is negligible, because the average distances between the molecules are so very great in comparison with the size of the molecules themselves.

Let us suppose, now, that our volume of gas is heated; the heat energy will serve to increase the kinetic energy of the molecules, and one of two things will happen. If we imagine the walls of the containing vessel to be perfectly elastic, the more energetic jostling among the molecules will increase the distances between them—i.e. the mean free path will be increased and the gas as a whole will expand. On the other hand, if the containing vessel is rigid, no expansion is possible, and the increased kinetic energy will manifest itself in increased force of collision among the molecules themselves and against the containing-vessel walls—i.e. the pressure will increase. It is well to note that, while the pressure of the gas as ordinarily measured is the resultant of the impacts of all the molecules at the *surface* of the gas, a similar pressure must exist among the molecules in the interior. In gases under certain conditions this intrinsic or internal bombardment pressure may be much higher than the pressure superficially exerted, and in liquids it is normally so.

Cooling the volume of gas will reverse these effects. If the cooling is carried on under conditions allowing of contraction in volume, the molecules will come closer and closer together with the progressive reduction in their kinetic energy. Their mutual attractive force will increase, and therefore the internal bombardment pressure will become progressively higher than the pressure manifest externally. With still further shrinking of volume a point will come at which the effect of constant collision in separating the molecules is overbalanced by their mutual attraction. When this point is reached the substance, previously gaseous, becomes liquid. It has now lost the gaseous property of diffusing equally through all available space, and the external pressure which it manifests is limited to the comparatively small vapour-pressure. This vapour-pressure is produced by the few molecules at the surface, which happen by their position and direction of motion to escape from the attraction of their fellows into the surrounding atmosphere. Because of the mutual attraction of its molecules, a liquid forms a coherent but readily deformable mass, and because of the proximity of one molecule to another, it is relatively incompressible.

Further cooling of the substance, now in the liquid state, will result in such a close approximation of the molecules that, though they still vibrate, they are practically unable to wander among one another; the substance has now passed into the solid state. If in this state of aggregation the molecules are definitely orientated to one another, the solid assumes a crystalline form, whereas if the arrangement is irregular, the solid is amorphous.

These changes of state have been described as the result of lowering the temperature of a substance, but it is obvious that theoretically it would be possible to produce similar changes by progressive increase of pressure externally applied, and within certain limits this is true in practice. However, above a certain temperature, which varies with different gases but is characteristic for each gas, it is impossible by increase of pressure, no matter how great, to condense the gas to a liquid. This limiting temperature is known as the critical temperature, and the pressure necessary to produce liquefaction at this critical temperature is known as the critical pressure.

The Gas Laws – We must now consider some of the fundamental laws of the behaviour of gases.

The first of the gas laws, as enunciated by Robert Boyle in 1662, states that "at constant temperature the pressure of a gas is inversely proportional to the volume"—that is, if the pressure is doubled the volume is halved, and *vice versa*. Expressed in another way, the law means that the product of pressure and volume is constant provided the temperature remains constant —in symbols :

$$pv = \text{constant} \qquad . \qquad . \qquad . \qquad (1)$$

The second law, Charles's or Gay Lussac's (1802), states that "the volume of a given quantity of gas is directly proportional to its *absolute* temperature, provided the pressure remains constant." Gay Lussac derived this generalisation from his experimental finding that the volume at 0° C. of any gas is increased by $\frac{1}{273}$ part for every degree C. of rise of temperature —in symbols:

$$v_1 = v_0 \left(1 + \frac{1}{273} t \right) \qquad . \qquad . \qquad . \qquad (2)$$

where v_1 is the volume at $t°$ C., and v_0 the volume of the same mass of gas at 0° C.

Provided the volume is kept constant, a similar relation holds for the increase of pressure with rising temperature, *i.e.*

$$p_1 = p_0 \left(1 + \frac{1}{273} t \right) \qquad . \qquad . \qquad . \qquad (3)$$

If the gas is cooled below 0° C. a similar diminution of $\frac{1}{273}$ per degree in volume at constant pressure, or in pressure at constant volume, will occur. This means that theoretically the volume and pressure of a gas would be annihilated at −273° C., and hence this temperature is known as the absolute

zero.   In physical chemistry temperatures are usually referred
to this zero instead of to 0° C.

Now if we take the above formulæ and substitute for t
(the temperature measured with reference to 0° C.), T (the
temperature measured from absolute zero), the two formulæ
become

$$v_1 = v_0\left(\frac{T}{273}\right) \qquad . \qquad . \qquad . \qquad (4)$$

and

$$p_1 = p_0\left(\frac{T}{273}\right) \qquad . \qquad . \qquad . \qquad (5)$$

Finally, under conditions in which the temperature is changed
and both pressure and volume are allowed to alter simultaneously, by combining the relations expressed in equations
(4) and (5) above, it can be shown that

$$PV = \frac{p_0 v_0}{273} T \qquad . \qquad . \qquad . \qquad (6)$$

where P and V are the values of the pressure and volume
at the absolute temperature T, and p_0 and v_0 are respectively
the pressure and volume of the same mass of gas at 0° C.

Leaving this equation for a moment, let us recall the third
great law of gas behaviour, that of Avogadro (1811), which
states that "all gases under the same conditions of temperature
and pressure contain in unit volume the same number of
molecules," or, differently expressed, "the gram-molecular
weights (*i.e.* molecular weight in grams) of all gases will
occupy the same volume under the same conditions of temperature and pressure."   We return to equation (6) with Avogadro's
law in mind.   It is evident that, however many different gases
we take, provided that we take a mass of each related to the
mass of the others in the same ratio as their molecular weights,
$\frac{p_0 v_0}{273}$ will be the same for them all.   When, therefore, 1 gram-

molecule or 'mole' is the mass of gas being considered, $\frac{p_0 v_0}{273}$

will have for all gases a certain value depending only on the

units in which pressure and volume are measured, and this
value of $\frac{p_0 v_0}{273}$ is usually designated R, the very important 'gas
constant.' The equation then reads PV=RT, the form in
which it is usually stated. The gas constant R is thus the
coefficient of increase or diminution with the absolute temperature of the product of the pressure and volume of 1 mole of
any gas.

Measuring pressure in atmospheres and volume in litres, as
is commonly done, what will be the value of R? Careful
experiment has established the fact that 1 mole of gas at 0° C.
and 1 atmosphere pressure (*i.e.* at normal temperature and
pressure, or N.T.P.) occupies a volume of 22·4 litres. Under
N.T.P. conditions, therefore, $p_0 v_0 = 22 \cdot 4$, and $\frac{p_0 v_0}{273}$ or $R = \frac{22 \cdot 4}{273}$
or 0·082. Therefore PV=0·082T. This equation refers to
1 mole of gas, but obviously can be made to refer to any weight
of gas by expressing the weight in moles (*n*) and using the
equation PV=$n \times 0 \cdot 082$T, or more generally, for any units of
measurement of P and V, PV=nRT. This equation is a most
important one to many sciences, and it will be well to consider
its significance and use a little further.

It has the obvious use of enabling one, knowing the number
of moles present (*n*) and the absolute temperature (T), to state
the volume corresponding to any pressure, or *vice versa*; or,
in fact, with any two values known, to calculate or graph the
variability of the remaining two relative to one another.

But the equation has a further significance in that the product
PV represents so much energy, and the changes in this product,
when either the pressure or the volume of the gas, or both,
are altered, will be a measure of the work done on or by the gas
in so altering. Consider 1 mole of gas at N.T.P. occupying
22·4 litres in which the product of P and V is therefore 22·4
litre-atmospheres. If this gas could exist as gas at the
absolute zero, the values of P and V would be 0. The ex-
pansive work represented by 1 mole of gas at N.T.P. is therefore 22·4 litre-atmospheres, which we may convert into
gram-centimetres and finally into calories as follows:—

P=1 atmosphere=76·0 cm. Hg=76×13·6 grm. per sq. cm. =1033 grm. per sq. cm.

V=22·40 litres =22,400 c.c.

∴ PV=22,400×1033 grm.-cm., or 231·39 kg.-mt. =542·3 calories.

This figure of 542·3 cals. represents the energy change involved in the expansion of 1 mole of any gas from absolute zero to 0° C., or through a range of 273° C. From this we may deduce that the heat energy required for the expansion of 1 mole of gas per degree Centigrade against atmospheric pressure is $\dfrac{542\cdot3}{273}$=1·98, or approximately 2 cals. In other words, the value of R in heat units is 2 cals.

It has been shown, mainly by Amagat (1880), that in actual fact gases deviate to some extent from their expected behaviour as described by the above laws. He found deviation most marked when the experimental conditions were such that the gas was close to the point at which it changes into the liquid state.

The errors in expecting a gas to follow the simple equation PV=RT under all conditions, are two—first, that of regarding P as always being equivalent to the external pressure, and secondly, that of regarding V as being equivalent to the volume of the gas as ordinarily measured. For the purposes of the equation PV=RT, the pressure P should be a measure of the pressure existing within the gas itself, the intrinsic or 'internal bombardment pressure,' and not just the externally produced pressure. Under ordinary conditions of temperature and pressure, and with ordinary gases, the externally produced pressure and the internal bombardment pressure are almost the same, but when either by extreme cooling or by extreme pressure the component molecules of the gas are brought within the sphere of strong mutual attraction, the internal bombardment pressure rises much higher than the external pressure. To allow for this increased pressure, van der Waals has modified the P of the original formula to $p+\dfrac{a}{V^2}$, the $\dfrac{a}{V^2}$ representing the supplement to the external pressure p which is due to the attractive force of the molecules, and the significance of the V^2 being that this extra pressure is inversely proportional to the square of the volume.

The other error in the simple $PV = RT$ equation is the assumption that the total volume, V, of the gas is compressible. In the theoretical or 'perfect' gas of the physicist this is so, but in real gases the molecules themselves are so nearly incompressible that it would be more correct to take as the compressible volume $V - b$, where b represents the volume occupied by the molecules themselves. The equation as thus modified would read:

$$\left(p + \frac{a}{V^2}\right)(V - b) = RT,$$

and, in this form, is known as van der Waals's equation of state. In this equation a and b are constants which must be determined experimentally for each gas, but with such determined values, the equation is capable of predicting with considerable accuracy the behaviour of gases under exceptional conditions of pressure and temperature.

In liquids, the internal pressure due to mutual attraction among its molecules must be of very great magnitude. How great one may begin to appreciate by calculating, from $PV = nRT$, what pressure (P) would be necessary to compress an ideal gas to the molecular concentration found in water. To do this, let us write the equation as $P = \dfrac{nRT}{V}$; in this form, since $n =$ moles and $V =$ litres of gas, $\dfrac{n}{V} =$ moles per litre. Now, the molecular weight of H_2O being 18, there will be $\frac{1000}{18}$ moles in 1000 grm. of water, or 55·5 moles per litre. P would therefore be 55·5 RT or, at 0° C., $55·5 \times 0·082 \times 273·1 = 1262$ atmospheres. In this calculation no account has been taken of the volume occupied by the molecules themselves (the b of van der Waals's equation). In point of fact, the molecules themselves occupy the greater part of the volume of the water, and $V - b$ would be very much smaller than the V used in the above calculation. The calculated value of 1262 atmospheres, striking though it is, thus represents only a part of the internal pressure of the fluid.

Diffusion of Gases – Considering that gases, according to the kinetic theory, consist of rapidly moving molecules separated by immensely larger spaces, it is not surprising that two gases brought into contact with one another diffuse completely and rapidly, the molecules of one gas moving into the intermolecular spaces of the other. The law governing the rate of diffusion was formulated by Graham in 1831 as follows: "The rate of diffusion of a gas is inversely proportional to the square root of its molecular weight." This behaviour fits well into the kinetic theory, since the kinetic energy of a molecule of a gas is $\frac{1}{2}mv^2$, and is the same for all gases under identical conditions of pressure and temperature. The heavier the molecules, therefore, the smaller must be their velocity.

Where diffusion of gases occurs in living organisms, the diffusion has almost invariably to take place across moist intercellular membranes. Under such conditions the rapidity of the diffusion of a gas is usually more dependent on its solubility in the fluid moistening the membrane than on its own density. The following table gives the solubilities in water of the three gases most important in biology :—

SOLUBILITY PER 100 c.c. WATER AT 38° C. AND 760° cm. Hg

Oxygen	2·37 c.c.
Nitrogen	1·2 c.c.
Carbon dioxide	55·5 c.c.

Partial Pressures – Given a mixture of gases, it is often important to know what part of the total pressure is attributable to each component of the mixture. Dalton's Law of Partial Pressures states that the "total pressure of a mixture of gases is equal to the sum of the pressures which each gas would exercise if it alone filled the vessel." This means that, in a gaseous mixture, the total pressure of the mixture is divided between the component gases in proportion to their relative volumes. For example, if we take 79 per cent. nitrogen and 21 per cent. oxygen as approximate figures for the composition of air, then the partial pressure of oxygen in air at 760 mm. Hg would be $\frac{21}{100}$ of 760 mm. or 159·6 mm., and the partial pressure of nitrogen similarly $\frac{79}{100}$ of 760 mm. or 600·4 mm.

CHAPTER IV

LIQUIDS AND SOLIDS

IT is a useful generalisation that the mean kinetic energy per molecule of matter in any state of aggregation is constant for any one temperature, but it must be borne in mind that this is, after all, only true of the average of a great number of particular instances. Individually considered, the kinetic energies of the molecules at any one moment are widely various, and in any one molecule over a period of time, the kinetic energy is constantly changing from zero at the moment of collision to a maximum value between collisions.

In liquids the mean molecular kinetic energy is lower than it is in gases. The 'mean free path' of the molecules has been so far reduced as to bring each molecule within the sphere of powerful attraction by its neighbours. On such mutual molecular attraction depend many of the specific phenomena observed in liquids.

In the interior of a liquid the molecules are all closely hemmed in by surrounding molecules. This is not so at a surface, where the liquid is, let us suppose, in contact with a gaseous phase such as the atmosphere. The gas molecules are relatively far apart and are separated by large intervening spaces, into which the liquid molecules can easily penetrate if they are free to do so. This penetration actually occurs with a small proportion of the liquid molecules which, by reason of a kinetic energy momentarily higher than the average and a favourable superficial position, break free from the attraction of the molecules surrounding them in the liquid. If the space above the liquid is unrestricted, as in a liquid exposed in an open vessel in a room, a small number of the molecules which leave the surface of the liquid will rebound from the gaseous molecules of the atmosphere and return to the liquid, but the great majority will pass into the large intermolecular spaces in the gaseous phase, and move further and further away from the liquid. There is thus a continuous movement of molecules from the surface of the liquid into the adjoining atmosphere, and the liquid evaporates. Moreover, since the process of evaporation is produced by the removal of molecules possessed of a higher than average kinetic energy, the mean kinetic energy of the remaining molecules of the liquid must be diminished. Hence, evaporation is always accompanied by a fall of temperature in the evaporating liquid.

If, instead of exposing the liquid to the surrounding air, we imagine it to be enclosed in a vessel whose volume exceeds that of the liquid, the space unoccupied by liquid being empty, then the same movement of molecules from the surface of the liquid into the vacuous space will occur. After a certain number of molecules have evaporated into the originally vacuous space, it will be so filled that any further movement of molecules from liquid to space will, by mutual collision, be accompanied by a return of an equal number from space to liquid, and the system will be in equilibrium. The presence of these molecules in the space above the liquid will evidently produce a pressure within the space. This pressure is the 'vapour-pressure' of the liquid. Moreover, a vapour-pressure of exactly equal amount exists even if the liquid is exposed to a gas or a mixture of gases, and not to a vacuous space, the vapour-pressure in this case being a partial pressure.

It is evident that the vapour-pressure of a liquid is dependent on the temperature of the liquid and will increase with increase in temperature. If the temperature of a liquid in contact with a gaseous phase (*e.g.* air) is progressively increased, an increasingly larger proportion of the liquid molecules have their kinetic energies raised to a value consistent with their existence in gaseous form. When the individual kinetic energies of a sufficiently large number of neighbouring molecules are so raised, a visible bubble of vapour forms within the liquid and, as the heating is still further continued, a point is reached at which the kinetic energy of all the molecules of liquid is *on the average* equal to the kinetic energy of the gaseous molecules adjoining it. At this point the vapour-pressure is equal to the external pressure, and the liquid boils. The boiling-point of a liquid is therefore dependent on the external pressure to which the liquid is exposed, being higher the greater the external pressure. This is turned to practical account in the autoclave, an apparatus in which water is heated in a strong-walled, steam-tight vessel. As steam forms, it is unable to escape and raises the pressure within the vessel, so raising the boiling-point of the water. Temperatures above 100° C. can thus be conveniently attained.

To the biologist two properties of liquids are of especial importance—viscosity and surface tension.

Viscosity – It is a matter of common observation that some liquids, such as water, are readily poured, while others, for example syrup or thick oil, flow with comparative diffi- culty. Physically, the more mobile liquid is said to have the lower viscosity. The

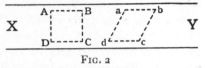

FIG. 2

difference in mobility is due to the different resistances offered to internal deformation. Consider a section of a stream flowing in the direction from X to Y (fig. 2). The deepest layer of the stream will tend to remain stationary owing to its friction against the stream bed. The layer immediately above this will move somewhat faster, the next layer faster still, while the layer on the surface of the stream will be moving fastest of all. An imaginary vertical section of the stream having the square form ABCD when the water is at rest, will thus be changed to the form *abcd* by the motion of the stream. The resistance which the liquid offers to such deformation is its viscosity. The coefficient of viscosity, usually represented by the Greek letter η, is, in absolute units, the force required to move a layer of the liquid of unit area, through unit length in unit time, past a stationary layer of the same area, situated at unit distance from the first layer. Water has a viscosity in absolute units of 0·010 dynes per sq. cm. at 20° C. A rise of temperature diminishes, and a fall increases, the viscosity of non-colloidal liquids.

In practice, the viscosity of a liquid is usually estimated by timing, under a certain driving force, its rate of flow through a capillary tube, and comparing this with the time required, under an equal driving force, for the passage of an equal

3

volume of water. In this way there is obtained the viscosity of the liquid relative to that of water, whose absolute viscosity is known.

Surface Tension – One of the most important properties of liquids is the tendency of their surfaces to contract; the surface behaves as though it were an elastic skin constantly endeavouring to diminish in area. A simple demonstration of this tendency of liquid surfaces to shrink is the following. To one point of a circular metal ring a loop of thread is tied, and the whole is dipped into soap solution, so as to form across the metal ring a complete film in which the thread loop is suspended. With a wet needle-point it will be found possible to move the loop freely about in the soap film, and to make the loop take on any shape. If, however, the part of the film within the loop is broken, as may be conveniently done with a pointed piece of filter-paper, the loop will be drawn out into a circular form by the contraction of the portion of film remaining between metal ring and loop. Any attempt to alter the shape of the loop now meets with considerable resistance. Again, it is a matter of common observation that free drops of liquid are almost spherical in shape, and, in fact, were it possible to free them from the influence of gravity, they would be perfectly spherical. Since a sphere has the smallest ratio of surface area to volume, we have here another illustration of the natural tendency of liquid surfaces to diminish in area.

It is convenient to regard this tendency to shrink as due to a force acting everywhere in, and parallel to, the surface of the liquid, and to speak of this force as the surface tension of the liquid. Thus, if an imaginary line is taken in the surface of a liquid, the part of the surface on one side of the line may be imagined as constantly pulling on the part on the other side, and surface tension is measured, in absolute units, in terms of the pull in dynes on such a line when the line is 1 cm. long. In other words, surface tension is the force of contraction at right angles to a line of unit length in the surface.

While it is convenient to regard surface tension in this way, in actual fact the tendency to contract is due to forces of molecular attraction which act perpendicularly to the surface of the liquid. Consider a drop of liquid surrounded by air or any other gas. Owing to the great distances between the gaseous molecules, mutual attraction between them is negligible, but in the liquid the molecules are so close that each is strongly attracted by its neighbours. Compare the molecules at the surface of the liquid drop with the molecules in its interior. The internal molecules, surrounded on all sides by their fellows, are equally attracted in every direction. A molecule at the surface of the drop is, however, experiencing an attraction which is stronger towards the centre of the drop than in other directions, because the attractive force of the many closely packed liquid molecules is greater than the attractive force of the comparatively few and sparsely placed molecules outside the drop. Every surface molecule is thus subjected to an unbalanced force tending to draw it towards the centre, and, as a result, the surface of the drop as a whole tends to shrink.

A similar tendency to contract in area, better called inter-facial tension, though often also surface tension, and similarly due to molecular cohesion, is found at the contact surface between two immiscible liquids, or between a liquid and a solid. In both of these cases we must consider not only the molecular cohesion among the molecules of each of the components of the interface, but also the attraction of the molecules of one component for the molecules of the other *across* the interface; it is this molecular pull across the line of contact that causes the greater or lesser adhesion existing between any two liquids, or between a liquid and a solid. The interfacial tension of the line of contact between two liquids is always less than the higher of the surface tensions of the two liquids that form the interface, because molecular attraction across the interface tends to prevent the surface shrinkage of each component.

At a solid-liquid interface the liquid may either tend to spread out over the solid (water and glass), or may tend to shrink away from the solid (mercury and glass). This tendency is often expressed by saying that water 'wets' and mercury does not 'wet' the glass. A water surface where it meets a vertical glass surface is thus curved upwards, while mercury similarly placed curves downwards. The angle which the surface of a liquid makes with the glass (or other solid) is known

as the angle of capillarity; for perfectly pure water this angle
is 0°, *i.e.* the water should spread completely over the glass ;
but the slightest contamination of the water, such as is
caused even by its exposure to air, increases the angle above
its zero value. For perfectly pure mercury the angle of
capillarity is 148°; contamination reduces the angle. Whether
a liquid wets or does not wet a solid, or, in other words, the
size of its angle of capillarity, depends on the relation between
the surface tension of the liquid and its strength of adhesion
to the solid. If its strength of adhesion is as great or greater
than its surface tension, it will spread over the solid, and the
angle of capillarity will be 0°; if its adhesive strength is
relatively small, the angle of capillarity will be large.

Measurement of Surface Tension – The surface tension
of liquids may be determined in various ways. One of the
simplest is by means of a stalagmometer. This apparatus is
similar to a pipette, but with its delivery end of capillary bore
so that liquids emerge from it in drops. The pipette has two
marks, one above and one below the bulb, and its tip is ground
to a perfectly flat surface. The apparatus is set in a vertical
position and filled with distilled water, whose absolute surface
tension is known. The water is allowed to run out, and the
number of drops formed as it falls from the upper to the lower
mark is noted. This number is then compared with the
number of drops formed in an exactly similar experiment with
the liquid whose surface tension is to be estimated. From
these observations the surface tension of the unknown liquid
can be obtained as follows. The ratio between the surface tension of the unknown liquid and that of water is the
same as the ratio between the weights of their drops, because
each drop of either liquid will be held attached to the tip of the
stalagmometer until it has grown in size and weight to such an
extent that the force of gravity overcomes the surface tension.
The greater the surface tension of the liquid, the heavier will
its drops become before they fall. But the weight of a drop is
its volume × its density, so that

$$\frac{T_1}{T_2} = \frac{v_1 d_1}{v_2 d_2},$$

where T_1 and T_2 are the surface tensions, d_1 and d_2 the densities, and v_1 and v_2 the individual drop volumes, of the two
liquids.

The individual drop volume is not determined directly, but
the same *total* volume of liquid is used in each of the comparative experiments, and the *number* of drops formed from
that volume is counted. The ratio between these numbers
(n_1 and n_2) will obviously be the inverse ratio of the individual
drop volumes, or

$$\frac{v_1}{v_2} = \frac{n_2}{n_1}.$$

Thus

$$\frac{T_1}{T_2} = \frac{n_2 d_1}{n_1 d_2},$$

and, since T_2 (surface tension of water) is known, T_1 may be
found.

Surface Energy – If the surface of a liquid is in a state
of tension, work must be done when the surface diminishes;
surface tension is, in fact, the intensity factor of surface energy,
the capacity factor being the area of the active surface. The
ability to do work may be demonstrated by dipping an inverted
filter funnel into soap solution, forming a film over its wide
end. This film will be found to move up into the narrow
part of the funnel in order to diminish its surface as much
as possible. In so moving, the film is doing the work of lifting
its own weight.

Alterations in Surface Tension – In living tissues, surfaces of contact are multitudinous, and alterations in surface
tension are probably responsible for very many of the phenomena of physiological processes. The influences by which
such alterations may be produced therefore demand some
consideration.

In surfaces of contact in which one component, or both, is
liquid, alterations of surface tension result from (1) temperature
changes, (2) the solution of substances in the liquid, and (3)
alterations in electrical potential differences at the interface.

(1) *Temperature* – Surface tension is dependent on the co-
hesive forces between molecules, so that rises in temperature,

by increasing the intermolecular distances, will diminish the surface tension. The range of temperature variation in biological processes is, however, so small that this cause of variation of surface tension is biologically of little importance.

(2) *Presence of Dissolved Substances* – The presence of a substance in solution alters the surface tension of a liquid. Most substances dissolved in water *lower* its surface tension; some, such as bile salts and saponin, effect this lowering of surface tension to a very pronounced degree. The ordinary test for the presence of the bile salts in urine depends on this fact. Normal urine in which bile salts are absent has a sufficiently high tension to support the weight of finely divided sulphur sprinkled on its surface, but the presence of the bile salts so lowers the surface tension that the sulphur particles sink.

The action of solutes in lowering surface tension gives us an explanation of the phenomenon of adsorption, a most important process for the biologist. In the chapter on Energy we saw that free energy always tends towards a minimum, so much so, that if a process is going to result in diminution of free energy we may safely predict that such a process will occur. Now take the case of water to which has been added some substance which, as most solutes do, lowers its surface tension. The added substance is obviously going to be most effective in lowering surface tension if it concentrates itself where that tension manifests itself—that is, wherever there are interfaces between the water and other phases. This is exactly what the substance does, and this process of concentration at surfaces is known as adsorption. In a vessel of solution, most solutes will therefore be present in relatively high concentration within the surface layers of the liquid; and in a solution with insoluble suspended particles dispersed through it, a similar concentration of solute will occur around each particle. We may note in passing, though it is of less concern to us, that a solute which raises the surface tension of a liquid will, on a similar principle, be less concentrated at the surface than in the general body of the solution.

Moreover, since adsorption results from a diminution of free energy at the surface of contact, its occurrence may be predicted not only when surface tension will be reduced thereby, but when any form of free energy existing at the interface will, by this means, be lowered. Now the surface of contact between solid and liquid, or between two immiscible liquids, is almost invariably electrically charged; a positive charge exists on one side of the interface and a corresponding negative charge on the other. The reasons for the existence of such electrical conditions will be considered in the chapter on Colloids, but meantime it is sufficient to note that their existence implies the presence of free electrical energy at the interface. The addition to one of the components of the interface of any substance which will diminish this electrical energy will necessarily result in the adsorption of the added substance at the surface of contact. This electrical adsorption is a prominent feature in the case of electrolytes, because of their dissociation into electrically charged ions.

As examples of electrical adsorption we may take the following. Most insoluble substances, e.g. charcoal, filter - paper, immersed in water, develop a negative charge at their surfaces. The addition to the water of, e.g., an electro-positive colloid will therefore be followed by the adsorption of the colloid at the charcoal-water or paper-water interface. Similarly, the addition of an electrolyte will result in the adsorption of its positively charged ion (cation). The latter may readily be demonstrated by partially immersing strips of filter-paper in water, adding to the water certain dissociable dyes, and observing to what extent the dye spreads over the moist non-submerged portion of the paper. Most dyes are of the nature of dissociable salts, in which the colour may be associated with either the basic or acid radical of the salt. If the dye is one (e.g. night-blue) in which the colour is associated with the basic radical and, therefore, forms the positively charged cation, adsorption by the negative paper will limit its spread, but not that of the water. On the other hand, a dye like congo-red whose coloured portion is the anion, is relatively slightly adsorbed, and spreads with the water. At electro-positively charged surfaces, electrical adsorption of anions and electro-negative colloid particles will occur.

The amount of substance adsorbed at a surface, other factors being constant, is diminished by rise of temperature. This is a necessary consequence of the effect of increase in temperature in lowering surface tension.

The quantitative relations between the amount of substance adsorbed and its concentration in the general body of the solution are of importance, and may be expressed in a general way as follows. As the concentration in the solution is increased, although the absolute amount of substance adsorbed at the surface also increases, the relative amount adsorbed becomes less and less, until, finally, a saturation-point is reached, beyond which further additions of adsorbable material to the solution are unattended by any more adsorption. Thus, on doubling the concentration of adsorbable substance, the increased amount of adsorption that is obtained is always less, and frequently much less, than twice the pre-existing amount.

(3) *Electrical Alteration of Surface Tension* – We have just seen that electrical charges of opposite sign exist on either side of most interfaces. A difference of potential must therefore exist at such surfaces. Diminution of this potential difference results in an increase of surface tension, while increase of the potential difference lowers the surface tension. Practical use is made of this fact in the capillary electrometer, an apparatus used for detecting slight differences in potential in electric circuits. In this instrument, an interface between mercury and sulphuric acid is formed within a capillary tube (A, fig. 3). At this interface the mercury assumes a positive charge with respect to the H_2SO_4.

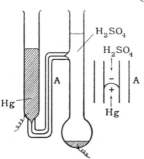

FIG. 3—Capillary electrometer

The Hg in the left-hand limb and the H_2SO_4 in the right-hand limb meet in the capillary tube at A.   An enlarged section of this point is shown on the right

If from two points of different potential in an electrical circuit one lead be taken to the mercury and the other to the sulphuric acid, the difference in potential in the circuit will be shown by a change in the position of the mercury meniscus. If the leads are so connected that the natural positive charge on the mercury is increased, and the charge on the sulphuric made correspondingly more negative, then the increase of the interfacial potential will lower the surface tension and the mercury meniscus will fall in the capillary. Conversely, if the leads are connected so as to diminish the natural interfacial potential, surface tension increases and the mercury meniscus rises in the capillary. In actual practice the mercury is always connected to the negative pole of the external circuit so as to avoid the formation of mercurous sulphate. As the movements of the meniscus are small, observations on it are made by means of a microscope. The instrument may readily be made sensitive to potential differences of 0·001 volt. It is chiefly used for detecting the null-point, that is, the point of balanced e.m.f., in a Wheatstone bridge or potentiometer wire.

Two simple but striking experiments to show the effects produced by alterations in surface tension may be prepared as follows. Into a clean Petri dish put a globule of clean mercury. Cover with water slightly acidified with nitric acid, and some distance away from the globule put a small crystal of potassium bichromate. The bichromate will dissolve and diffuse towards the mercury globule. When the bichromate solution reaches the globule, surface tension is lowered at that point, and the mercury shoots out an amœboid process along the path of the bichromate. This usually diffuses the liquid sufficiently to spread the bichromate solution in even concentration around the globule, and the mercury comes to rest until more bichromate dissolving from the crystal causes a repetition of the movements.

The other experiment, due to Ostwald, and often known as the 'physical heart,' depends on the electrical alteration of surface tension. A large clock glass is almost filled with 15 per cent. sulphuric acid, to which sufficient potassium bichromate solution has been added to turn it a pale yellow. A globule of mercury about the size of a halfpenny is run in below this solution. A clean sewing needle fixed in a cork, which for convenience is best held in the clamp of an adjustable stand, is now brought just into contact with the periphery of the mercury globule. If the adjustment is carefully made, the mercury will execute rhythmic contractions and expansions, hence the name given to the experiment. In this experiment we have essentially a miniature galvanic cell, the mercury forming the positive, and the carbon in the needle the negative element. When the two elements are in contact the difference of potential disappears, and consequently, surface tension increasing, the mercury globule shrinks away from the needle. A difference of potential is then re-established with accompanying fall in surface tension, the mercury flattening out till it once more touches the needle, when the cycle of events is repeated. In the presence of the bichromate, which prevents polarisation, the movements may go on for hours.

Molecular Orientation at Interface – Certain investigations by Hardy, and later by Harkins, on the force of adhesion between water and various organic liquids, showed that adhesion is greatest in the case of these organic liquids possessing a chemical grouping of high water-affinity, *e.g.* a COOH group in a fatty acid. This led to the conclusion that, at the interface between these substances and water, the molecules must have a definite orientation, the water-soluble or so-called 'polar' groups being next the water-surface. Such an orientation of the surface molecules has been definitely shown to exist by Langmuir, and later by Adam, by their investigations of the films of insoluble fatty acids spread on a water-surface. The method of investigation was briefly as follows.

A solution of a known small amount of fatty acid in benzene was placed on a water-surface. The benzene evaporated, and

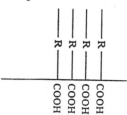

FIG. 4—Orientation of fatty acid molecules
Horizontal line—water-surface

the fatty acid spread out in a thin film over the water. By measurement of the area of this film, and knowing the number of molecules in the film from the amount of fatty acid used, it was shown that the film was only one molecule in thickness. By repeating the experiment with fatty acids of varying length of chain, it was found that the area occupied per molecule was the same in all the saturated acids. This could only mean that the fatty acid molecules were orientated perpendicularly to the surface (fig. 4).

With alterations in temperature, such monomolecular films exhibit changes in state comparable with the solid-liquid-gas

changes which we find in matter in mass, but with this difference, that the attachment of the molecules to the water-surface
by their COOH groups prevents their movement in a direction
vertical to the water-surface, so that the separation of the
molecules, due to increase in their kinetic energy, can only take
place in the plane of the water-surface.   The states in which
such films may exist, therefore, are those of (1) a solid in which
the film is rigid; (2) a liquid in which the film, though mobile,
is still composed of molecules packed together in close apposi-
tion; and (3) a condition known as 'expanded,' in which the
molecules are separated from one another laterally, but are
still anchored to the water-surface by their polar groups.   The
last has been described as that of a "gas in two dimensions
instead of three."

These conditions pass one into the other at more or less
defined temperatures, but generally at much lower temperatures than the solid-liquid-gas changes for the same substance
existing in mass.   The state of expansion of a monomolecular
film can also be altered, without temperature variation, by the
addition of certain substances to the material composing the
film.   The probable importance of these monomolecular films
in accounting for the permeability changes in living cells will
be referred to in Chapter XI.

Diffusion in Liquids – Diffusion occurs between two
miscible liquids just as with gases, but the process is much
slower owing to (1) the lower kinetic energy of the molecules,
and (2) the much smaller intermolecular spaces available for
the molecules to move about in.

Solids – If the temperature of a liquid is sufficiently lowered
one of two things may happen.   As we have seen, the viscosity
of most liquids increases with falling temperature, and this
increase in viscosity may proceed progressively until by in-
definable degrees the liquid passes into a so-called 'amorphous
solid.'   On reheating such a solid it gradually softens and
returns to the liquid condition.   Glass is an example.

On the other hand, most liquids when they cool come to
a point at which they are suddenly transformed into a collection of rigid bodies whose size may vary considerably, but
whose shape is constant for any particular substance.   The

liquid is said to crystallise.   On reheating such crystals there is an equally sudden return to the liquid condition, occurring at the same temperature as that at which the liquid crystallised on cooling.   The crystals have thus a definite melting-point in distinction to the amorphous solids, which change gradually from solid to liquid.   Moreover, the melting-point is so characteristic for any specific substance that it is often used as a criterion of purity.

Crystals of a pure substance have the same geometric form, the angles between the corresponding faces being the same whatever the size of the crystal; substances of similar chemical composition have similarly shaped crystals; the physical properties of crystals are not the same in all axes; all these facts suggest that the atoms constituting the crystal must have a definite geometrical arrangement within it.   Proof was lacking until Laue, in 1912, conceived the idea that, just as a diffraction grating may produce spectra from light waves, the latticework arrangement of the atoms within a crystal might be of suitable dimensions to produce spectra from X-rays, which are similar to light waves but of very much shorter wavelength.   Laue not only found that the transmission of X-rays through a crystal did indeed produce such spectra, but also that from the spectra so obtained information could be gained as to the internal arrangement of the atoms within the crystal. More recently, work of this type has been carried further by W. H. and W. L. Bragg, and a great deal has been learned about the structure of crystals.

CHAPTER V

SOLUTIONS AND OSMOTIC PRESSURE

THE word 'solution' in common usage generally refers to the mixture obtained by dissolving some solid substance in a liquid. The term should not be so limited; it is appropriate for any mixture of substances in any of the states of aggregation, provided that the mixture is chemically and physically homogeneous, constituting a one-phase system. Thus there are solutions of gases, liquids, or solids in gases; solutions of gases, liquids, or solids in liquids; and solutions of gases, liquids, or solids in solids. Of these nine types only a few are important biologically, and these are chiefly the solutions in liquids, since practically all biological reactions take place in fluid media. In addition to these types of true solution, many substances form colloidal dispersions, often called colloidal solutions, but incorrectly, because they are not homogeneous, but are two-phase systems. They will be discussed in a later chapter. In dealing with solutions of one substance in another it is customary to speak of one as the solvent and the other as the solute, and to apply the term 'solvent' to the substance present in greater amount, and 'solute' to the other.

Solution of Gases in Gases – All gases mix homogeneously with one another in any proportion, and in the solution so resulting the properties of the mixture are simply the sum of the properties of the components, provided no chemical reaction has occurred between these components. Air is therefore a solution of gases in gases.

Solution of Gases in Liquids – A gas only dissolves in a liquid up to a certain point, at which point the liquid is said to be saturated with the gas. The solubility of a gas in any particular solvent varies with (1) the specific gas, (2) the temperature, and (3) the pressure of the gas. The specific solubility of different gases is very unequal; ammonia, for example, is some 60,000 times as soluble in water as hydrogen at normal

temperature and pressure.   The effect of increase of temperature is invariably to lower the solubility of gases in liquids,
an effect readily explained by the kinetic theory.   Increase of
pressure increases the solubility of gas, the increased amount
in solution being related to the increased pressure according
to Henry's Law.   Henry found that if a volume of liquid at
saturation contains a certain *weight* of a gas under atmospheric
pressure, at twice this pressure twice the weight of a gas will
be taken up by the liquid before it is saturated.   Tripling the
pressure allows of the uptake of three times the original weight
of gas, and so on.   Since from Boyle's Law the volumes
occupied by x grm. of a gas at atmospheric pressure, $2x$ grm.
at two atmospheres, and $3x$ grm. at three atmospheres are
identical, it follows that the *volume* of gas dissolved by a liquid
is the same at all pressures provided the temperature remains
constant.   The 'coefficient of solubility' of a gas for any
particular solvent is the volume of gas (reduced to N.T.P.
values) saturating unit volume of the liquid at a given
temperature.

It is convenient at this point to refer to the significance of
the word 'tension' as applied to the gas content of liquids.
When a liquid is brought into contact with a gas it takes up
a certain amount of the gas, according to the pressure and
temperature and the coefficient of solubility.   When equilibrium is reached, that is in terms of the kinetic theory, when the
penetration of the liquid by gas molecules is equalised by the
escape of gas molecules from the liquid, the gas is said to be
present in the liquid at a 'tension' equivalent to the pressure
of gas above the liquid.   If the liquid is exposed to a mixture
of gases, the tension of each gas in the liquid is the equivalent
of its partial pressure in the gaseous mixture;   for example,
a mixture of 20 per cent. oxygen, 5 per cent. CO_2, and 75 per
cent. nitrogen at 760 mm. contains these gases at partial
pressures respectively of $\frac{1}{5}$ of 760 or 152 mm.; $\frac{1}{20}$ of 760 or
38 mm.; and $\frac{3}{4}$ of 760 or 570 mm.   The 'tensions' of these
gases in a fluid exposed to such a gas mixture, and allowed
time to come into equilibrium with it, would be 152 mm.
for oxygen, 38 mm. for carbon dioxide, and 570 mm. for
nitrogen.   Exposure of a liquid, containing a gas at a certain

tension, to an atmosphere in which the partial pressure
of the gas is lower, will, of course, result in the liberation
of some gas from the liquid. Conversely, exposure to a
higher partial pressure will result in the uptake of more of
the gas.

Solution of Liquids in Liquids – Some liquids, such as
alcohol and water, are miscible in all proportions; others, like
ether and water, possess a limited type of solubility. The
first type, though it may appear to resemble the gas-gas type
of solution, differs in that the mixture of two liquids usually
results in some degree of physical change. The total volume
of the mixture is generally not the sum of the separate volumes
of the components, which in itself indicates some molecular
rearrangement; there is also often further evidence in a change
of temperature, in some cases a rise, in others a fall. With
partially miscible liquids, we have to consider each liquid
alternately in the rôle of solute and solvent, so that if we have
two liquids, A and B, at a definite temperature, A has a certain
solubility in B, and B a different solubility in A. In a mixture
of these liquids where there is more of A than will completely
saturate B, we have the two liquids so apportioning themselves
as to form partly a saturated solution of A in B, and partly a
saturated solution of B in A. A mixture of ether with water
is an example. If more ether is added than will saturate
the water, the mixture will be found to separate into two
layers, the lower consisting of a saturated solution of ether
in water, and the upper of a saturated solution of water in
ether.

Rise of temperature as a rule increases the solubility of
liquid in liquid, though in a few exceptions it acts in the
reverse direction. The effect of increasing temperature is
exerted on both aspects of the liquid-liquid solution, and
with progressively rising temperature a point will be reached
at which the solubilities of A in B and B in A are so much
increased that A and B will be miscible in all proportions.
The temperature at which this occurs is known as the critical
solution temperature.

Solution of Solids in Liquids – When any solid substance
is placed in a liquid, more or less of it is always dissolved,

the so-called insoluble substances having an extremely low solubility. On the other hand, the solubility of a solid in a liquid may be very high, but a saturation-point is always reached beyond which it is impossible to dissolve any more; that is, the solubility of solids is always limited.

Apparently when a solid and liquid are brought into contact, the liquid molecules exert an attraction on the surface molecules of the solids sufficient to effect their liberation from the attraction of neighbouring solid molecules, and to enable them to diffuse out among the liquid molecules. A number of these dissolved solute molecules, by collision with the solvent molecules and with one another, will eventually return to the solid, and this number will increase as the proportions of solute molecules in the solvent increases. Saturation is reached when the proportion of solute molecules in the liquid rises so high that the number of molecules returning to the undissolved solid just balances the number leaving the solid to go into solution, so that a condition of dynamic equilibrium is reached.

The solubility of the great majority of solids increases with heating, but with a few, rise of temperature diminishes solubility. The usual measure of the solubility of a solid in a liquid is the amount of the solid in grams which will saturate 100 c.c. of the solvent at a given temperature.

Depression of the Freezing-Point – Two very important effects are produced in a solvent by dissolving a solid in it— the vapour-pressure is lowered, with the result that the boiling-point at any particular pressure is raised, and the freezing- or melting-point is lowered. For example, the boiling-point of a solution of 25 grm. potassium chloride per 100 grm. of water is 103·44° C. at 760 mm. pressure, and the freezing-point of the same solution is −10·9° C. Raoult, in 1886, in the course of a quantitative investigation into the depression of the freezing-points of solvents by various solutes, made the very important discovery that, for any particular solvent, the lowering of the freezing-point is, for many solutes, proportional to the number of gram-molecules (moles) dissolved in a given weight of solvent. Thus for a great number of different solutes dissolved in water, if the number of moles of solute per 1000 grm. of water is multiplied by a constant 1·86, the resulting figure gives the depression of the freezing-point in degrees C. This figure of 1·86 is known as the 'cryoscopic' constant for water. Different cryoscopic constants are given by other solvents. These constants are extremely useful, since, if we know the weight of substance dissolved in a certain solvent and can determine the depression of the freezing-point, we may calculate the molecular weight of the substance from these data and the cryoscopic constant for the solvent. For this purpose, and for the estimation of osmotic pressures, the accurate determination of the freezing-point of a solution is of the greatest importance. The apparatus used for such a determination is that of Beckmann, and is illustrated in fig. 5.

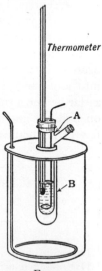

Fig. 5

The solution whose freezing-point is to be determined is placed in the inner tube A, in which it can be kept mixed by a stirrer. Surrounding this tube is a larger tube B, which acts as an insulating air-jacket. Both tubes are placed in a large vessel containing a second stirrer. A freezing mixture is placed in the outermost vessel, and the temperature at which freezing of the solution occurs is noted on a sensitive Beckmann thermometer (readable to 0·001° C.), placed with its bulb just immersed in the solution. Freezing-point depressions are usually signified by the Greek letter Δ.

Raoult, in his work on the quantitative relations of freezing-point depressions, found great discrepancies in the solutions of inorganic salts, which in most cases gave much greater depressions than were to be expected from application of the cryoscopic constant. Raoult was unable to account for these discrepancies, but the explanation was given by Arrhenius in 1887, in his classical paper on the "Dissociation of Substances Dissolved in Water." In this paper Arrhenius put forward the view that the molecules of many salts in solution break up into smaller fragments carrying an electric charge, and that these fragments are identical with Faraday's ions. Arrhenius further showed that the relative number of molecules breaking up into ions, or the percentage ionisation, can be determined from the conductivity of the solution, since the ions are responsible for the carriage of the current, and he found that the percentage ionisations so determined were correlated with the abnormalities in Raoult's freezing-points. The cause of these abnormally low freezing-points, therefore, apparently lay in the fact that in such solutions the solute was not wholly present in molecular particles, but more or less subdivided into ions, and that these ions acted as independent particles as far as concerned their effect on vapour-pressure, and hence on boiling- and freezing-points. The following table gives a few of Arrhenius's data:—

Substance	Molar Depression of F.P.[1]	
	From Experiment	Calculated allowing for Percentage Ionisation
Cane sugar (non-electrolyte) .	1·00	1·00
Potassium hydrate . . .	1·91	1·93
Hydrochloric acid . . .	1·83	1·81
Potassium chloride. . .	1·86	1·86
Barium chloride . . .	2·63	2·54

(Haldane, *Gases and Liquids*)

Osmotic Pressure – If we pour some strong cane-sugar solution into the centre of a vessel of water, the mixture, though not at once homogeneous, gradually becomes so by diffusion of the sugar through the water and the diffusion of the water through the sugar. If instead of placing the cane-sugar solution directly in the water, we enclose it in a sac impermeable to sugar molecules but permeable to water molecules, and immerse the sac in the vessel of water, a homogeneous distribution cannot then be attained by the diffusion outwards of the sugar. Dilution of the sugar nevertheless takes place by the diffusion of water into the interior of the sac. If the apparatus is arranged as in fig. 6, with a

---

[1] Figures are depressions ÷ 1·86.

vertical tube inserted through a tightly fitting cork into the interior of the sac, then the passage of water inwards will be obvious from the rise of the diluted sugar solution in the vertical tube. This experiment shows, too, that the inward movement of water occurs in spite of the fact that by so doing it increases the pressure within the sac; in fact the intrusion of the water will go on until the hydrostatic pressure of the water column in the tube balances the tendency of the water to pass into the sac. Such a process of water or other solvent passing through a membrane which is impermeable to a solute is called osmosis, and the pressure developed is called osmotic pressure. Membranes exhibiting these properties are called semi-permeable membranes. Since all living cells are surrounded by such semi-permeable membranes, and since, in all probability, there are many such even inside the cell, subdividing it into compartments, osmotic processes must evidently be of the greatest biological importance.

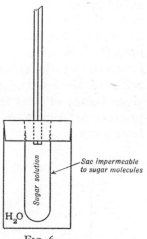

FIG. 6

This process of osmotic movement of water was first observed and so named by Dutrochet in 1827, in living plant cells. In 1861 Graham published his experiments on diffusion, in which he showed that parchment was permeable to some substances in solution but not to others. He classified substances into crystalloids and colloids, according to whether they did or did not diffuse through the parchment. The name colloids was given to the non-diffusible materials because they mostly formed viscous gluey solutions ($\kappa o\lambda\lambda\eta$=glue) and could not be crystallised, in contradistinction to the diffusible crystalloids, which were substances like the inorganic salts that crystallised readily. Some six years later Traube showed that it was possible to prepare membranes, e.g. copper ferrocyanide membranes, which were impermeable not only to Graham's colloids but to many crystalloids as well, while

yet retaining their permeability to water. These copper ferrocyanide membranes as prepared by Traube were unable to
resist any great pressure, but Pfeffer prepared the copper
ferrocyanide membrane in the pores of an ordinary porous
porcelain pot, thus obtaining a supported membrane which
would resist considerable pressure. By fitting up an osmometer similar to the one in fig. 6, in which the porous pot
replaced the sac and a closed manometer replaced the vertical
tube, Pfeffer carried out measurements of the osmotic pressures
produced by various strengths of cane sugar and other solutions.
Some of his results for cane sugar (at approx. 15° C.) are
given below. Pfeffer further studied the relation of osmotic
pressure to temperature, and found it to increase with rise of
temperature.

Per cent. Sucrose	O.P. in mm. Hg
1·0	535
2·0	1016
2·74	1518
4·0	2082
6·0	3072

Pfeffer's experiments were published in 1877, and ten
years later van't Hoff, from a critical review of Pfeffer's data,
perceived that the phenomena of osmotic pressure show a
remarkable similarity to the behaviour of gases. In the first
place, the osmotic pressure varies as the concentration of dissolved substance, as is evident from the above table; the smaller
the volume in which a definite weight of substance is dissolved,
the greater the pressure produced. This statement is evidently
analogous to Boyle's Law for gases (that the volume varies
inversely as the pressure, temperature being constant). In
the second place, the variation of the osmotic pressure with
temperature was found to follow Charles's Law (the volume,
or pressure, varies directly as the absolute temperature,
pressure, or volume, being constant). In the third place,
Pfeffer's data for different solutes showed that, in many cases
at least, taking equal volumes of different solutions having the

same osmotic pressure at the same temperatures, these solutions all contain the same number of molecules of solute—in other words, equimolecular solutions of many substances produce equal osmotic pressures. This relationship is obviously homologous with Avogadro's Law (equal volumes of gases under the same conditions of temperature and pressure contain equal numbers of molecules).

The applicability of these main gas laws to osmotic pressure, together with other theoretical considerations, led van't Hoff to the view that the osmotic pressure developed by a substance in solution is the same pressure as that which the substance would exert if converted into a gas having the same temperature and volume as the solution. The gas equation $PV = nRT$ should, therefore, hold for solutions if P is taken to represent osmotic pressure and the other symbols have their usual significance. To see if this is valid, let us take the 1 per cent. sucrose solution in Pfeffer's data above, and use the equation to calculate the theoretical osmotic pressure as follows:—

$$PV = nRT \quad \text{or} \quad P = \frac{n}{V}RT.$$

$\dfrac{n}{V}$ = moles/litre of sugar solution = $\frac{10}{342}$ or 0·029.

R = ·082 when P and V are in atmospheres and litres respectively.

T = 273 + 15 = 288.

P = 0·029 × 0·082 × 288 = 0·684 atmospheres = 520 mm.

The result, 520 mm., is a close approximation to the directly observed value. Note that in this calculation the concentration of sugar solution is measured in terms of gram-molecules per 1000 c.c. of solution.

Now Pfeffer was unable to measure with his apparatus osmotic pressures much above 6 atmospheres, because beyond this pressure his apparatus began to leak. The technical difficulties of leaks were, however, surmounted by Morse (1901), and by Berkeley and Hartley (1906), and these workers were able to measure the osmotic pressures developed by much more concentrated solutions. The general result of their work was to show that, while the equation $P = \dfrac{n}{V}RT$ gives a fairly good approximation to the osmotic pressures at low solute concentrations, there is considerable disagreement at the higher concentrations. This is shown in the following table, in which the osmotic pressures actually found by Berkeley and Hartley, for various strengths of cane sugar, are given along with the theoretical values of the osmotic pressure calculated from the simple gas equation.

OSMOTIC PRESSURE OF CANE-SUGAR SOLUTIONS

Concentration	Osmotic Pressure in Atmospheres		
Moles Sugar per litre	Actually observed	Calculated from Gas Equation	Calculated according to Morse's Weight-concentration
0·097	2·23	2·17	2·22
0·281	6·85	6·29	6·66
0·533	14·21	11·95	13·44
0·754	21·87	16·90	20·04
0·822	24·55	18·41	22·22
1·585	67·74	35·48	53·19
1·933	100·13	42·20	73·14
2·201	134·84	49·31	92·37

(Haldane, *Gases and Liquids*, from data in Berkeley and Hartley, *Proc. Roy. Soc.*, 1916, **A, 92,** p. 480)

In fact, the case is comparable with that of gases in which the simple equation $PV = nRT$ no longer holds under extremely high pressures or low temperatures, owing to the close approximation of the gaseous molecules.

Morse showed from his results that much better approximation of theoretical and observed values could be obtained if the concentration of solute was measured, not as $\dfrac{n}{V}$, *i.e.* moles per litre, but as moles solute per 1000 grm. of solvent. This was considered to make allowance for the volume of the solute molecules themselves, and is comparable to the introduction of the *b* factor in the van der Waals equation for gases (p. 29). While somewhat better agreement (last column of table above) between observed and theoretical values is undoubtedly obtained in this way, there is still considerable divergence in the more concentrated solutions. Many attempts have been made to obtain better agreement by further modification of the simple gas equation, but their consideration is rather beyond the scope of the present work. We may, however, remind the reader that the simple gas equation is only strictly applicable to an ideal gas, and that it is inaccurate even with real gases under conditions in which their molecules are closely approximated. It is not surprising, therefore, that its direct application to solutions, in which molecules are still more closely packed, meets with only partial success, and that only when the solutions are very dilute ones.

Isotonicity and Osmotic Pressure of Dissociated Solutes – Owing to the difficulty of obtaining an artificial membrane completely impermeable to inorganic salts and yet permeable to water, the measurement of the osmotic pressure of such salts has never been carried out directly. While Pfeffer was working with his osmometer, however, de Vries, a Dutch botanist, was investigating osmosis in living plant cells. He found that by placing pieces of vegetable tissue in a comparatively strong solution, fluid would pass from the interior of the cell through its walls, which acted as a semi-permeable membrane, into the surrounding solution. The loss of this water from the interior of the cell was microscopically evident from a shrinkage of the protoplasm away from the cell wall. On the other hand, if the cells were placed in a weak solution, passage of water occurred from the solution to cell interior, producing an increase of pressure within the cell. Between these two extremes there was a concentration of external solution which was in equilibrium with the cell contents, and with which, therefore, no movement of water was apparent. Using the plant cell as his indicator, de Vries determined the concentrations of different solutes, including inorganic salts, which were in equilibrium with the cell contents. Such solutions must evidently be in equilibrium with one another, and

therefore possess equal osmotic pressures. De Vries introduced
the term 'isotonic' for such solutions in osmotic equilibrium;
and isotonic, hypertonic (meaning of greater osmotic pressure),
and hypotonic (of lesser osmotic pressure) are the terms now
commonly used to express the osmotic relations of two
solutions.

Van 't Hoff, examining de Vries' results, found them in many
cases to verify his expectation that when two solutions are
isotonic they contain the same number of gram-molecules per
litre. To this general rule the solutions of inorganic salts
were notable exceptions, their osmotic pressures being higher,
and often much higher, than would be predicted from their
molar concentration. Van't Hoff was unable to explain these
abnormalities, but the explanation appeared when Arrhenius
brought forward evidence that many inorganic salts and other
substances in solution were dissociated into ions. Arrhenius
was able to show that the excess osmotic pressure of a dissociated substance was proportionate to the extent to which
it dissociated into ions. If ions were produced in the process
of solution they, as far as osmotic pressure was concerned,
were able to function as separate particles, just as they function
in producing an excessive lowering of the freezing-point. We
may just note at this point that the opposite condition is also
found, viz. osmotic pressures lower than we should expect from
the molecular strengths. This is a characteristic of many
colloidal dispersions, and we must assume that in these dispersions the ultimate particles are not single molecules, but
aggregates of several molecules. In correspondence with their
low osmotic pressure, such substances produce an abnormally
small depression of the freezing-point.

Measurement of Osmotic Pressure – The direct measurement of osmotic pressure is always difficult, partly owing to
the difficulty of obtaining a membrane completely impermeable
to the solute and free from other defects, and partly owing to
the difficulty of leaks in the apparatus when the measurement
of high pressures is attempted. An indirect method is therefore to be preferred, and the student will already have perceived that in the measurement of the freezing-point depression
we have a very suitable means, because by this method the

actual particulate concentration of the solution is measured regardless of whether the particles are ions, individual molecules, or aggregated molecules. It has already been noted that Raoult found that the depression caused by a molar, or apparently molar, solution in water was 1·86° C. For dilute . solutions, to which it may validly be applied, the gas equation tells us that a molar solution of any substance will produce an osmotic pressure of 22·4 atmospheres at 0° C. (p. 27). The osmotic pressure at 0° C. of any aqueous solution whose Δ has been determined will therefore be

$$\frac{\Delta}{1·86} \times 22·4 \text{ atmospheres.}$$

CHAPTER VI

ELECTROLYTIC DISSOCIATION

IT was known from the beginning of the nineteenth century that certain substances in solution could be decomposed by passing an electrical current through the solution, and such substances were called electrolytes. In the first chapter we saw that Faraday, in 1834, stated two important laws of electrolytic phenomena. The second law stated that the mass of the substance liberated by a current per unit time is proportional to the chemical equivalent weight of the substance (*i.e.* the atomic weight or sum of the atomic weights divided by the valency). For instance, if the same quantity of electricity is passed through solutions of silver nitrate, cuprous chloride, cupric chloride, and gold chloride, the relative amounts of the metals liberated are as follows:—

$$\text{Ag from AgNO}_3, \quad \frac{107 \cdot 88}{1}$$

$$\text{Cu from CuCl}, \quad \frac{63 \cdot 57}{1}$$

$$\text{Cu from CuCl}_2, \quad \frac{63 \cdot 57}{2}$$

$$\text{Au from AuCl}_3, \quad \frac{197 \cdot 2}{3}.$$

The real nature of this process of electrolytic decomposition of solutions remained obscure until Arrhenius propounded his theory that substances dissolved in water exist in the form of electrically charged particles—ions. This theory, though by no means universally accepted at that time, has offered satisfactory explanations of the quantitative aspects of so many phenomena that it is now practically never contested. In the present chapter we must examine this process of electrolytic dissociation in greater detail.

Suppose we have a vessel containing a solution of cupric

chloride into which are placed two electrodes, a negative cathode and a positive anode, and that a current of electricity is passed through electrodes and solution from a battery (fig. 7). The battery causes electronic movements in the external circuit and in the material of the electrodes, such that there develops an excess of negative electricity (accumulation of electrons) at the cathode and a corresponding positive charge (diminution of electrons) at the anode. According to the dissociation theory, the majority of the dissolved $CuCl_2$ molecules exist in the solution as positively charged Cu^{++} ions and negatively

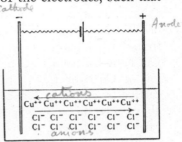

FIG. 7

charged chlorine Cl^- ions. The former, owing to their positive charge, are attracted towards the negatively charged cathode, and the latter move towards the anode. When a copper ion, which is positively charged because it has lost two electrons, comes in contact with the cathode, it will regain its lost electrons from the accumulation of electrons in the electrode, thus becoming an uncharged copper atom, in which form it is deposited on the electrode. In symbolic form the reaction occurring at the cathode may be represented thus, ($^-$) signifying a free electron:

$$Cu^{++} + 2(^-) = Cu.$$

When the chlorine ions, which are negatively charged, having each one excessive electron, reach the anode, each ion gives up its electron to the anode where there is a deficiency of electrons, and becomes atomic chlorine, which is liberated in gaseous form. The anodal reaction may be represented in symbols as:

$$Cl^- - (^-) = Cl.$$

The ions accumulating from the solution at the cathode (in this case Cu^{++}) are called the cations; those accumulating at the anode (in our example Cl^-), anions.

Other electrolytes dissociate in similar fashion, *e.g.*

$$KCl \longrightarrow K^+ + Cl^-$$
$$HCl \longrightarrow H^+ + Cl^-$$
$$CaCl_2 \longrightarrow Ca^{++} + 2Cl^-.$$

Now, as stated in Faraday's second law, the same quantity of electricity that liberates the atomic weight of potassium from KCl, liberates only half the atomic weight of Cu from $CuCl_2$ or Ca from $CaCl_2$. It is obvious, therefore, that each ion of Cu^{++} or Ca^{++} must carry twice the positive charge carried by an ion of K^+, as indicated by the double $^{++}$ symbol above. In the same way the ion of a trivalent element would carry three charges, a quadrivalent four, and so on.

In the above examples the ion is, in each case, a charged atom, but many ions consist of charged groups of atoms; *e.g.* sulphuric acid and acetic acid dissociate as follows:—

$$H_2SO_4 \longrightarrow 2H^+ + SO_4^=$$
$$CH_3COOH \longrightarrow H^+ + CH_3COO^-.$$

The modern theory of atomic structure offers a good explanation of this dissociation phenomenon. Chlorine as an atom, in which state it is electrically neutral, has one electron less than the number required to form a stable electronic pattern, potassium as an atom has one electron in excess. In their combination to form a KCl molecule, the potassium atom gives up its excessive electron to the chlorine atom, thereby making each, as a component of the molecule, stable in electronic pattern, but at the same time electrically unbalanced. The potassium, having lost an electron, becomes positively charged (K^+), and the chlorine, which has gained an electron, becomes negatively charged (Cl^-). When the KCl is dissolved in water, the mutual attraction of these two oppositely charged components of the molecule is so far diminished that they act, in many respects, like separate particles. Because of their movement in an electrical field they were called 'ions.' Divalent atoms have two transferable electrons, and therefore, in ionic form, will carry twice the charge, positive or negative, of a monovalent ion. On the other hand, in ions formed by groups of atoms, *e.g.* the $SO_4^=$ ion, the atoms within the grouping are probably united by 'shared' electrons (p. 12), and thus there is no tendency to further dissociation of the grouping. Similarly, in non-electrolytes the whole molecule is made up of atoms united by shared electrons, so that there is no tendency to dissociation of the molecule at all.

Avogadro's Number – Faraday's second law states that the amount of electricity liberating one gram-equivalent of all elements is constant. This constant, called a 'faraday,' has been measured very accurately, and found to be 96,500 coulombs. From the discussion above it is evident that this quantity of electricity is equal to the aggregate charge on all the ions in one gram-equivalent. Now, in the ions of one gram-equivalent of an element, the total number of excessive or lacking electrons is equal to the number of atoms in one gram-atom of the element, since the excess or deficiency of electrons per ion is numerically equal to the valency. If, therefore, the charge on an electron is known, from it and Faraday's constant the number of atoms in a gram-atom of any element may be calculated. The charge on one electron is $1 \cdot 59 \times 10^{-19}$ coulombs. The number of atoms per gram-atom of any element, which is known as Avogadro's number, is thus:

$$\frac{96,500}{1 \cdot 59 \times 10^{-19}} = 6 \cdot 06 \times 10^{23}.$$

Percentage Dissociation and Electrical Conductivity – Not all the molecules of a solution of electrolyte dissociate, but only a certain percentage of them, a percentage depending on (1) the nature of the electrolyte, and (2) its dilution. Arrhenius, in developing the theory of ionisation, pointed out that as the dissociated ions are responsible for the carriage of the current through the solution, the extent to which it is ionised can be determined from its electrical conductivity. In fact, his main proof of his theory was that the percentage number of molecules ionised, as determined by the electrical conductivity, indicated the presence in the solution of just that number of extra particles which would account for the excess osmotic pressure found with such electrolytes.

The electrical conductivity of a solution of an electrolyte is of such importance as a means of assessing the percentage dissociation of the electrolyte, that we must now consider the units and technique involved in its measurement. Electrical resistances of conductors are ordinarily measured in terms of the current flowing when a defined potential difference exists between the two ends of the conductor. The unit of resistance is the ohm. A conductor has a resistance of 1 ohm when a potential difference of 1 volt between its two ends causes a current of 1 ampere to flow through it. The conductivity of a conductor is expressed as the reciprocal of its resistance, the unit being called the mho.

The conductivities of solutions may be expressed in terms of either their specific, their equivalent, or their molecular conductivity. The specific conductivity, denoted by L, is the conductivity (or reciprocal of the resistance) of a cube of the solution whose edge is 1 cm. long. The equivalent conductivity, denoted by Λ, is the conductivity measured between two parallel electrodes 1 cm. apart, of a volume of the solution which contains 1 gram-equivalent of the electrolyte. Similarly, the molecular conductivity is the conductivity measured between two parallel electrodes 1 cm. apart, of a volume of the solution which contains 1 gram-molecule of the electrolyte.

The relation between specific and equivalent conductivities is the following:—

$$\Lambda = LV,$$

where V is the volume in c.c. of solution which contains 1 gram-equivalent of the electrolyte. If the concentration of the solution (C) be expressed as gram-equivalents per litre, then

$$\Lambda = \frac{1000L}{C}.$$

The actual measurement of the conductivity of a solution is carried out by placing it in a 'conductivity vessel.' Inside this vessel are two platinum plates fixed at the ends of two glass tubes by platinum wires sealed into the glass. Electrical connection between the external leads and these platinum wires is made by small amounts of mercury in the bottom of each tube. The glass tubes are fixed to the cover of the vessel in such a way as to allow of adjustment of the distance between the platinum electrodes.

This conductivity vessel (X) is connected up with an induction coil, accumulator, bridge wire AC, telephone receiver, and variable resistance (*e.g.* P.O. Box) Y, as shown in fig. 8.

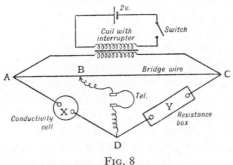

FIG. 8

The current in the primary circuit of the induction coil, interrupted by the usual interrupter, induces an alternating current in its secondary circuit. This current will at A and C apportion itself between the two circuits ABC and ADC according to their resistances. If point B is not at the same potential as D, some of the alternating current will flow through the telephones and produce a humming sound. By moving B along AC, a point may be found at which there is a minimum of sound or none; B and D are then at the same potential. Under these conditions the fall of potential from A to B equals the fall from A to D, and the potential drop from B to C equals that from D to C. This means that:

Resistance of portion of wire AB : Resistance of portion of wire BC : : Resistance of X : Resistance of Y.

The wire AC being uniform in material and cross-section throughout, the resistance of its two parts will be in the ratio of the lengths of the two parts. Thus we have:

Length AB : length BC : : X : Y,

or

$$X = \frac{Y \times \text{length AB}}{\text{length BC}};$$

AB and BC being measured on a scale fixed adjacent to the wire and Y being known, X is readily found.   The induction coil is used because the alternating current supplied from it avoids the accumulation of ions at the electrodes of the conductivity cell, which would occur with a direct current.   This ionic concentration around an electrode, called polarisation, would produce a reverse e.m.f. in the circuit and give an erroneously high result for the resistance of the solution.

From the definitions of specific and equivalent conductivities it is evident that, if these are to be measured directly, the area of the conductivity vessel electrodes and their distance apart must be known.   In practice this is avoided by carrying out a measurement when the vessel is filled with a solution (*e.g.* N/15 KCl) whose conductivity is known, and, from the results, determining a 'constant' for the vessel which may be used in subsequent estimations on unknown solutions.

Variation of Conductivity with Dilution – The specific conductivity is the conductance between opposite faces of a cube of the solution of 1 cm. edge.   As the solution is diluted, the number of ions in a cubic centimetre becomes less, and hence the specific conductivity diminishes with dilution.   The equivalent conductivity, we have seen, is related to the specific conductivity by the formula $\Lambda = LV$, where Λ and L are respectively equivalent and specific conductivities, and V is the volume of solution containing 1 gram-equivalent of the solute.   Now, on progressive dilution, if no change in the percentage number of molecules ionised took place, L would diminish in the same proportion as V increased, and Λ would therefore remain constant.   Experimentally, however, Λ is found to increase with dilution, the increase becoming less and less, until at extreme dilutions it is almost constant. This is shown, for KCl solutions, in the accompanying table.

This can only mean that with progressive dilution the relative number of molecules undergoing ionisation becomes greater until, at infinite dilution, all the molecules are dissociated, and the equivalent conductivity will be constant. The equivalent conductivity at infinite dilution is, of course, impossible to measure, but it may be estimated by extrapolation from the values obtained at finite dilutions.   Thus

EQUIVALENT CONDUCTIVITY OF KCl AT 18° C.

Dilution. Gram-equivalent per litre	Conductivity. Mho
1·0	98·3
0·1	112·0
0·01	122·4
0·001	127·3
0·0001	129·1

Λ_∞ for KCl at infinite dilution is 130·1 mho. Having obtained a value for Λ_∞, the relative number of molecules ionised, *i.e.* the degree of dissociation, at any dilution V will be given by the relation $\dfrac{\Lambda_V}{\Lambda_\infty}$. For example, a KCl solution containing 0·1 gram-equivalent per litre having been found to have a conductivity of 112 mho, will be $\dfrac{112}{130\cdot1}$, or approximately 86 per cent. dissociated. The degree of dissociation is usually represented by the symbol α.

Cryoscopic Method of Determining Degree of Ionisation – Another method of estimating the degree of ionisation in a solution has been already indicated in the chapter on Osmotic Pressure. We saw there that an aqueous solution containing 1 gram-molecule of solute per 1000 c.c. H_2O will have a freezing-point 1·86° below 0° C., provided that no dissociation of the molecules of solute occurs. If each molecule of the solute dissociated into two ions, and dissociation was complete, a molar solution (1 gram-molecule solute per 1000 c.c. solvent) would contain twice the number of ultimate particles, and the Δ would be $2 \times 1\cdot86° = 3\cdot72°$ C. Similarly a molar solution of an electrolyte, whose molecules each gave rise to three ions, would, if dissociation were complete, have a Δ of 5·58° C., and so on for electrolytes producing larger numbers of ions per molecule. Hence, by observing the freezing-point of a solution of an electrolyte, deducing from the observation the molar depression, and comparing the figure

5

so obtained with 1·86° C. if the solution be an aqueous one, or with the appropriate constants for other solvents, the degree of ionisation may be estimated. For example, a solution of 5·85 grm. of NaCl in 1000 c.c. of water will be found to have a Δ of 0·342° C. Since the molecular weight of NaCl is 58·5, such a solution is of 0·1 molar strength. The depression in molar solution deduced from the observation would be therefore 3·42° C. The excess of depression (3·42–1·86) will be to 1·86 as the extra number of particles produced by dissociation is to the total number of molecules of NaCl. Now if each molecule is capable of giving rise to n ions, then the extra particles *per molecule* will be $n-1$, if dissociation is complete, and $a(n-1)$ when dissociation is incomplete and a represents the degree of ionisation. Thus we have in general that

(molar Δ from observation $-1·86$) : $1·86$: : $a(n-1)$: 1,

or

$$a = \frac{d - 1·86}{1·86\,(n-1)},$$

where d is the molar Δ from observation. In the example above, where $NaCl \longrightarrow Na^+ + Cl^-$ and $n=2$, we have

$$a = \frac{3·42 - 1·86}{1·86},$$

or 84 per cent.

Rôle of the Solvent – We have been making considerable use of the cryoscopic constant 1·86° C. It must be repeated that this constant refers only to solutions in water, and that the molar depression of the freezing-point is not identical in all solvents. For example, the molar depression of the freezing-point of substances dissolved in benzine is 5·0° C.

Again, the degree of ionisation of an electrolyte varies with the particular solvent. It is relatively high in aqueous solutions, because water has a high 'dielectric constant.' The dielectric constant of a medium is a measure of its influence on the attractive or repulsive forces between electrically charged bodies separated by it. If the dielectric constant of the medium between two oppositely charged bodies is high, there will be comparatively little attractive force exerted between them, and conversely when the constant is low. The ability of ions to exist as separate entities will thus obviously depend on the dielectric constant of the solvent. In water, with its high dielectric constant of 75, conditions are favourable for ionisation; in petroleum, on the other hand, with its low constant of 2, ionisation occurs only to a very small extent.

Ionisation of Water – Water itself dissociates into hydrogen and hydroxyl ions according to the reversible reaction:

$$H_2O \rightleftharpoons H^+ + OH^-.$$

The degree to which pure water is ionised may be estimated, as with electrolytes, by conductivity measurements. Such measurements show that its degree of ionisation is very low. In pure water at 22° C. 1 litre contains only 10^{-7} grm. ions of H^+, and an equivalent quantity of OH^- ions. The importance of these figures will be apparent when we come to deal with the measurement of acidity and alkalinity in terms of hydrogen-ion concentration.

Mobilities of Ions – If one estimates the equivalent conductivities of a number of different electrolytes at infinite dilution, they will be found to differ considerably, even although the electrolytes are so chosen that each dissociates into ions of equal valency. Now, the current is carried by the charges on the ions, and the charges on ions of similar valency are equal. Further, dissociation is complete at infinite dilution, and therefore, in comparing equivalent conductivities at infinite dilution, we are dealing with identical ionic concentrations. Charge per ion and number of ions being equal, the only possible explanation of different equivalent conductivities is that there are differences in the speed with which different ions move through the solution. Determination of the relative speeds of the different ions shows that the H^+ and OH^- ions have a much higher velocity of migration than that of any other ion. The relative speed of an ion is controlled partly by the mass of the ion itself, but also largely by the degree to which it is hydrated—that is, by the number of water molecules which are associated with it, and have to be carried with it in its movement through the solution.

CHAPTER VII

ACIDS, BASES, AND BUFFERS

A REVIEW of what is meant by equilibrium and velocity constants will aid in the understanding of the subject-matter of the present chapter. In 1867 the 'Law of Mass Action,' which is the basis of all chemical kinetics, was announced by Guldberg and Waage. According to this law, provided the temperature, and therefore the kinetic energy, of the reacting particles remains constant, "the velocity of a reaction is proportional to the product of the molecular concentrations of the reacting substances." If we represent the molecular concentrations of two combining substances A and B by the usual method of enclosing them within square brackets, the symbolic expression of the mass-action law becomes

$$V \propto [A] \times [B]$$

or

$$V = k \times [A] \times [B] \qquad \text{(where } k \text{ is a constant).}$$

The reason why the velocity is proportional to the product will be evident from the following simple illustration. In a certain volume represented by each of the squares in fig. 9, imagine the presence (1) of one molecule each of A and B, and (2) of three molecules of A and two of B. In a given time, under the same conditions of kinetic energy (same temperature), there will be six times the opportunity for combination of any A molecule with any B molecule in (2) that there is in (1), because in (2) we may have combination in any of the following ways:—

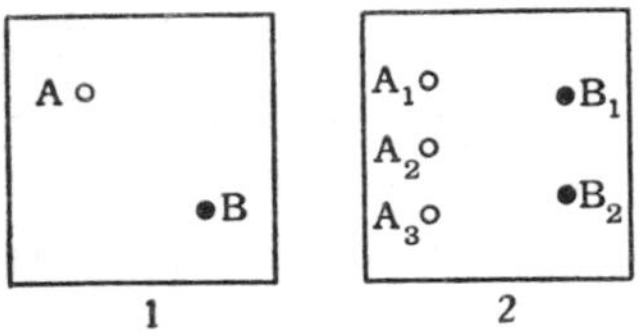

FIG. 9

$$A_1B_1; \qquad A_2B_1; \qquad A_3B_1; \qquad A_1B_2; \qquad A_2B_2; \qquad A_3B_2.$$

The rate of combination in (2) will therefore be six times the rate of combination in (1).

Now such an equation as $V=k[A][B]$ is of little value as it stands, because the concentrations of the two combining substances A and B are incessantly altering as the chemical reaction proceeds. We must therefore endeavour to find an equation relating the change of concentration to the time during which such change occurs. Let us take a case simpler than that given above, in which single molecules of one substance A undergo change into another substance or set of substances B. Let a be the number of gram-molecules of A present before the reaction begins, and let t be the period of time during which the original concentration a moles has fallen to $(a-x)$ moles, x moles having been chemically changed during the period. The velocity of the reaction may be expressed as $\dfrac{dx}{dt}$,[1] and according to the mass-action law this velocity is proportional to the concentration of A, which at the end of time t is $a-x$. We have thus

$$\frac{dx}{dt}=k(a-x) \quad \text{or} \quad k=\frac{\dfrac{dx}{dt}}{a-x}.$$

On integration (*cf.* p. 94) this becomes

$$k=\frac{1}{t}\log_e\frac{a}{a-x}.$$

k is called the velocity constant of the reaction, and may be found from the above equation by determining t, a, and x experimentally. A reaction such as this is called a unimolecular reaction, or a reaction of the first order.

When two substances react together, one molecule of one combining with one of the other, or when two molecules of the same substance are involved, the reaction is bimolecular, or of the second order. Such reactions may be represented as follows:—

$$A+B \longrightarrow \text{products}$$

or

$$2A \longrightarrow \text{products}.$$

---

[1] dx in this expression signifies an infinitesimally small amount of the change x, and dt the infinitesimally short period of time that dx occupies.

Reasoning similar to the above shows that the velocity constant of such reactions is given by

$$k = \frac{1}{t(a-b)} \log_e \frac{b(a-x)}{a(b-x)},$$

where a and b are the molar concentrations of the reacting substances at the beginning, and x is the amount changed in time t. Where A and B are initially present in equimolar concentration the equation simplifies to

$$k = \frac{1}{t} \frac{x}{a(a-x)}.$$

Similar expressions may be found for trimolecular reactions (reactions involving three molecules). Reactions of orders higher than the third are very rare.

Equilibrium Constant – Most of the reactions with which the biologist has to deal are reversible. As a general example of a reversible reaction we may take the following:—

$$A + B \rightleftharpoons C + D.$$

The two substances A and B not only combine together and form the two products C and D, but the reaction may proceed in a reverse direction, C and D combining together to form A and B. Reversible reactions, no matter in which direction they are proceeding, never go on to completion, though they may apparently do so. The reason for this can be made explicit as follows. Suppose we start the reaction with certain quantities of A and B, C and D being absent entirely from the system. The reaction will proceed rapidly in the direction of the upper arrow in accordance with the law of mass action, because the concentrations of A and B are relatively high. The velocity in this direction will become less and less as the concentrations of A and B diminish. A and B are diminishing, however, by forming C and D, and as soon as any of these latter are formed, a reaction in the direction of the lower arrow will begin, and the velocity of this reaction will progressively increase with increasing concentrations of C and D. We thus have the reaction A and B $\rightarrow$ C and D slowing down, and simultaneously the reaction C and D → A and B speeding up. After a certain time the two velocities will become equal, and the reaction will have *apparently* ceased, though, really, both reactions are proceeding at equal rates, and therefore the composition of the mixture does not alter. The point at which this dynamic equilibrium is reached is called the equilibrium position of the reaction. In many cases the equilibrium position is so near the point of complete change in one direction that the reaction is for practical purposes a one-way reaction. Note also that a reversible reaction will be changed to a one-way reaction if provision is made by any means for the removal of the products as fast as they are formed. If, for some reason, C and D are removed from the system as fast as they are formed, there will never be any reverse reaction, and complete one-way conversion of A and B into C and D will be secured. Such constant removal of products is of very frequent occurrence in living organisms.

Now, in our example the velocity V_1 in the direction $A+B \rightarrow C+D$ will, according to the law of mass action, be proportional to the product of the concentrations of A and B, or

$$V_1 = k_1 [A] [B].$$

Similarly, the velocity of the reverse reaction V_2 will be proportional to the concentrations of C and D:

$$V_2 = k_2 [C] [D].$$

At the equilibrium position $V_1 = V_2$, and therefore

$$k_1 [A] [B] = k_2 [C] [D],$$

or

$$\frac{k_2}{k_1} = \frac{[A] [B]}{[C] [D]}.$$

This ratio between the two constants k_2 and k_1 must itself be a constant, which we may designate as K. Then

$$K = \frac{[A] [B]}{[C] [D]}.$$

K is called the equilibrium constant of a reversible reaction.

This relationship is a general one. No matter how many

different kinds of reactants take part, nor how many different kinds of products are formed, the equilibrium constant K is equal to the ratio of the product of the concentrations of reactants to the product of the concentrations of resultants. Similarly, where two molecules of the same substance take part in the reaction the concentration of that substance is squared. For example, in a reaction of the type $2A+B \rightleftharpoons 2C+D$,

$$K = \frac{[A][A][B]}{[C][C][D]}$$

$$= \frac{[A]^2[B]}{[C]^2[D]}.$$

Ionisation Constants – The law of mass action is equally applicable to the reversible reaction of the formation of ions from dissociating substances. For instance, in the dissociation $NaCl \rightleftharpoons Na^+ + Cl^-$ an equilibrium is reached, and the relation

$$\frac{[Na^+][Cl^-]}{[NaCl]} = K_{NaCl}$$

holds good. In these ionisation reactions the equilibrium constant (K_{NaCl} above) is called the ionisation constant. Similarly, the ionisation constant of hydrochloric acid is

$$K_{HCl} = \frac{[H^+][Cl^-]}{[HCl]},$$

and of the base sodium hydroxide is

$$K_{NaOH} = \frac{[Na^+][OH^-]}{[NaOH]}.$$

Acids and Bases – The feature common to all substances having an acid reaction is their ability to give rise either directly or indirectly to hydrogen ions. The feature common to all basic substances is their direct or indirect production of hydroxyl ions. Neutrality, on the ionic interpretation, consists in an exact balance of H^+ and OH^- ions. Such a balance obviously exists in pure water, since each H_2O molecule which dissociates must give rise to one H^+ ion and one OH^- ion.

Further, the reactivity of an acid as acid depends on the

concentration of H^+ ions to which it gives rise, and similarly the reactivity of a base as base on its production of OH^- ions. Now it will be apparent from the equations just given for the ionisation constants of HCl and NaOH, that this constant will be large when the concentration of H^+ or OH^- ions is high. The ionisation constant gives, therefore, some measure of the strength of an acid or base.

We have just considered a monobasic acid, viz. HCl. In the case of polybasic acids similar dissociation into H^+ ions occurs, but each molecule of acid will give rise to more than one hydrogen ion. The liberation of the several hydrogen ions does not, however, occur simultaneously, but in a series of steps, as is shown for carbonic acid (H_2CO_3) and phosphoric acid (H_3PO_3) below:

$$(1)\ H_2CO_3 \rightleftharpoons H^+ + HCO_3^-;$$
$$(2)\ HCO_3^- \rightleftharpoons H^+ + CO_3^=.$$

$$(1)\ H_3PO_4 \rightleftharpoons H^+ + H_2PO_4^-;$$
$$(2)\ H_2PO_4^- \rightleftharpoons H^+ + HPO_4^=;$$
$$(3)\ HPO_4^= \rightleftharpoons H^+ + PO_4^{\equiv}.$$

The law of mass action applies to each of these steps, so that there is a different ionisation constant for each step. The same features are common to bases producing on dissociation more than one OH^- ion. The following ionisation constants will serve as illustration:—

Acid	K_1	K_2	K_3
Acetic acid .	1.8×10^{-5}		
Lactic acid .	13.8×10^{-5}		
Carbonic acid .	3.3×10^{-7}	6.0×10^{-11}	
Phosphoric acid .	9.0×10^{-3}	8.8×10^{-8}	3.6×10^{-13}

A number of substances, though not themselves possessing potential H^+ or OH^- ions, give rise to such indirectly by hydrolytic dissociation. For instance, sodium carbonate in solution in water has an alkaline reaction. This is due to the occurrence of the following dissociations:—

$$Na_2CO_3 \rightleftharpoons 2Na^+ + CO_3^=.$$

Now whenever $CO_3^=$ ions and H^+ ions are simultaneously present, most of them will combine, since the ionisation constants of carbonic acid are low (*i.e.* carbonic acid can only exist dissociated to a slight degree).

Many $CO_3^=$ ions, then, unite with some of the hydrogen ions formed by dissociation of the water in which the Na_2CO_3 is dissolved, forming in the first instance HCO_3^- ions, and secondly, H_2CO_3 :

$$H_2O \rightleftharpoons H^+ + OH^-$$

$$\downarrow$$

$$H^+ + CO_3^= \rightleftharpoons HCO_3^-$$
$$H^+ + HCO_3^- \rightleftharpoons H_2CO_3.$$

As a result of these reactions an excess of OH^- ions remains over from the dissociated water molecules, and the solution has an alkaline reaction.

The following dissociation formulæ explain similarly why NaH_2PO_4 in solution in water has an acid reaction, and solutions of Na_2HPO_4 an alkaline reaction. In the NaH_2PO_4 solution the following dissociations occur:—

$$(1) \ NaH_2PO_4 \rightleftharpoons Na^+ + H_2PO_4^-;$$
$$(2) \ H_2PO_4^- \rightleftharpoons H^+ + HPO_4^=.$$

By equation (2) the solution gains an excess of H^+ ions, and the reaction becomes acid. In the case of the Na_2HPO_4 solution we have the following:—

$$(1) \ Na_2HPO_4 \rightleftharpoons 2Na^+ + HPO_4^=;$$
$$(2) \ H_2O \rightleftharpoons H^+ + OH^-;$$

$$\downarrow$$

$$(3) \qquad H^+ + HPO_4^= \rightleftharpoons H_2PO_4^-.$$

The $HPO_4^=$ ions produced by equation (1) unite with some of the H^+ ions arising from the dissociation of the water molecules (2), so as to satisfy the equilibrium demanded by equation (3). The removal of some of the H^+ ions of the water thus leaves an excess of OH^- ions, and the reaction of the solution is alkaline.

Buffer Substances – When an acid such as HCl is added
to water the concentration of free H^+ ions rises markedly,
because the HCl dissociates almost completely, and practically
all the H^+ ions formed from it remain in the ionic state.
Similarly, there is a pronounced increase in OH^- concentration
on addition of an alkali to water. There are, however, many
substances which in solution can withstand the addition of
considerable amounts of acid or base without any very great
alteration in H^+ or OH^- ion concentration. Such substances
are called buffers, and are prevalent in living tissues for obvious
reasons. The mechanism of the buffering phenomenon may
be illustrated by one or two examples. A solution of sodium
acetate alone will act as a buffer towards acid. On the addition
of acid, say HCl, to such a solution we have the following ions
and undissociated molecules in the solution (Ac^- representing
CH_3COO^-):—

$$NaAc + Na^+ + \underbrace{Ac^- + H^+}_{HAc} + Cl^- + HCl + NaCl.$$

Now the ionisation constant of $NaAc \rightleftharpoons Na^+ + Ac^-$ is high,
so that comparatively little sodium acetate will exist in the
undissociated form, most of it having given rise to Na^+ and
Ac^- ions. On the other hand, the ionisation constant of
$HAc \rightleftharpoons H^+ + Ac^-$ is low, and therefore when H^+ ions and
Ac^- ions are both present, the majority of them combine
together to form the undissociated HAc. This is exactly
what happens in the above example, the H^+ ions dissociating
from the added HCl combining for the most part with the
Ac^- ions dissociated from the sodium acetate. The hydrogen-
ion concentration of the solution does not therefore rise to
any great extent.

In this example we have a solution with a buffering action
towards acid alone. A buffer solution proper resists not
only changes in H^+ ion concentration, but also changes in
OH^- ion concentration. Such buffers are usually mixtures of
a weak acid and a salt of the same acid with a strong base,
or, conversely, a mixture of a weak base and its salt with a
strong acid. If, instead of using sodium acetate alone, we
use a mixture of sodium acetate and acetic acid, we have a

very good example of the first type. The ions and undissociated molecules resulting in such a mixture may be represented as follows:—

$$\overset{\left(\substack{\text{from}\\\text{NaAc}}\right)}{} \quad \overset{\left(\substack{\text{from}\\\text{HAc}}\right)}{}$$

$$\underset{(s)}{\text{NaAc}} + \underset{(l)}{\text{HAc}} + \underset{(l)}{\text{Na}^+} + \underset{(l)}{\text{Ac}^-} + \underset{(s)}{\text{Ac}^-} + \underset{(s)}{\text{H}^+}$$

Sodium acetate being highly dissociated, there will be relatively few undissociated molecules of NaAc, most of these molecules having formed Na^+ and Ac^- ions. On the other hand, HAc dissociates only slightly, so that the numbers of Ac^- and H^+ ions arising from it will be small in comparison with the number of undissociated HAc molecules. These relations have been roughly indicated by the insertion of the symbols (s)=small and (l)=large, under each molecule or ion.

On addition of a strong acid, e.g. HCl, to the above mixture, the same effects will follow as in the case of NaAc alone. The free H^+ ions of the HCl will be largely taken up by combination with the Ac^- ions, a plentiful supply of which is present from the NaAc dissociation, so forming more of the very feebly dissociating HAc. Other ionic transferences will, of course, simultaneously occur in order to readjust the $NaAc \rightleftharpoons Na^+ + Ac^-$ and $HAc \rightleftharpoons H^+ + Ac^-$ equilibria in accordance with their respective ionisation constants, but the important point for us at the moment is that, on the whole, a large proportion of the added H^+ ions are transferred to the non-dissociated state as HAc. The H^+ ion concentration of the mixture, therefore, alters only slightly. On the other hand, if one adds a strong base to such a mixture, the OH^- ions of the base may be taken up by combining with the H^+ ions from the HAc, thus forming undissociated water molecules. Readjustment of the equilibria will then occur by other reactions, such as slight further dissociation of the HAc, and the taking up of the excess Ac^- ions (which have lost their corresponding H^+ ions), by recombining with the Na^+ ions to form NaAc. Again, the important change is the transformation of the OH^- ions to the undissociated condition. The reader should observe that, in both cases, the possibility of absorption of H^+ or OH^- ions is not unlimited; for example, the absorption of the OH^- ion will cease when all, or nearly all, of the HAc has been dissociated. The buffering action of such mixtures is, therefore, limited to a certain range, beyond which additions of H^+ or OH^- ions produce practically as much alteration in H^+ ion or OH^- ion concentration as they would do in water.

Two other examples of buffer action may be mentioned: (a) that of a solution containing both Na_2HPO_4 and NaH_2PO_4, and (b) a solution of $NaHCO_3$, which contains also free H_2CO_3. In (a) the two salts by their dissociation will give rise to $H_2PO_4^-$ ions and $HPO_4^=$ ions. These two ions will be present in such relative concentrations as to preserve the equilibrium of the reaction:

$$H_2PO_4^- \rightleftharpoons H^+ + HPO_4^= \qquad . \qquad . \qquad (1)$$

On the addition of an acid to such a solution, the H^+ ions of the acid will be largely removed from the ionic condition by becoming associated with the $HPO_4^=$ ions, forming more $H_2PO_4^-$ ions. On the other hand, the free OH^- ions of a base will be for the most part rendered inactive by combining with the H^+ ions on the right-hand side of equation (1) to form undissociated water molecules. The equilibrium of the reaction (1) will then be restored by further dissociation of the $H_2PO_4^-$. Thus the hydrogen-ion concentration of such a solution does not alter much by the addition (within limits) of either acid or alkali.

The second case (b), that of H_2CO_3 in equilibrium with $NaHCO_3$, being a mixture of a weak acid and its salt with a strong base, is analogous to the acetic acid and sodium acetate combination already described. These phosphate and bi-carbonate buffer systems play a large part in the preservation of the neutrality of the blood and tissue-fluids of the body.

Amphoteric Electrolytes – Some substances can give rise to both hydrogen and hydroxyl ions on dissociation, and have therefore the property of combining either with a base or with an acid. Such 'amphoteric' action is shown by the proteins, and biologically is of very considerable importance. Proteins are compounds of amino-acids, the union between each pair of amino-acids being a peptide linkage, i.e. the

NH$_2$ group of one amino-acid combines with the carboxyl group of another, with elimination of water, e.g.

$$CH_2(NH_2)CO \cdot OH + H \cdot HN \cdot CH_2 \cdot COOH = CH_2(NH_2)CO \cdot$$
$$NH \cdot CH_2COOH + H_2O.$$

In this example there are shown two molecules of glycine combining to form the dipeptide glycyl-glycine.

An amino-acid is an amphoteric substance, since it possesses an NH$_2$ group through which it may combine with acid, e.g.

$$CH_2(NH_2)COOH + HCl = CH_2NH_3Cl \cdot COOH,$$

and a COOH group, by which it is able to combine with bases, e.g.

$$CH_2(NH_2)COOH + NaOH = CH_2(NH_2)COONa + H_2O.$$

Now proteins, as compounds of amino-acids, are also amphoteric. Although many of the NH$_2$ groups and COOH groups of the component amino-acids are mutually combined, there are always a number free, because, in addition to the free groups at the ends of the peptide chain, many of the amino-acids contain two NH$_2$ groups or two COOH groups (or both) in their molecule.

If, therefore, we represent a protein symbolically thus,

$$P\!\!\begin{array}{l} \diagup NH_2 \\ \diagdown COOH \end{array}$$, we have, as with amino-acids, the possibility of

the formation of a compound with acid, e.g. $P\!\!\begin{array}{l} \diagup NH_3Cl \\ \diagdown COOH \end{array}$, and

with a base, e.g. $P\!\!\begin{array}{l} \diagup NH_2 \\ \diagdown COONa \end{array}$. These compounds, like any

other salts, are dissociated to a considerable extent, their ionisation taking place as follows:—

$$(1)\; P\!\!\begin{array}{l} \diagup NH_3Cl \\ \diagdown COOH \end{array} \rightleftharpoons \left(P\!\!\begin{array}{l} \diagup NH_3 \\ \diagdown COOH \end{array} \right)^{+} + Cl^{-};$$

$$(2)\; P\!\!\begin{array}{l} \diagup NH_2 \\ \diagdown COONa \end{array} \rightleftharpoons \left(P\!\!\begin{array}{l} \diagup NH_2 \\ \diagdown COO \end{array} \right)^{-} + Na^{+}.$$

In other words, in acid solution, the protein behaves like a base, and on dissociation forms the cation; in alkaline solution its behaviour is that of an acid radical, and it forms the anion.

There obviously must be some intermediate point at which neither of the above reactions occurs. This point is called the iso-electric point, and, at it, the ionisation of the protein is usually considered to be minimal, any dissociation that exists resulting in equal numbers of protein cations and protein anions. (L. J. Harris has, however, brought forward evidence for the view that iso-electric protein is maximally ionised, the protein forming 'zwitterions':

$$P \begin{cases} NH_3^+ \\ COO^- \end{cases}$$

i.e. ions carrying both positive and negative charges. On either view, iso-electric protein ionises equally as acid and base.) The iso-electric pH is specific for each protein.

A number of the physical properties of a protein are at a minimum at the iso-electric point. It is evident from the above that the combining capacity of the protein for other ions is then minimal. This is turned to practical use in the purification of proteins by dialysis. If dialysis is carried out at the iso-electric point, the inorganic ions previously associated with the protein pass through the dialysing membrane into the dialysate. Again, since proteins are most feebly dissociated at the iso-electric point, their conductivity will then be at its lowest. Another feature is that non-iso-electric protein, being either anion or cation, will move towards either cathode or anode when an electric current is passed through its solution. This is frequently used as a method of determining the iso-electric point; by trial and error, a hydrogen-ion concentration is found at which no migration occurs. The viscosity, imbibition capacity, and osmotic pressure of proteins are also all at a minimum value at the iso-electric point.

Solutions of proteins, because of their weakly acid or basic properties, act as buffers. At the pH of the body fluids, their proteins are combined with base. When acid enters such a fluid, some of the base is displaced and its position taken by the H^+ ions of the acid. Simultaneously the ionisation of the protein is reduced, so that many of the H^+ ions are transferred to an undissociated condition and the rise in H^+ ion concentration is small.

The Donnan Membrane Equilibrium – The capacity of proteins to combine with other ions leads us to a discussion of the effect of proteins in disturbing the ionic equilibria on the two sides of a membrane impermeable to the protein. Let us suppose that AB represents a membrane permeable to sodium and chlorine ions but impermeable to the much larger protein ions. Imagine on side 1 of the membrane some protein and some NaCl, the hydrogen-ion concentration being such that the protein and base may combine. On side 2 let there be, to begin with, water. We may arbitrarily represent the relative concentrations of the ions by the bracketed figures, the sodium being, of course, associated partly with the protein ions and partly with the chlorine ions.

	A				A		
(6) P^-				(6) P^-			
(12) Na^+				(8) Na^+		Na^+ (4)	
(6) Cl^-				(2) Cl^-		Cl^- (4)	
	B				B		
1		2		1		2	

Now when diffusion occurs, although the membrane is permeable to both Na^+ and Cl^-, equilibrium is not reached by the equalisation of the concentrations of these ions on the two sides. At equilibrium the concentrations are *unequal*, for the following reason. The protein ions cannot pass through the membrane, and by their electrostatic attraction on the sodium ions associated with them, they prevent these also from going through. We thus find the ionic concentrations arranging themselves as in the second figure, with a higher concentration of Na^+ ions on the protein side than on side 2, and a higher concentration of Cl^- ions on side 2 than on side 1.

By thermodynamic treatment of this question, Donnan proved that, at equilibrium, the products of the diffusible ion concentrations on each side must be equal, *i.e.* in our example,

$$[Na_1][Cl_1]=[Na_2][Cl_2],$$

or

$$\frac{[Na_1]}{[Na_2]}=\frac{[Cl_2]}{[Cl_1]}.$$

The ratio $\frac{[Na_1]}{[Na_2]}=\frac{[Cl_2]}{[Cl_1]}$ or, in general, $\frac{[cations_1]}{[cations_2]}=\frac{[anions_2]}{[anions_1]}$, is known as the 'Donnan Ratio.'

The difference in the concentrations of the diffusible ions on the two sides produces a difference of electric potential, and it is possible to calculate what these differences of potential should amount to with ions of different valency. The mathematical deductions of Donnan have been experimentally confirmed by Loeb, using an arrangement similar to that to be described for the measurement of H+ ion concentration in the next chapter. This Donnan equilibrium is one factor in the explanation of the differences in ionic concentration which are often found to exist between a cell and its surrounding tissue-fluid.

CHAPTER VIII

HYDROGEN-ION CONCENTRATION

In the last chapter we have observed that acids are character-ised by the fact that they give rise on dissociation to free H^+ ions, and bases by their capacity for dissociating into OH^- ions. We must now concern ourselves with the measurement of the degree of acidity or alkalinity of a solution in terms of its hydrogen-ion concentration.

One says that hydrochloric acid is a much 'stronger' acid than acetic acid, meaning thereby that if, say, an N/10 solution of HCl is compared with an N/10 solution of acetic acid, the former exhibits those properties which are commonly associated with acidity to a much higher degree than the latter. This is because the degree of ionisation of HCl is much higher than that of acetic acid, and consequently there are many more free H^+ ions in the solution of the HCl. At N/10 dilution HCl is 91 per cent. dissociated, and will give rise to a hydrogen-ion concentration of $\frac{91}{100}$ of N/10 or 91×10^{-3} N, whereas the percent-age dissociation of N/10 acetic acid is only 1·36, and its hydrogen-ion concentration will be $\frac{1\cdot36}{100} \times \frac{N}{10}$, or $1\cdot36 \times 10^{-3}$ grm. ions per litre. In terms of its hydrogen-ion concentration, therefore, N/10 HCl is $\frac{91 \times 10^{-3}}{1\cdot36 \times 10^{-3}}$, or approximately 70 times as 'strong' as N/10 acetic acid.

Titration of an acid with a base until an indicator, such as phenolphthalein, changes colour can give no measure of the initial concentration of H^+ ions in the solution, for, of course, 10 c.c. of N/10 HCl, or 10 c.c. of N/10 acetic acid, equally requires 10 c.c. of an N/10 solution of an alkali, such as N/10 NaOH, to neutralise them. Titration with alkali gives only a measure of the *total* amount of replaceable hydrogen in the acid, because during titration the acid is induced to go on ionising until all its hydrogen atoms have passed through the ionic stage and have become combined with the hydroxyl ions of the base to form water. If, for example, we start with a solution of acetic acid, before any alkali has been added, a certain proportion of the acid will be ionised, such that $\dfrac{[H^+][Ac^-]}{[HAc]} = k_{HAc}$ (representing the CH_3COO^- anion as Ac^-). As soon as the titration is begun, the OH^- ions of the alkali will combine for the most part with the H^+ ions to form undissociated water molecules. The numerator in the above equation will hence be diminished, and, in order to re-establish the equilibrium represented in the equation, some of the hitherto undissociated HAc molecules will dissociate, providing a fresh supply of H^+ ions. These in turn will be combined with OH^- ions, and so the process will go on until *all* the acetic acid has dissociated. The same sequence of events will occur with any acid no matter what its original dissociation into hydrogen ions, and hence any quantity of any acid will always be neutralised by the chemically equivalent quantity of any alkali.

Units of Measurement of Hydrogen-ion Concentration – Our previous chapter should have taught us that in any solution where both H^+ ions and OH^- ions are present the law of mass action demands that these ions will coexist with undissociated H_2O molecules in such proportions that

$$\frac{[H^+][OH^-]}{[H_2O]} = k,$$

where k is the ionisation constant for water. Now water dissociates so slightly that the proportion of undissociated water molecules to its dissociation products, H^+ and OH^- ions, is always very great; in fact so great that the error is negligible if we consider the molar concentration of water, *i.e.* the denominator of the above equation, as constant under all conditions. We might therefore write the above equation as

$$\frac{[H^+]\times[OH^-]}{k_1} = k,$$

or, rearranging, $[H^+]\times[OH^-] = kk_1$, and putting K_w in place of the product of the two constants k and k_1, we have

$$[H^+]\times[OH^-] = K_w.$$

This important equation is the numerical basis for all measurements of H^+ ion concentration, since the value of K_w can be directly obtained by determinations of the conductivity of pure water, in which the only ions present are the H^+ and the OH^- ions. The value of K_w at $22°$ C. has been found to be almost exactly 10^{-14}.

In any solution at $22°$ C. in which both hydroxyl and hydrogen ions are present, the product of the concentrations of these must therefore be 10^{-14}, i.e.

$$[H^+] \times [OH^-] = 10^{-14}.$$

Now neutrality, according to the ionic theory, exists when the concentrations of H^+ ions and OH^- ions are equal. From the above equation, substituting [H] for [OH] since they are equal, we find that the concentration of H^+ ions in a neutral solution must be 10^{-7} N:

$$[H^+] \times [H^+] = 10^{-14}$$
$$[H^+] = \sqrt{10^{-14}} = 10^{-7}.$$

A neutral solution will therefore contain 1 grm. of H^+ ions in 10^7 or 10,000,000 litres, and in the same quantity of solution an equivalent weight, i.e. 17 grm. of OH^- ions. Now suppose a neutral solution, e.g. pure water, has some acid added to it. Acids dissociate into H^+ ions, so that the H^+ ion concentration of the water or solution must be increased. It may rise to 1 grm. in 1,000,000 litres, 1 grm. in 100,000 litres, 1 grm. in 10,000 litres, and so on according to the amount of acid added and its degree of dissociation. The concentration of hydrogen ions (written cH) would rise from the neutrality value 10^{-7} N to 10^{-6} N, 10^{-5} N, 10^{-4} N, and so on. In spite of this increase of hydrogen-ion concentration, the equation $[H^+] \times [OH^-] = 10^{-14}$ must be satisfied, so that in a slightly acid solution of cH 10^{-6} N the hydroxyl-ion concentration must have fallen to 10^{-8} N. In the more acid solution of cH 10^{-5}, cOH must be 10^{-9}, and so on. We see, then, that an acid solution must have a cH equal to a negative power of 10 less than 7, the index figure being *smaller* the more strongly acid the solution.

On the other hand, suppose that we add a base to a neutral solution, or to water.   The OH⁻ ion concentration will rise to 10^{-6} N, 10^{-5} N, 10^{-4} N, and so on, according to the quantity and degree of dissociation of the added base, and just as rises in H⁺ ion concentration are accompanied by corresponding falls in OH⁻ ion concentration, so will rises in the latter necessitate falls in the former.   For instance, a cOH of 10^{-6} N demands a cH of 10^{-8} N; a cOH of 10^{-5} N, a cH of 10^{-9} N; and so on.   It is apparent, therefore, that we can measure both acidity and alkalinity in terms of *either* cH or cOH.   It is unnecessary and confusing to use the one for acid solutions and the other for alkaline solutions, and the cH is customarily used for defining degrees of both acidity and alkalinity.   To summarise:

Acidity	Neutrality	Alkalinity
cH	cH	cH

$\ldots 10^{-4}$ N, 10^{-5} N, 10^{-6} N ; 10^{-7} N ; 10^{-8} N, 10^{-9} N, 10^{-10} N, $\ldots$

So far, for simplicity's sake, we have taken the index figure as a whole number, but of course there are all intermediate degrees of acidity.   For example, a solution may have a cH between 10^{-5} N and 10^{-6} N, say $10^{-5.301}$ N.   In the cH notation these intermediate values are not usually expressed in this way, where the whole of the index figure (exponent) is negative, but are transformed as follows, so as to have the power of 10 always a whole number. $10^{-5.301}$ equals, in ordinary logarithmic notation where the fractional part of the exponent is always positive, $10^{\overline{6}.699}=$ antilog 0.699×10^{-6} $=5 \times 10^{-6}$.   The cH would thus be expressed as 5×10^{-6}.

The cH notation has been superseded to a great extent by the pH (p=exponent) notation of Sørensen.   The pH is the negative power of the base 10, of the solution's normality in hydrogen ions, the minus sign being omitted.

In the pH notation the solution just discussed would have a pH of 5·301—that is, the exponent alone is used, both integer and fraction being negative.

As the cH notation is frequently used in the older literature, the two following examples of conversion may prove useful:—

Convert a cH of $1·5 \times 10^{-5}$ into pH:

$$pH = -\log cH$$
$$pH = -\log (1·5 \times 10^{-5})$$
$$\log (1·5 \times 10^{-5}) = \log 1·5 + \log 10^{-5}$$
$$= +0·1761 - 5$$
$$= -4·8239$$
$$\therefore pH = 4·82.$$

Convert pH 6·2 into cH:

$$pH = -\log cH$$
$$-\log cH = 6·2$$
$$\log cH = -6·2$$
$$= \bar{7}·8$$
$$\therefore cH = 6·31 \times 10^{-7} \quad (\text{antilog } 0·8 = 6·31).$$

The pH of neutrality is therefore 7, of an acid solution something less than 7, the number being *smaller* the *more acid* the solution; and of an alkaline solution something greater than 7, the number rising with increasing alkalinity.

Since the pH figures are logarithms, a very small difference in pH number means a surprisingly large change of hydrogen-ion concentration. For instance, a fall of pH number by 0·3 means a doubling of the hydrogen-ion concentration, a diminution of pH number of 1 indicates a tenfold increase in hydrogen-ion concentration.

Methods of Measurement of Hydrogen-ion Concentration. - Indicators – The indicator method is the simplest way of determining hydrogen-ion concentration, and is sufficiently accurate for many biological purposes.

The student is already familiar with the use of indicators for detecting the end-point of an acid-alkali titration. At the end-point of such titrations the pH change is a comparatively large one and takes place rapidly, so that the change in indicator colour is correspondingly rapid and marked; but when the pH changes slowly, the colour of the indicator will alter slowly from its acid to its alkaline tint, each intermediate shade being characteristic of an intermediate pH value.

The range over which any indicator shows its complete change of colour is comparatively small, and the range in which the colour change is decided enough to be clearly distinguished is smaller still, only about 1·6 pH units. Different indicators, however, show their colour changes over different pH ranges, so that by using a series of indicators it is possible to cover the whole pH range. A few common indicators with their pH ranges are given in the following table:—

	Strength	Colour Changes	Range of pH
	Per cent.		
Thymol blue (acid range) . . .	0·04	Red-yellow	1·2–2·8
Brom-phenol blue .	0·04	Yellow-blue	3·0–4·6
Methyl red . .	0·02	Red-yellow	4·4–6·0
Brom-cresol purple .	0·04	Yellow-purple	5·2–6·8
Brom-thymol blue .	0·04	Yellow-blue	6·0–7·6
Phenol red . .	0·02	Yellow-red	6·8–8·4
Cresol red . .	0·02	Yellow-red	7·2–8·8
Thymol blue . .	0·04	Yellow-blue	8·0–9·6

(Clark and Lubs)

By putting a definite amount (5 drops) of, *e.g.*, phenol red into a fixed volume (10 c.c.) of a series of solutions of *known* pH varying between 6·8 and 8·4, we obtain a series of standard colours each one of which corresponds to a definite pH between 6·8 and 8·4. All that is then necessary to determine the pH of a fluid whose H^+ ion concentration lies within this range is to take 10 c.c. of it, add 5 drops of phenol red, and match it against the series of standard colours. A similar method is adopted for the other ranges, using the appropriate indicator. For making up the series of standard colours, mixtures of solutions of buffer salts are used in order to get a solution whose pH is very stable, and determinable with sufficient accuracy from the relative amounts of buffer salts in each mixture. For the phenol-red range one may use mixtures of $M/5$ KH_2PO_4 and $M/5$ NaOH in the following proportions (p. 88).

If pure materials are used and the quantities are accurately measured, the pH may be taken from tables such as the above, but, if desirable, the pH of each mixture may be actually

c.c. KH$_2$PO$_4$	c.c. NaOH	pH
50	23·6	6·8
50	29·6	7·0
50	34·9	7·2
50	39·3	7·4
50	42·8	7·6
50	45·2	7·8
50	46·8	8·0

determined by the hydrogen-electrode method, which we will describe later. To save trouble in locating the appropriate indicator and buffer mixtures to use for fluids whose pH is not even approximately known, there are composite indicator solutions such as the 'B.D.H. Universal,' which give roughly the pH of the unknown.

Hydrogen-ion concentrations may be determined by the indicator method with an accuracy of about 0·1 pH unit, but the method is liable to give fallacious results when the tested solutions contain considerable quantities of either protein or inorganic salts. Difficulty will also be found in estimating the pH of coloured solutions by this method, but the difficulty may often be overcome by the device of superimposing a standard colour tube over a tube of the unknown *without* indicator, and matching these two viewed together against the tube of unknown *with* indicator, superimposed on a tube of clear water.

Dale and Evans have introduced a simple and ingenious indicator method for obtaining the pH of blood. A small quantity of blood (2 to 3 c.c.) held in a closed collodion sac is dialysed against 1 c.c. of 0·85 per cent. NaCl contained in a flat-bottomed tube of very slightly greater diameter than the sac. After dialysis has continued for twenty minutes, the pH of the dialysate is equivalent to that of the blood and is measured in the following way.

Three solutions containing KH$_2$PO$_4$ and NaOH in the following concentrations are prepared :—

	c.c. M/5 KH_2PO_4	c.c. N NaOH	c.c. N/10 NaOH	c.c. Boiled distilled Water
Solution No. 1	33·33	..	56	
,, No. 2	33·33	..	21·33	to 100
,, No. 3	33·33	7·33	..	

One c.c. of No. 1 solution is placed in a tube exactly similar to that containing the dialysate. To both these tubes the same quantity of phenol red or neutral red is added, and the colour of the phosphate solution adjusted to match the colour in the dialysate tube by adding No. 2 solution from a graduated pipette. The pH of the dialysate and hence that of the blood can then be read off from the middle curve (fig. 10). The matching of the two solutions is done in a comparator in which the solutions are illuminated only through the bottoms of the tubes.

The addition of No. 2 to No. 1 solution as described covers a pH range from 7·0 to 7·5. If the dialysate is more alkaline than pH 7·5, its colour may be matched by starting as before with 1 c.c. of No. 1 and adding to it the necessary amount of No. 3 solution, the pH then being read from the upper curve. Similarly, if the dialysate is on the acid side of pH 7·0, the colour is matched by adding the necessary amount of No. 1 solution to 1 c.c. of No. 2 solution, the pH being given by the lowest of the three curves.

We may now consider why indicators change colour at all, why their change is limited to a certain pH range, and what are the theoretical quantitative relations between pH and colour changes. In general, indicators are either salts of a weak acid or a weak base, or are themselves weak acids or bases, and Ostwald first suggested that their colour change was simply an effect of their own dissociation, one of the dissociated ions differing in colour from that of the undissociated molecule. The colour of a solution containing an indicator would thus vary according to whether the undissociated indicator or indicator ions were predominant. For example, let us take an indicator which is a weak acid, whose undissociated molecule

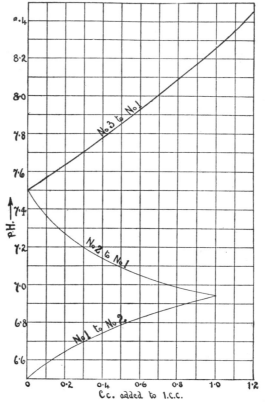

FIG. 10—Mixing chart for phosphates used in dialysis method for determining pH of blood

(Dale and Evans, *Journ. Physiol.*, 1920)

is yellow and whose dissociated anion is red.   The dissociation of such an indicator may be represented as follows:—

$$HIn \rightleftharpoons H^+ + In^-,$$
$$\text{(yellow)} \qquad \text{(red)}$$

and the equilibrium between ions and undissociated molecules will be such that

$$\frac{[H^+][In^-]}{[HIn]} = K_{HIn},$$

where K_{HIn} is the ionisation constant of the indicator.

Now when such an indicator is placed in an acid solution, the H^+ ions of the acid will momentarily increase the numerator of the equation, disturbing the equilibrium. To restore the equilibrium and keep K_{HIn} constant, a reassociation of H^+ and In^- to form undissociated HIn molecules will occur. The colour of the solution will tend, therefore, more towards the yellow, since undissociated indicator now predominates. Addition of alkali, on the other hand, will lower the value of the numerator in the equilibrium equation by the combination of the OH^- ions of the alkali with the H^+ ions. More of the undissociated HIn will ionise in order to preserve equilibrium conditions. More In^- ions are therefore formed, and their predominance will cause the colour of the solution to tend towards red.

It will be apparent, then, that the colour of the solution is dependent on the degree of dissociation (a) of the indicator. When a is zero the indicator is completely yellow, when $a = 100$ per cent. it is completely red.

To turn now to the determination of the relationship between a, the degree of dissociation (to which colour change is proportional), and pH. Let us begin with the equation:

$$K_{HIn} = \frac{[H^+]\,[In^-]}{[HIn]}.$$

If the concentration of total indicator be represented by X, then the concentration of the undissociated portion equals X less the concentration of its dissociated ion. In symbols,

$$[HIn] = X - [In^-].$$

Substituting this value in the equation above,

$$K_{HIn} = \frac{[H^+]\,[In^-]}{X - [In^-]}.$$

$$\therefore \quad K_{HIn}X - K_{HIn}[In^-] = [H^+]\,[In^-],$$

$$K_{HIn}X = [H^+]\,[In^-] + K_{HIn}[In^-],$$

$$K_{HIn}X = \{[In^-]\}\{[H^+] + K_{HIn}\},$$

$$\frac{K_{HIn}}{K_{HIn} + [H^+]} = \frac{[In^-]}{X}.$$

But $\dfrac{[In^-]}{X}=$ degree of dissociation $= a$.

Hence

$$a=\dfrac{K_{HIn}}{K_{HIn}+[H^+]}.$$

From this last equation a most important relationship emerges —when $a=\frac{1}{2}$, $K_{HIn}=[H^+]$. In words, this means that the indicator is half dissociated, and is therefore at the mid-point of its colour change, at a hydrogen-ion concentration numerically equal to its dissociation constant. While these relations

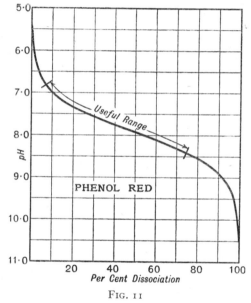

FIG. 11

have been developed here for the specific case of an indicator acid, it is worth noting that they hold for any weak acid.

Taking now phenol red as an example, given that K for this indicator $=1\cdot2\times10^{-8}$, we may calculate from the equation the pH values which will correspond to different values of a. These are tabulated below, and graphed in fig. 11. Similar curves are given by other indicators, but, their dissociation constants being different, they lie at different positions in relation to the pH axis.

pH . .	5·93	6·23	6·41	6·64	6·97	7·32	7·55	7·74	7·92
a, per cent.	1	2	3	5	10	20	30	40	50

pH . .	8·10	8·29	8·52	8·87	9·20	9·43	9·61	9·92
a, per cent.	60	70	80	90	95	97	98	99

From the figures and the graph we see that the range of colour change for phenol red extends from pH 5·9 (yellow) to pH 9·9 (red). Its range of practical utility for hydrogen-ion determination is much smaller, however. In the first place, at the two extremes of the range, large differences in pH are accompanied by relatively small alterations in percentage dissociation and hence in colour; this limits the useful range to a small portion of the theoretical range. Secondly, this useful range is not equally distributed on either side of the 50 per cent. dissociation point, but has its mid-point considerably nearer the undissociated end of the curve. The main reason for this is that the eye finds it easier to discriminate between shades of yellow with only a small admixture of the more dominant colour red, than between shades of red admixed with small amounts of yellow. While, therefore, the theoretical change of colour in phenol red extends from pH 5·9 to pH 9·9, its range for practical purposes is only from pH 6·8 to pH 8·4—that is to say, from a point at which it is approximately 8 per cent. dissociated to a point corresponding to about 75 per cent. dissociation.

In the above discussion it has been assumed that Ostwald's original theory offers a sufficient explanation of the colour changes. Later work has shown, however, that the colour alteration in many indicators is a matter of 'tautomeric' change or molecular rearrangement. As the degree of dissociation determines which tautomer predominates, the general applicability of the argument given above is not affected.

Electrometric Methods – The indicator method just described is, after all, only an indirect comparative method, the pH of an unknown being established by comparison with a known pH. In the hydrogen electrode and other electrometric methods, the pH of an unknown may be directly determined by the measurement of certain potential differences. Before considering the methods themselves it will be well to deal first with the theoretical basis of such methods, beginning with some discussion of the relationship between electrical potential and pH. The equation involved is only one of the many important applications of the mathematical calculation of the work done in gas expansion. This calculation can be applied to so many diverse aspects of biology, that it is well worth the student's while, even though he may be ignorant of the methods of the calculus, to have at least some idea of its derivation.

Imagine a gas expanding from a volume V_1 to a volume V_2 under conditions in which the temperature remains constant. During this expansion the gas could do a certain amount of work (say by expanding within a cylinder fitted with a piston, and driving out the piston against some resistance). Let the work done be W. Now during the whole of this expansion the pressure of the gas will alter, but we might divide up the process of expansion into a series of infinitesimally small expansions, during each of which the pressure may, with negligible error, be assumed to remain constant. Let the small increase of volume in each of these fractional expansions be dV (d meaning an infinitesimally small fraction). The work done during each small expansion will then be the product of the pressure P (which has been assumed to remain constant) and the increment of volume dV, that is PdV. The total work done in expansion from volume V_1 to volume V_2 will be the sum of all the products PdV between the volume limits V_1 and V_2; in symbols, where $\int$ means 'sum of':

$$W = \int_{V_1}^{V_2} P dV . \qquad . \qquad . \qquad . \qquad (1)$$

Now although P has been considered constant in *each* of the infinitesimally small increments of expansion, it cannot be considered constant throughout the whole range of volume change V_1 to V_2. The gas equation $PV = RT$ is, however, a general relationship holding under all conditions, and we may therefore substitute $\dfrac{RT}{V}$ for P. Equation (1) will now read—

$$W = \int_{V_1}^{V_2} RT \frac{dV}{V}.$$

R being a constant and T having been taken as constant, these may be brought outside the ∫ sign, since they are not subject to variation with alteration of volume from V_1 to V_2. Therefore

$$W = RT \int_{V_1}^{V_2} \frac{dV}{V}.$$

Now the equation as it stands is of no practical value, because dV represents an infinitesimal and unmeasurable change of volume. The calculus tells us, however, that the value of the part inside the ∫ sign, when we are dealing with *finite* changes of volume, such as V_1 to V_2, is $\log_e \frac{V_2}{V_1}$.

The work done is thus given by

$$W = RT \log_e \frac{V_2}{V_1}.$$

In this equation the logarithm of $\frac{V_2}{V_1}$ is taken to the base *e*. It may be converted so as to be used with common logarithms by multiplying by 2·303 thus:

$$W = 2 \cdot 303 RT \log_{10} \frac{V_2}{V_1}.$$

Now, by Boyle's Law, the pressure of a gas is inversely proportional to its volume, hence $\frac{V_2}{V_1} = \frac{P_1}{P_2}$, and we may write the above equation so as to calculate the work done from the change in pressure and not from the change in volume:

$$W = 2 \cdot 303 RT \log_{10} \frac{P_1}{P_2}.$$

It is in this form that the equation is biologically useful. We have seen that the gas laws are directly applicable with only slight error to dilute solutions, and we may take P_1 and P_2

in the above formula to represent osmotic pressures. Now osmotic pressures are proportional to the concentrations of solutes in solutions, so that if we wished to calculate the work done in concentrating a solution from a molar concentration C_1 to a molar concentration C_2, we could obtain it from the above formula written as—

$$W = 2 \cdot 303 RT \log_{10} \frac{C_1}{C_2}.$$

In this form the equation may be used for estimating the work done by a gland in secreting or excreting a substance from the blood, the concentrations of the substance in blood and secretion or excretion being known.

We will now consider the application of this formula to electrode potentials.

It is a familiar fact that some substances dissolve in a solvent more readily than others. This fact is expressed physico-chemically by saying that the more readily soluble substances have higher *solution pressures*. Moreover, when a solvent becomes saturated with a dissolving substance, it does so because the solution pressure of the dissolving substance is then equalised by the osmotic pressure of the molecules already in solution.

Now when a metal plate is placed in water, its solution is not grossly evident, but it is believed to have a similar tendency to dissolve. In this case, however, the particles tending to pass into solution are not molecules, but *ions* of the metal. This tendency of a metal to go into solution is called its electro-lytic solution pressure. It varies with different metals, but is a characteristic for any one metal; some, like zinc, have a high solution pressure; others, like copper, have a low solution pressure.

If the metal plate is placed, not in contact with water, but in contact with a solution of one of its own salts, a similar tendency of the ions of the metal to migrate from plate to solution exists, provided that the solution pressure of the metal is in excess of the osmotic pressure of the metallic ions already in solution. If the contrary holds, then ionic migration will tend to occur in the opposite direction, and metallic ions will tend to leave the solution to be deposited on the plate as metallic atoms. In either case, as described below, a difference of potential will be set up between plate and solution. If solution pressure and osmotic pressure are equal, there will be no tendency to ionic interchange at all.

In fig. 12 is represented a plate of zinc immersed in a solution of zinc sulphate. Owing to the relatively high electrolytic solution pressure of zinc, the solution has been invaded by a number of zinc ions ($\oplus$). As a result of this migration

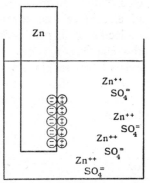

there has arisen an increased concentration of positively charged ions in the layer of solution adjacent to the plate, and the plate itself is now negatively charged by the electrons 'left behind' by the emigrating ions. A difference of potential is thus created between plate and solution. Now the electrostatic attraction between these two oppositely charged layers will evidently prevent this process of electrolytic solution going beyond a certain

FIG. 12

limit, and equilibrium will be reached when the electrostatic attraction equals the metal's tendency to dissolve. It will also be apparent that this equilibrium will be the more quickly attained the greater the number of positively charged zinc ions that are already present in the solution before the metal is brought into contact with it. The higher the initial zinc-ion concentration, the less is the ionic emigration from the plate, and the lower the difference of potential set up.

What are the energy changes involved in reaching this equilibrium? If we regard the solution pressure of the metal as comparable with osmotic pressure, then a certain amount of energy has been lost by the Zn^{++} ions in being brought from the higher solution pressure of the metal to the lower osmotic pressure of the ions in the solution. Let the solution pressure of the metal be P and the osmotic pressure of the ions in the solution be p. Then applying the formula derived from the

7

work done in gas expansion, the osmotic work done per gram-molecule is:

$$RT \times 2{\cdot}303 \log \frac{P}{p}.$$

Corresponding to this loss of osmotic energy there has appeared an amount of free electrical energy, equivalent to the electrical work involved in transporting the positively charged ions from the plate to the solution. Now electrical energy=quantity of electricity multiplied by difference of potential. The quantity of electricity due to the charges on the ions of one gram-molecule of any substance is one faraday $\times$ the valency (n) of the element, i.e. nF. If, then, a difference of potential, E, exists between plate and solution, the electrical energy gained $=n$FE.

The osmotic energy and the electrical energy must be equal, hence

$$n\mathrm{FE}=\mathrm{RT} \times 2{\cdot}303 \log \frac{P}{p},$$

or

$$\mathrm{E}=\frac{\mathrm{RT}}{n\mathrm{F}}2{\cdot}303 \log \frac{P}{p}.$$

If, therefore, E could be measured, the above equation would give the ratio $\frac{P}{p}$. Unfortunately, E cannot be determined without making a second metallic connection to the solution,

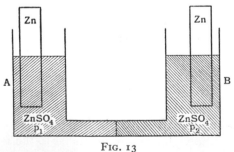

FIG. 13

so as to provide two leads for an electrical measuring instrument. If, however, we set up an arrangement like fig. 13, in which there are two zinc sulphate solutions of different concentrations, exhibiting osmotic pressures due to their zinc ions of p_1 and p_2 respectively, and each solution having a zinc plate immersed in it, then the potential E_1 between plate and solution in half-cell A would be

$$E_1 = \frac{RT}{nF} 2 \cdot 303 \log \frac{P}{p_1}.$$

Similarly, in half-cell B, if the potential difference between plate and its solution be E_2,

$$E_2 = \frac{RT}{nF} 2 \cdot 303 \log \frac{P}{p_2}.$$

These two potential differences are acting against one another, and will be unequal if the concentrations of zinc sulphate differ. The difference between them will show as a potential difference between plate and plate.

If this potential difference be E, then

$$E = E_1 - E_2 = \frac{RT}{nF} 2 \cdot 303 \log \frac{P}{p_1} - \frac{RT}{nF} 2 \cdot 303 \log \frac{P}{p_2}$$

$$= \frac{RT}{nF} 2 \cdot 303 \log \left(\frac{P}{p_1} \div \frac{p_2}{P} \right)$$

$$= \frac{RT}{nF} 2 \cdot 303 \log \frac{p_2}{p_1},$$

and, since the osmotic pressures p_2 and p_1 are proportional to the respective zinc-ion concentrations, which we may call C_2 and C_1,

$$E = \frac{RT}{nF} 2 \cdot 303 \log \frac{C_2}{C_1}.$$

This potential E is readily measurable, because we have now two external points to which an electrical measuring instrument may be connected. By the arrangement of two half-cells we have obtained a system in which the potential difference can be measured, and we have also, in the mathematical equation, got rid of the unknown electrolytic solution pressure P.

E is now expressed in terms of the ratio between the concentrations of zinc ions in the two half-cells, and if one of these concentrations were known, the other could be calculated.

It will now be realised that, if the electrodes could be made of hydrogen instead of zinc, a similar arrangement would enable the ratio between the *hydrogen*-ion concentrations of two solutions to be determined.   An electrode which, for practical

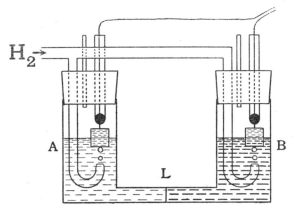

FIG. 14—Diagram of two hydrogen half-cells in liquid junction at L
(Clark, *The Determination of Hydrogen Ions*, Baillière, Tindal & Cox)

purposes, functions as a hydrogen electrode may be made by using a platinum electrode coated with platinum black and exposed to an atmosphere of hydrogen.   The platinum black absorbs the hydrogen, and the electrode acts as though it were a hydrogen plate.   Such an arrangement is shown in fig. 14.

The same formula will be applicable, and since we are now dealing with hydrogen of valency=1, the n may be omitted. Therefore

$$E = \frac{RT}{F} 2 \cdot 303 \log \frac{C_2}{C_1}.$$

Now if the concentration of hydrogen ions in the solution in the half-cell B be made normal, *i.e.* 1 gram-equivalent per litre, C_2 will equal 1 and the formula becomes

$$E = \frac{RT}{F} 2 \cdot 303 \log \frac{1}{C_1},$$

C_1 being the concentration of hydrogen ions in the half-cell containing the unknown solution. By measuring E, the hydrogen-ion concentration of the fluid in half-cell A could be calculated.

So far we have taken no account of another source of potential difference, viz. the potential that is created when two solutions of different concentrations are brought into contact, as at L in the figure. This contact potential may in some cases be calculated, but is usually in practice brought to a negligible value by using saturated KCl as the junction medium between the two solutions. KCl is used because the velocities of the migrations of its ions are almost equal, and the contact potentials of the double junctions formed on either side of it are constant and negligibly low.

The arrangement in fig. 14 demands a half-cell of normal hydrogen-ion concentration. Such a half-cell is very difficult to prepare. Instead, a calomel half-cell, which has a stable potential and is easily reproducible, is used, and the difference between its potential and the potential of a normal hydrogen-ion half-cell is allowed for in calculation. One form of the calomel half-cell is shown in fig. 15. It will be seen that it is comparable to the zinc-zinc sulphate cell previously described, the metal in this case being mercury and the salt of mercury being calomel. The addition of the KCl improves the conductivity of the calomel and

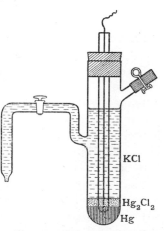

FIG. 15—Calomel half-cell

serves for connection to the remainder of the concentration chain. This KCl may be N/10 or saturated, the potential of the half-cell being different in each case.

The difference between the potential of a calomel half-cell containing N/10 KCl and that of a half-cell of normal H^+ ion concentration is 0·338 volts at 18° C. The above formula, using such a cell, would therefore be

$$E - 0.338 \text{ volts} = \frac{RT}{F} 2.303 \log \frac{1}{[H^+]},$$

$[H^+]$ being the hydrogen-ion concentration of the solution under measurement. This formula may now be simplified further by inserting values for the constants R and F. Since we are dealing with electrical measurements, R must be given its value in electrical units $= 8.3129$. F in coulombs $= 96,500$, and hence, if the measurements are carried out at $18°$ C. when $T = 291$,

$$E - 0.338 \text{ volts} = \frac{2.303 \times 8.3129 \times 291}{96,500} \log \frac{1}{[H^+]},$$

$$E - 0.338 \text{ volts} = 0.058 \log \frac{1}{[H^+]}.$$

But

$$\log \frac{1}{[H^+]} = pH.$$

Hence

$$pH = \frac{E - 0.338}{0.058}.$$

Determination of the pH of a solution by the hydrogen electrode consists then, in brief, of measuring the potential difference between a platinum electrode, saturated with hydrogen and immersed in the solution, and the mercury of a calomel half-cell which, through KCl, is also in contact with the solution. This gives E of the above formula, from which the pH may be calculated.

Fig. 16 shows diagrammatically a simple form of the complete chain for hydrogen-ion concentration measurement, consisting of a hydrogen electrode A, immersed in the solution B whose pH is to be determined, and electrically joined by a KCl agar bridge [1] to a connecting vessel of saturated KCl (C), into which dips the tip of the calomel electrode D. The leads E and F are taken to some type of potentiometer.

Potentiometers are of varied complexity, but the principle of them all is represented by fig. 17. AB is a bridge wire of uniform resistance throughout its whole length, and, say, 1.018 metres long. A difference of potential between A and B is

[1] A tube filled with a gel of agar saturated with KCl.

set up by the battery C, the magnitude of this p.d. being controlled by the variable resistance D.   A Weston Standard

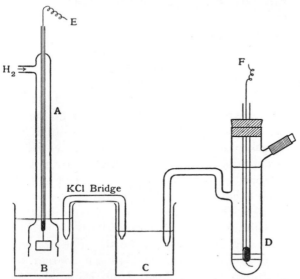

FIG. 16—Simple arrangement for pH determination by hydrogen electrode

Hydrogen gas fed into the outer tube of A displaces the level of the fluid in the bell-shaped lower portion and bubbles out through holes on a level with the platinum plate.   The plate and solution around it are thus kept saturated with hydrogen

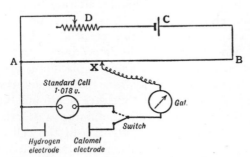

FIG. 17—To illustrate principle of potentiometric measurement of electrode potentials

Cell (which has a very constant e.m.f. of 1·018 volts) and the concentration chain of hydrogen and calomel half-cells are connected, through a two-way switch and galvanometer, between the movable contact X and one end of the bridge wire.   Both standard cell and concentration chain are set so that their e.m.f.'s oppose the e.m.f. of the battery C.   By operating the switch either can be placed in circuit as desired.

Now, by varying D, the p.d. between A and B (1·018 metres apart) may be adjusted so as to be 1·018 volts.   This adjustment is made by placing the movable contact X at B with the standard cell in circuit, and adjusting D until the galvanometer shows no deflection.   The wire has now a potential drop along it of 1 millivolt per millimetre.   Having made these adjustments, the standard cell is switched out and the gas chain switched in.   The movable contact is now shifted until there is again no galvanometer deflection.   The potential difference of the concentration chain is then equal to the potential drop along the tapped-off piece of wire XA.   This potential drop (in millivolts) is equivalent to the length in mm. of XA.

The hydrogen-electrode method just described is capable of giving results with an accuracy of 0·01 pH or less, but it is not universally applicable.   Like the indicator method, it is liable to error in solutions of high salt content, and there is also a 'protein error.'   Apart from these, the method is obviously inapplicable to solutions of substances which are easily reduced.   Neither is it applicable to blood without special precautions, as the saturation of the blood with hydrogen would alter its CO_2 tension, thereby altering its pH.

Two other electrometric methods may be briefly mentioned.   One is the quinhydrone electrode.   In this method the solution whose pH is to be determined is saturated with quinhydrone in a vessel containing a platinum, or preferably a gold, electrode.   The quinhydrone half-cell so formed is then connected by a KCl bridge to either a calomel half-cell or another quinhydrone half-cell containing a standard buffer solution.   The difference of potential in the cell so formed having been measured in the usual way, the pH may be calculated as follows.   The potential difference in a chain of quinhydrone half-cell and calomel half-cell is given by the formula

$$E = E_K - \frac{2 \cdot 303RT}{nF}\, pH_q + \text{potential of calomel half-cell,}$$

where E_K is a constant and pH_q is the pH of the solution in the quinhydrone half-cell.   By measuring E when this pH is known, a value for E_K can be obtained, which can subsequently be used for determining the unknown pH of another solution.   The method is simple and rapid, but fails at pH's greater than 8 or 9.

A third electrometric method is the glass-electrode method introduced by Haber and elaborated by P. T. Kerridge.   In this the solution whose pH is to be measured is separated from a buffer solution of known pH by a very thin glass membrane.

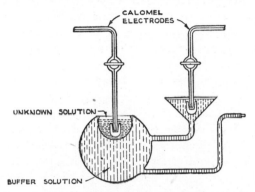

FIG. 18—Kerridge glass electrode
(Kerridge, *Principles of Physical Chemistry for Medical Students*)

This, in the Kerridge electrode, is achieved by placing the two solutions, one in the outer and the other in the inner bowl of a glass electrode shaped as in fig. 18.   A difference of electrical potential, related in magnitude to the pH difference, is established between the two solutions.   This potential difference is measured by connecting the two solutions through KCl to calomel electrodes, so arranged that their e.m.f.'s oppose each other.   The method is rapid, requires extremely small quantities of fluid, and can be applied to blood.   Unfortunately, owing to the extremely high resistance of the glass membrane, the potentials produced are incapable of causing any measurable flow of current.   They have therefore to be measured with an electrometer, which necessitates shielding from atmospherical electrical disturbances, and the preservation of a very high standard of insulation in the whole apparatus.

CHAPTER IX

COLLOIDS

THE difference between the true solution and the colloidal solution is that, in the former, the dissolved substance is present in the solvent in a state of molecular or ionic subdivision, while in the latter the substance is present in the solvent or, more correctly, in the dispersing medium, as particles of size larger than the *usual* molecule or ion. Their larger size may be due to aggregation of the molecules, as we saw in the chapter on Osmotic Pressure, but colloidal solutions are also obtained where the dispersed substance is one whose individual molecules are exceptionally large (*e.g.* proteins). The essential feature in both cases is that the dispersed particles present to the surrounding dispersing medium a large effective surface, at which all the phenomena of surface tension are manifest, and on which several other molecules or ions of ordinary size may be adsorbed. With particles of ionic or ordinary molecular dimensions, such as occur in true solution, these surface phenomena are not exhibited.

Although some two or three years previously Faraday had prepared colloidal dispersions of gold, our knowledge of colloids and of the colloidal state may be said to begin with the researches of Graham in 1861. Graham, in studying the diffusion of dissolved substances through parchment membranes, observed that while salt solutions diffused through the membranes easily, others, like gelatine, starch, and albumin, passed through very slowly or not at all. He noticed also that those substances which readily diffused were also easily crystallised, and he classified them on that account as 'crystalloids.' Those that did not pass through crystallised either with difficulty or not at all, and on account of their frequently gluey consistency he called them 'colloids' (κολλη=glue). We now know that there is no distinct division of substances into crystalloids and colloids, as Graham appeared to believe, because many substances occurring naturally as crystalloids may, by suitable treatment, be obtained in the form of colloidal solutions, and conversely, many natural colloids have been crystallised in the laboratory and, in certain solvents, will form a true molecular solution. For example, sodium chloride in benzol forms a colloidal dispersion, while the soaps of the higher fatty acids which may be colloidal in water form a true solution in alcohol. It is more correct, therefore, to speak of the colloidal and crystalloidal states than to regard them as two different classes of substances.

A colloidal dispersion is a heterogeneous system consisting of two 'phases,' one forming the 'dispersed' or 'internal' phase, and the other the dispersing medium, frequently called the 'continuous' or 'external' phase. The possible combinations yielding such dispersed systems are tabulated in the following table along with common examples of each:—

No.	Dispersed Phase	Continuous Phase	Example
1	Gas	Solid	Gases in minerals.
2	,,	Liquid	Foam.
3	Liquid	Gas	Steam.
4	,,	Another immiscible liquid	Emulsions (when particles large). Emulsoid (when particles small).
5	,,	Solid	Jellies.
6	Solid	Gas	Smoke.
7	,,	Liquid	Colloidal gold.
8	,,	Solid	Ruby glass.

The most important of these biologically are Nos. 4, 5, and 7, particularly Nos. 4 and 5.

Size of Colloidal Particles – The difference between crystalloidal and colloidal solution is one of the size of particle dispersed through the solvent. To come down to actual figures, the molecular particles in crystalloidal solution are in the neighbourhood of $\frac{1}{10,000,000}$ mm. in diameter, in colloidal dispersion the particles range from $\frac{1}{1,000,000}$ to $\frac{1}{10,000}$ mm. It must not be thought that there is a sharp dividing line between the two; these numerical limitations are chosen arbitrarily in a continuous scale. Crystalloidal solutions with large particles merge into the smaller colloidal dispersions, and the colloidal solutions with large colloidal particles pass by degrees into the finer suspensions, and these again into coarser suspensions, until we reach matter in its gross state.

The large size of the colloidal particles compared with ordinary molecules can be actually demonstrated in a number of ways. The particles are not large enough to be visible under the ordinary microscope, because, in the microscope, objects are viewed by light transmitted through them, and the smallest particle that can be made visible in this way must have a diameter greater than half the wave-length of the light used for illumination. Since the wave-lengths of visible light vary from about 0·80 to 0·40 μ, this sets the limits of visibility in the ordinary microscope at approximately $\frac{1}{4}$ μ, and we have roughly gauged the diameter of colloidal particles at $\frac{1}{10}$ to $\frac{1}{1000}$ μ. But the particles will reflect and scatter from their surfaces a strong beam of light, projected through the colloidal solution. Macroscopically, this is known as the Faraday-Tyndall phenomenon, and may be produced as follows. If a glass vessel of pure dust-free water is placed in the track of a beam of light, it is found that the track of the light-beam through the water is practically invisible when the vessel is viewed in a direction at right angles to the direction of the light. It would be quite invisible were it technically possible to prepare water absolutely free from any impurities. If now a colloidal solution is substituted for the water, the track of the light-beam through the solution becomes plainly visible owing to the scattering of light by the colloidal particles dispersed through the solution. Each particle acts as a secondary source of light, and the combined effect of all these secondary light sources produces the appearance of the illuminated beam in the solution.

Now if one could contrive to focus a microscope on the illuminated part of the solution, it would be possible to see, not the particles themselves certainly, but a series of spots of light produced by the light rays scattered from each particle. The ultramicroscope invented by Siedentopf and Zsigmondy is such a contrivance. In its. original form the arrangement was what we have just described, the colloidal solution being held in a small open rectangular vessel, illuminated from the side by a powerful cone of light, and the illuminated track was observed through a microscope provided with a water-immersion objective. Other forms of the instrument have since been invented, one being shown in fig. 19. The apparatus

depicted takes the place of the ordinary substage condenser of the microscope, and consists of a paraboloid reflector provided with a central stop, A, to prevent any of the rays from the illuminating source entering the objective directly. The material on the slide is, as the arrows in the diagram show, illuminated by oblique reflected rays, and the only light which enters the microscope objective is that scattered

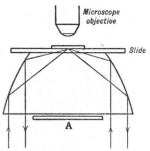

Fig. 19—Diagrammatic section of Wenham paraboloid condenser

from the particles in the material under examination.

There is theoretically no limit to the size of particle that could be rendered visible by such means; by using a sufficiently powerful source of light the presence of even single molecules should be detectable. Practically such intensity of illumination is impossible, and the smallest particles so far made visible are of the order of $\frac{1}{1,000,000}$ mm. Although what is seen through the ultramicroscope is not the particle itself but its diffraction image, it is possible by calculation to estimate the sizes of the particles from the number of images seen in a given volume, compared with the mass of the dispersed substance per unit volume.

Dispersed particles are often roughly classified as to size into (1) microns—those visible under an ordinary microscope; (2) submicrons—those invisible by ordinary microscope but visible by ultramicroscope; and (3) amicrons—those too small to be rendered visible by either. The following diagram (fig. 20) of Ostwald's gives a good idea of the relative size of molecules, colloidal and suspended particles, compared with the anthrax bacillus and a red blood corpuscle.

Further evidence of the comparatively large size of the colloidal particles is given by the fact that colloids will not diffuse through parchment or other similar membranes, as Graham found in his original experiments. More recently this non-diffusibility has been put to practical use in separating

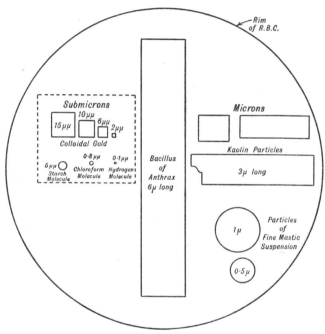

FIG. 20—Relative sizes of various particles compared with a red blood corpuscle. The magnification within the dotted rectangle is thirty-three times that of the remainder of the figure

(After Ostwald, *A Handbook of Colloid Chemistry*, Churchill)

colloidal particles of different size. Bechhold found it possible to prepare collodion or gelatin membranes with the diameter of the pores of the membrane varying according to the method of preparation. The actual diameter of the pores could be determined by blowing compressed air through them. A series of membranes may thus be prepared with gradually diminishing size of pore, and from the one with the smallest pores, which will just permit passage of a particular colloid, the diameter of the colloidal particles may be arrived at. The separation of colloidal particles of different size by such means is known as ultra-filtration. This process of ultra-filtration has uses apart from colloids, such as the separation of bacteria from the fluids containing them.

Brownian Movement – When fine suspensions or colloidal solutions are viewed through an ultramicroscope, the spots of light indicating the presence of particles are seen in constant and apparently chaotic motion. This movement was first observed by a botanist, Robert Brown, in 1827, in a suspension of pollen grains, and hence it is called the Brownian movement. For many years there was much speculation as to the cause of the movement, which is manifested in all fine suspensions and colloidal solutions; but evidence has gradually accumulated that it must be due to the hustling into motion of the colloidal particles by the continuous bombardment of the rapidly moving molecules of the liquid in which they are dispersed. The Brownian movement, in fact, constitutes one of the most direct proofs of the validity of the kinetic theory of matter, and, consequently, it has been studied in detail by several physicists. It is possible to compute, by accurate observation of the rate of displacement of the suspended particles, Avogadro's constant N (p. 61), and the values so deduced show good agreement with determinations by the method previously described. This has not only justified the assumption that molecular bombardment is the cause of the Brownian movement, but has given firm support to the kinetic theory in general.

N = no. of atoms per gram atom.

Maintenance of Colloidal Particles in Suspension – Judging by analogy with the coarser suspensions, one would expect that the particles of a colloidal dispersion would gradually sink to the bottom of the containing vessel. The following factors operate to prevent this. First, the Brownian movement, or rather the molecular bombardment which is the cause of the Brownian movement, tends to maintain an even distribution of the particles. Secondly, as we shall see later, the colloidal particles each bear an electric charge of the same sign, and the mutual electric repulsion between them will prevent their approximation. Other factors in the maintenance of suspension are the viscosity and density of the dispersing medium.

Types of Colloids – The colloidal dispersions with which we are primarily concerned may be differentiated into two great classes according to the amount of water associated with the particles of the dispersed phase.   In a colloidal suspension of gold, for instance, the dispersed phase consists of particles of solid gold and the continuous phase of pure water.   In a colloidal solution of a protein like albumin, the system consists of a dispersed phase of comparatively concentrated albumin solution suspended in a continuous phase of a more dilute solution of albumin.   These two classes are frequently differentiated as 'suspensoid' (gold) and 'emulsoid' (albumin) colloids respectively.   Other names have been used, such as hydrophobe, lyophobe, or irreversible for the suspensoid class, and hydrophile, lyophile, or reversible for the emulsoid class. In general, though not in particular instances, these names are synonymous.   Hydrophile (water-loving) and hydrophobe (water-fearing) are self-explanatory; lyophile and lyophobe are more general terms applicable to all media whether water or not; the terms reversible and irreversible indicate whether or not, after evaporation to dryness, a colloidal solution may be again produced by the simple addition of water.   Two other terms introduced by Graham may be noted.   Those colloidal solutions which were mobile and liquid he called 'sols,' or more particularly 'hydrosols,' 'alcosols,' according to whether the dispersion medium was water or alcohol.   Other colloids that he worked with formed gelatinous masses, and these he called 'gels.'   While the suspensoid colloid is always a sol, the emulsoid colloids may exist in either sol or gel form, the change from one form to the other being sometimes reversible, sometimes irreversible.   For example, ordinary white of egg is an emulsoid in sol form, but by boiling is converted into the gel condition, and after such conversion cannot be transformed to a sol again.   Gelatine, on the other hand, in a concentration of more than about 1 per cent., exists at ordinary room temperature as a gel, but by heating becomes a sol, returning to the gel condition on cooling.

Properties of Colloids – In the above discussion of the nature of colloids a number of their properties, such as their non-diffusibility through membranes, and the exhibition of

Brownian movement, have already been indicated. We may now consider some others.

(1) *Adsorption a Pronounced Phenomenon* – Adsorption, whether of molecules or of ions, is dependent on the extent of the effective surface of the adsorbing body. A sphere measuring 1 cm. in radius placed in water presents a surface of 12·6 sq. cm. to the water. Division of this sphere into particles of colloidal proportions would produce 10^{18} small spheres having an aggregate surface of 1260 *sq. metres*. In colloidal dispersions there is therefore an enormous surface between particle and dispersion medium on which mechanical and electrical adsorption of added substances may and does occur.

(2) *Osmotic Pressure* – Osmotic pressure is dependent on the number of entities of solute per unit volume of solution. Theoretically, therefore, the osmotic pressure of colloids must be low, as the number of particles per unit volume is always small compared with that of true solutions of the same percentage concentration. This is true not only for those colloids whose particles are aggregated molecules, but also for those in which the particles are single molecules of exceptionally large size. In the latter case, a solution of even high percentage concentration is only a fraction of molar strength, and hence its osmotic pressure will also be only a fraction of the 22·4 atmospheres associated with a solution of molar strength.

Where experimental evidence has been obtained, the theoretically small pressure of colloids has been confirmed by observation. Such observations of the osmotic pressures produced by colloids are apt to be unsatisfactory, because it is difficult to free the colloidal solutions from the electrolytes with which they are almost always associated. Electrolytes have a high osmotic pressure, and their presence even in very small amounts vitiates the observation of the much lower colloidal osmotic pressure. This refers, of course, only to electrolytes existing free in the dispersion medium. Where they are associated with the colloidal particles themselves, *e.g.* by adsorption thereon, they have no direct osmotic activity of their own, since they are not separate units. Thus associated, they often have, indeed, a depressant action on the

8

osmotic pressure, apparently through causing the colloidal particles to aggregate into larger units, and so reducing the number of osmotically active particles per unit volume of solution.

The depressant influence of electrolytes on osmotic pressure is dependent on the nature of both its cations and its anions. For the anions, Hofmeister, in 1890, found that the following was the order of their depressant action on osmotic pressure :—

$$Cl > SO_4 > NO_3 > Br > I > CNS.$$

As he found similar sequences in the relative effects of anions on several other properties of colloids, such as their imbibition and liability to precipitation, he came to regard them as of considerable importance. The arrangement of anions in the order given above is known as a Hofmeister series. The physico-chemical significance of the Hofmeister series has been severely criticised by Loeb, on the grounds that Hofmeister took no account of the varying effect of the salts which he used on the pH of the colloidal dispersions. Loeb has given evidence to show that, if the pH is controlled, the anions may be graded according to valency, and not in the somewhat puzzling order of the Hofmeister series. Loeb's criticisms are generally, but not universally, accepted.

The reaction of a colloidal solution also affects its osmotic pressure. In those colloids which are amphoteric (see p. 77) and possess an iso-electric point, the osmotic pressure is at a minimum at this point, and increases when the reaction changes from the iso-electric point either in an acid or alkaline direction. This is not surprising when we remember that the iso-electric condition is one of minimum ionisation, and that ionisation and association with inorganic ions increases on either side of this point.

(3) *Possession of Electric Charge by Particles* – A most important property of colloidal solutions is the existence of an electric charge on the dispersed particles. The sign of this charge is negative in some colloids and positive in others, but in either case, all the individual particles of any specific colloid are similarly charged. In some cases, e.g. the proteins, the sign of the charge varies according to the pH of the solution.

Colloids may thus be classed as electro-negative or electro-positive according to the nature of the charge on their particles, and the following list gives a few examples of each class :—

Electro-negative	Electro-positive
Platinum, Silver, Gold. Mercury, Iodine, Sulphur. Stannic acid. Arsenic sulphide. Proteins on alkaline side of iso-electric point. Glycogen, Starch. Soaps, Lecithin, Phosphatides.	Bismuth, Lead, Iron. Copper. Iron hydroxide. Aluminium hydroxide. Proteins on acid side of iso-electric point. Histones and Protamines.

The presence of the electric charge and the nature of its sign may be demonstrated by the process of 'cataphoresis.' A U-tube, which can be filled from the bend and which is provided with two platinum electrodes at the upper extremities of its two limbs, is partially filled with water, to which some alcohol may be added to lower its density. The colloidal solution to be tested is then carefully run in below the water so as to push it up into contact with the two electrodes, thus leaving a distinct boundary line between colloid and water at the same level in each limb. If a current is now passed through the solution, the positions of the boundary lines will alter, the colloid moving towards the electrode whose sign is opposite to that of the charge of its particles, and retreating from the electrode of sign similar to that of its particles.

The explanation of the existence of an electric charge on colloidal particles is not in all cases clear. In some it is probably the result of electrolytic dissociation of the surface molecules of the colloidal particles. This would explain, for instance, the electro-negative nature of silicic acid and the positive charge on metallic hydroxides. The silicic acid particle, by losing dissociated H^+ ions, would become nega-tively charged, and the loss of dissociated OH^- ions would leave the colloidal iron particle with a positive charge. Such an explanation will not suffice for the colloidal metallic solutions like gold, platinum, etc.   According to one view, the charge in these is due to a preferential adsorption of one of the ions produced by dissociation of the dispersion medium. Thus, in a colloid dispersed in water, if there is a preferential adsorption of the H^+ ion of the water by the colloidal particles, these will take a positive charge.   Adsorption of the OH^- ion, on the contrary, would give the colloid electro-negative properties.

The presence of electric charges on the colloidal particles implies the presence of charges of opposite sign on the medium in which the particles are dispersed.   The opposite charge on the continuous phase may be brought into evidence by carrying out an experiment similar to the cataphoresis experiment, but keeping the colloid fixed in position in the lower part of the U-tube.   This may be achieved by using a colloid such as gelatine or agar in stiff gel form.   When a current is passed under such conditions, the colloid is immovable, but the water moves.   If, for example, the colloid is electro-negative, the water is positively charged and therefore rises in the limb containing the cathode.   This passage of water through a colloid under the influence of an electrical current is called 'electrical endosmose.'

(4) *Precipitation of Colloids by Electrolytes* – We have seen that one of the factors in maintaining colloidal particles in suspension is the existence on the particles of charges of similar sign.   If, therefore, an electrolyte is added to a colloidal solution, the ion whose charge is opposite to that of the colloidal particle tends to be adsorbed, with resulting neutralisation of the colloidal charge.   The first effect of this neutralisation will be an aggregation of the original colloidal particles to form a suspension of a much smaller number of larger particles, and, if only a small amount of electrolyte has been added, these more highly aggregated particles may remain in suspension. If, however, more than a certain amount of electrolyte be added, the neutralisation of the colloidal charge will be nearly or quite complete, and the colloidal suspension will precipitate. These effects may be beautifully seen in the gold sols, in which the colour of the colloidal solution varies with the magnitude of the particles.   On addition of an electrolyte to

a gold sol in an extremely fine state of subdivision and
therefore appearing red by transmitted light, the transmitted
colour will be observed to change as the particles become
aggregated into larger and larger units, until ultimately a black
precipitate of metallic gold will fall.

The amount of electrolyte required to precipitate a colloid
depends on the nature of both colloid and electrolyte. Suspensoids are much more sensitive to precipitation by this means
than emulsoids. Hardy first investigated quantitatively the
effect of different electrolytes in causing the precipitation of a
particular suspensoid, and showed that (1) the precipitating
ion was the one carrying an opposite charge to that of the
colloidal particle (Hardy's rule), and (2) the concentration of
the effective ion necessary to cause precipitation depended on
its valency, in such a way that if X were the precipitating
power of a monovalent ion, X^2 and X^3 would be the powers
of divalent and trivalent ions respectively. But it is found that
the precipitating power of divalent and trivalent ions is frequently far more than these ratios warrant, so that Hardy's
simple quantitative relationship is only true in a very general
way, and does not afford a complete explanation of the precipitating power of different electrolytes. If it did, the precipitating action on an electro-negative colloid of different salts
of, say, potassium, should all be the same, and this is found
experimentally not to be the case. Other factors, therefore,
must enter into the process. One of the most important of
these is the stabilising effect of the non-precipitating ion of
the electrolyte, *i.e.* the one of similar charge to that of the
colloid. Although this ion will not be electrically adsorbed
to the colloidal particle, experimental findings go to show that
it has some influence in modifying the effect of the precipitating ion. The precipitating action of electrolytes on suspensoid
colloids is thus a complex process which, though the valency
of the precipitating ion is of prime importance, may be influenced by the nature of the other ion of the electrolyte, and
by other factors which at present are somewhat obscure.

When we come to consider the effects of electrolytes on
colloids of the emulsoid class, experimental indications of a
similar dependence on valency are also to be found, but the

emulsoids in general are very much less sensitive to electrolytes, and frequently half- or fully-saturated solutions of electrolytes have to be used to cause precipitation.   The explanation of this phenomenon probably is that the dispersed and continuous phases of the emulsoids are similar in *composition* and differ only in *concentration*, and the system is thus more stable.   Moreover, the effect of electrolytes in precipitating emulsoids would seem to consist in a withdrawal of water, a dehydrating of the dispersed phase which brings them into a condition approaching that of a suspensoid, rather than a direct electrical neutralisation.   While emulsoids are relatively little affected by small concentrations of electrolytes, the addition of such small concentrations may frequently complete a process of precipitation which has been initiated by other means.   For example, heating alone will not precipitate a non-iso-electric solution of albumin or globulin provided they are salt-free, but it does produce such a change of condition in the protein solution (denaturation) that a subsequent addition of relatively small quantities of electrolyte will then cause precipitation.

The precipitates produced in emulsoids by almost saturated solutions of electrolytes can be redispersed to form a colloidal solution; this is contrary to what is found with suspensoids, in which electrolyte precipitation is usually an irreversible process.

Since the precipitation of colloids by oppositely charged ions is caused by electrical adsorption of the ion, one may expect to find considerable quantities of the ion in the colloidal precipitate.   In fact, it is often very difficult to separate the components of this ion-colloid complex, though another similarly charged ion may readily be substituted for the original one.

(5) *Precipitation by Oppositely Charged Colloid* – Just as a colloid may be precipitated by the ion of an electrolyte, so is it equally possible to precipitate an electro-negative colloid by the addition of an appropriate quantity of an electro-positive colloid.   This process is frequently of practical use in obtaining the complete precipitation of a protein, as, for instance, in the precipitation of the serum proteins which ordinarily are on the

alkaline side of their iso-electric pH, and hence are electro-negative, by the addition of colloidal iron, which is positively charged.

If too small or too great an amount of the oppositely charged colloid is added, precipitation may not occur, but we may have instead the formation of a colloidal complex consisting of two colloids associated together.   In the first case, the charge on the complex particles will be unchanged, but, in the second, where an excess of the oppositely charged colloid has been added, it is evident that a reversal of the charge must have occurred.

(6) *Protective Action* – A somewhat similar phenomenon is the protective action of emulsoids on suspensoids. As we have seen, suspensoids are much more readily precipitated by electrolytes than emulsoids, but if an emulsoid is added to a suspensoid, it is frequently found that the particles of the latter adsorb the former.   The suspensoid thus becomes super-ficially an emulsoid colloid, and hence less liable to precipita-tion. A good example of this phenomenon is the action of various emulsoids on the gold sols; and, indeed, the degree of protective action exhibited by different emulsoids is so characteristic that, to a certain extent, it may be used to identify them. The degree of protective action is measured in terms of Schulz and Zsigmondy's 'gold number,' which is the number of milligrams of the emulsoid which just suffices to prevent aggregation (shown by change in colour) of 10 c.c. of a bright red gold sol by 1 c.c. 10 per cent. NaCl.   Protective action has been used clinically to determine the relative amounts of albumins and globulins in the body-fluids. Alterations in the albumin-globulin ratio are readily detected by such a method, because globulins have a marked protective action while albumins have little.

(7) *Colour of Colloidal Solutions* – The Faraday-Tyndall phenomenon and ultramicroscopic images have as their basis the scattering of light by the suspended particles. When the particles composing the dispersed phase are of the size found in emulsoids and the larger-particled suspensoids, this scatter-ing involves a mixture of all the visible wave-lengths, and hence the scattered light appears white. If, however, the

particles in suspension are sufficiently small, as in the gold sols, the interference with light passing through the solution is selective, and certain wave-lengths will be absorbed or reflected by the particles, and the remaining wave-lengths allowed to pass through the solution. A solution of such finely divided particles will thus have one colour by reflected light and another by light transmitted through it. Further, the colours absorbed or transmitted should theoretically vary with the magnitude of the particles in suspension, and though the selective action on light waves of the dispersed particles is complicated by the optical properties of the dispersion medium, theoretical expectations can be to some extent confirmed by observation. In general, the more finely divided the colloidal suspension, the more effectively are the shorter wave-lengths (blue) scattered, leaving the longer wave-lengths (red) to be transmitted. A gold sol of high degree of dispersion thus appears blue when looked at from the side, and red when held up in front of the light. With increasing size of particle the transmitted wave-lengths become shorter, so that the transmitted colour changes from red to blue and violet.

This production of colour by light interference in highly dispersed systems is not only an interesting phenomenon in physical chemistry, but also offers an explanation of many natural colourings such as those of sea and sky. The colour of the human iris also is due to the presence of finely dispersed uncoloured particles. At birth the colour is always deep blue, but as the child grows the particles become larger and the blue becomes lighter in tone, while at the same time the development of more or less black pigment in the iris may alter the original blue to brown or black. If the pigment does not develop, the eyes remain blue.

(8) *Viscosity* – The viscosity of suspensoids is generally low, and, where water is the dispersion medium, differs little from that of water itself. Emulsoid colloids, especially in the gel form, have a relatively high viscosity, which is probably associated with the largeness of the emulsoid particle, and the fact that any deformation of the solution as a whole must also be accompanied by deformation of the individual dispersed particles. Amphoteric emulsoids with an iso-electric point

show a minimum viscosity at this point. This is probably because in the iso-electric condition the hydration of the emulsoid is minimal, *i.e.* the colloid is in a condition in which it approximates most closely to the suspensoid type.

(9) *Gel Formation* – The effect of rise of temperature on emulsoids varies in different colloids, increasing the viscosity in some (albumin), and diminishing it in others (gelatine). In some colloids this change in viscosity progresses until a solid or semi-solid elastic gel is formed. Gelation is produced in egg albumin by heating it above about 60° C., and in gelatine, dissolved in warm water, by cooling it to room temperatures. The temperatures at which such sol-gel transitions occur vary with the concentration of the colloid, with its pH, and with its content of electrolytes. Some sol-gel changes are reversible, *e.g.* gelatine; others, *e.g.* albumin, are irreversible.

The intimate physico-chemical nature of the change of a sol into a gel is not yet well understood. One aspect of the change appears to be a rearrangement of the two phases of the system. What was previously the dispersed phase becomes the continuous phase, and *vice versa*. If we consider an albumin sol as consisting of dispersed particles of a relatively strong albumin solution suspended in a much weaker albumin solution, then in the gel state the weaker albumin solution is now dispersed through a continuous phase of albumin sufficiently concentrated to give solidity to the whole mass. Fig. 21 shows this diagrammatically, the dark areas representing the more

Fig. 21—To illustrate the reversal of phases in gel-formation

(Bayliss, *Principles of General Physiology*)

concentrated phase of an emulsoid and the clear areas the less concentrated, so that A depicts the sol condition and B the gel condition. It is unlikely that this is the complete explanation of gel formation. By ultramicroscopic observation a number of investigators have been able to detect details of structure such as fibrils or crystal-like formations in certain gels, and it is very probable that there is still much to be observed and interpreted.

(10) *Imbibition* – A property of gels is their ability to soak up water and other fluids, the gel swelling in the process, but not at all commensurately with the volume of fluid taken up. It is evident, therefore, that the fluid imbibed must be in some way compressed. Water imbibed by a gel can be squeezed out only with difficulty, and gels under considerable external pressures can still imbibe a certain amount of water. The degree of compression in a water-logged gel may be calculated from the contraction observed when a known volume of free water is imbibed by a known volume of gel. These pressures are enormous, amounting in the case of gelatine to 300–400 atmospheres, and in starch to over 2500 atmospheres.

The property of imbibition, like so many other properties, is at a minimum at the iso-electric point of amphoteric colloids, and is increased by addition of either acid or alkali. It is diminished, in the same way as the osmotic pressure, by the presence of electrolytes, and Hofmeister, in observing the depression of imbibition of proteins, found that again the anions of salts were effective in the order of the series called by his name (p. 114). Loeb's criticism of the Hofmeister series is as applicable here as there.

(11) *Diffusion* – Colloidal solutions in contact with water or true solutions diffuse into them very slowly, because the large size of their particles is necessarily accompanied by sluggishness of movement. The true solutions, on the other hand, readily diffuse into the colloid, even into a gel, into which, as dialysis experiments show, another colloid will not enter. When such diffusion of a true solution into a gel is accompanied by a chemical reaction involving precipitation between the diffusing liquid and some other substance incorporated in the gel, a peculiar effect known as the Liesegang phenomenon is sometimes produced. The precipitation does not occur evenly all over the area occupied by the diffusing liquid, but in intermittent zones. If, for example, some gelatine in which some potassium bichromate is incorporated is allowed to solidify in a Petri dish, and then a drop of strong $AgNO_3$ is placed in the centre, the silver nitrate diffuses into the gel, forming silver bichromate. The silver bichromate is not deposited evenly, but in concentric rings with progressively

widening spaces between them. One explanation suggested for this phenomenon is as follows. As the silver nitrate advances into the gelatine, a very concentrated region of silver bichromate forms slightly behind the front line of advance and precipitates out. This precipitate acts like a crystal in a supersaturated solution, drawing towards itself further supplies of potassium bichromate from the region in front, thus forming more precipitate. The zone immediately in front of this deposit is thus freed of its potassium bichromate, and the silver nitrate has to advance across this space without causing any chemical reaction. When it has done so and has reached a new supply of bichromate, the cycle of changes is repeated, and a second ring of precipitate is formed. This and other explanations fail to account for the experimental fact that, with the same chemical reaction, stratification takes place in some gels and not in others.

CHAPTER X

ENZYMES

ONE of the most remarkable characters of animal and vegetable organisms is their ability to carry out, at low temperatures and in the absence of strong reagents, chemical reactions which in the laboratory can often be initiated only by the employment of most drastic chemical procedures. For many of these biochemical processes, what are called 'enzymes' are responsible. All the digestive changes that the proteins, carbohydrates, and fats of our food undergo in the alimentary canal are brought about by enzymes secreted from the various digestive glands : in the liver, an enzyme is responsible for the conversion of glycogen into glucose; from many of the tissues, extracts have been prepared which, apparently by enzymatic action, convert the purines, which are derived from nucleoproteins, into uric acid; and so on.

Enzymes are nowadays designated by adding the suffix *ase* or *lytic* to the name of the substance on which they act: *e.g.* an enzyme hydrolysing protein is a proteolytic enzyme, or protease; a fat-splitting enzyme, a lipase; and so on. However, a number of the original names given to the earlier known enzymes, such as pytalin, pepsin, trypsin, etc., are still retained. The substance on which the enzyme acts is called its substrate.

The table below gives a list of some of the more important enzymes with their substrates.

Of the nature of enzymes very little is known, except that in their actions they resemble very closely the catalysts of the pure chemist. It will be best, therefore, to recall the features of the ordinary chemical catalysts and then to compare the biological catalysts with them.

Chemical Catalysts – A 'catalyst' was defined by Ostwald as a "substance which alters the velocity of a chemical reaction without entering into the formation of the end-products of that reaction." The catalyst is, therefore, recoverable unchanged at the completion of the reaction.

Enzyme	Origin	Substrate
Ptyalin . .	Saliva	Starch.
Pepsin . .	Gastric mucosa	Protein.
Rennin . .	..	Caseinogen.
Trypsin . .	Pancreas	Protein.
Anylase . .	Pancreas, etc.	Starch.
Lipase . .	Pancreas, etc.	Fat.
Erepsin . .	Intestinal mucosa	Protein.
Invertase . .	,, ,,	Cane sugar.
Maltase . .	,, ,,	Maltose.
Urease . .	Soja bean	Urea.
Esterase . .	Various	Lower fatty acids.
Peroxidase . .	,,	H_2O_2 and other peroxides.
Deamidase . .	,,	NH_2 groups.

For instance, the following reaction of the splitting of cane sugar by hydrolysis to two mono-saccharide molecules occurs very slowly by itself,

$$C_{12}H_{22}O_{11} + H_2O = 2C_6H_{12}O_6,$$

but proceeds much more rapidly if a little acid such as HCl is added; and when the reaction has gone on to completion, it will be found that the HCl is still present unaltered and undiminished in amount. The HCl is said to 'catalyse' the reaction.

Since a catalyst is not used up in the reaction which it catalyses, it is not altogether surprising to find that minute quantities of them may be very active in accelerating the reaction. Take the reaction of hydriodic acid and hydrogen peroxide to form water and iodine: this particular reaction is catalysed by molybdic acid, and an accelerating effect can be detected when the concentration of molybdic acid is as low as 1 gram-molecule per 32 million litres. At the same time, the extent by which a catalysed reaction is accelerated is proportional to the amount of catalyst present; the greater the concentration of catalyst, the higher the velocity of the reaction.

So far we have spoken of catalysis as a process of acceleration of chemical reaction; there are instances, however, where the velocity of reaction is *diminished* by the addition of a substance which is not used up in the course of the reaction. Such substances are known as negative catalysts.

Does a catalyst induce a chemical reaction between substances which, in the absence of the catalyst, would not enter into combination at all? This is a question very difficult to answer, because, in the absence of catalyst, an immeasurably small amount of chemical reaction may or may not be taking place. For example, hydrogen and oxygen gases show an appreciable combination to form water at ordinary room temperatures, provided the reaction is catalysed by the presence of spongy platinum, but no detectable combination occurs at room temperature in the absence of the catalyst. On the other hand, an appreciable formation of water occurs, without catalyst, at temperatures above 500° C. Now the velocity of chemical reactions is, in general, halved by a fall in temperature of 10° C. A reaction with a velocity of 1 at 500° C. would therefore have a velocity of $\frac{1}{2}$ at 490° C., $\frac{1}{4}$ at 480° C., and $1/2^{49}$ at a room temperature of 10° C.; this means that an amount of change that occurred in one minute at 500° C. would take approximately 1,000,000,000 years to occur at 10° C.

The significance of the velocity constant of a reaction has been discussed in the chapter on Acids and Bases, and a practical equation derived for its determination. This equation in the case of a monomolecular reaction was as follows:—

$$k = \frac{1}{t} \log_e \frac{a}{a-x},$$

a being the molar concentration at the beginning, and $a-x$ the molar concentration at the end of time t. Now since a catalyst alters the velocity of a reaction, the values of k in a catalysed and an uncatalysed reaction will be different, k being greater in the catalysed reaction (in a case of positive catalysis). If one experimentally observes a, x, and t in a catalysed reaction and deduces k according to the above equation, a constant value should be found for it no matter whether the observations are taken at the beginning or towards the end of the reaction. Some experimental determinations of k in the inversion of cane sugar catalysed by acid are given below:

Time in Minutes	k
0	0·001330
30	1332
60	1352
90	1379
120	1321
150	1371
210	1465
330	1463
510	1386

(Bayliss)

Any *observed* deviation of k from its theoretically constant value will indicate some source of interference with the catalyst during the course of the reaction. If the interference is a favourable one, then k will tend to rise as the reaction proceeds; an unfavourable influence will tend to diminish k. The importance of this we shall see when we come to deal with enzymes.

The equation indicates another point. In any reaction, catalysed or uncatalysed, the progression of chemical change bears to the passage of time the same relation as a series of logarithms bears to the corresponding antilogarithms. Therefore, if we graph the course of the reaction, plotting amount of chemical change against time, we obtain a logarithmic curve.

Another point in the kinetics of catalysed reactions must be referred to. Many catalysable reactions are reversible; a good example is the hydrolysis of ethyl acetate to acetic acid and alcohol, which takes place slowly by itself but can be accelerated by the addition of a small quantity of acid,

$$CH_3COOC_2H_5 + H_2O \rightleftharpoons CH_3COOH + C_2H_5OH.$$

The equilibrium position of such reactions is the same, whether the reaction is catalysed or not. This must mean that the catalyst accelerates such a reaction in both directions, and to the same extent in each direction, because, as we have seen (p. 71), the equilibrium position of a reversible reaction can be defined by the ratio between the velocity constants of the two opposing reactions. If then, under catalysis, this ratio remains the same, as it must do if the equilibrium position is unaltered, the two velocity constants must be equally affected by the catalyst, or in other words, the two directions of the reversible reaction must be equally accelerated.

Little is known about the nature of catalytic action. Some catalysts appear to act by offering a large surface on which the reacting molecules are adsorbed. The high concentration of reactants so produced around the particles would account, by mass action, for the accelerated rate of their chemical combination. This type is well exemplified by spongy platinum, an instance of the action of which has just been given. Other catalysts appear to act as intermediate carriers, combining first with the reacting substances to form an intermediate compound, which then breaks down into the final products, at the same time freeing the catalyst for further action. If, for example, the chemical change of two substances A and B into another substance C can be accelerated by a catalyst X which acts as a carrier, the steps of the process may be represented as follows :—

Uncatalysed Reaction.   Catalysed Reaction.

$$A+B \longrightarrow C.$$

$$(1)\ A+X\ =AX.$$
$$(2)\ AX+B=C+X.$$

In a case of positive catalysis by such a method, the two stages of the catalysed reaction must obviously occupy less time than the single stage of the uncatalysed reaction. The chamber process for the manufacture of sulphuric acid is an example of this type of catalysis. Here nitric oxide acts as a carrier catalyst, causing the oxygen to combine with water and sulphur dioxide as follows:—

$$2NO+O_2 \longrightarrow 2NO_2.$$
$$NO_2+SO_2+H_2O \longrightarrow H_2SO_4+NO.$$

Many catalytic processes occur which cannot be explained by either of these modes of action, and, in fact, in the majority of catalytic actions the mechanism is entirely unknown. Hydrogen ions and hydroxyl ions act as catalysts in many reactions, as in the inversion of cane sugar already mentioned. Water itself is also a catalyst; many reactions occur with ease in the presence of perhaps the merest trace of water-vapour, which will not occur at all if the reacting substances are perfectly dry.

Before leaving the inorganic catalysts to consider the enzymes of living organisms, we may note two other phenomena in connection with catalysis—'autocatalysis' and 'poisoning' of catalysts. Some reactions are catalysed by their own products; e.g. Ag_2O is decomposed into silver and oxygen at high temperatures, and the reaction, once started, is catalysed by the silver which is produced in a finely divided condition. In a similar way a catalytic reaction may produce a substance which in its turn acts as a secondary catalyst for the reaction. Such a process is known as autocatalysis.

Substances which diminish the activity of catalysts are called catalytic 'poisons.' They are mostly known in connection with those catalysts which act by surface adsorption; for example, traces of HCN will very markedly diminish the catalytic activity of colloidal platinum.

Enzymes – We may now consider the propriety of regarding enzymes as catalysts, by comparing their action (or rather the action of extracts believed to contain them) with the phenomena of chemical catalysis just referred to. But, first of all, it may be well to impress the reader with the fact that our knowledge of the real nature of enzymes is practically nil. Enzymes, with one doubtful exception, have never been isolated in a pure state. It is quite true that extracts which behave like catalysts can be prepared from many tissues, but the investigation of the chemical nature of the enzymes believed to be present in such extracts is very difficult, because they are present only in minute amount and intimately associated with the other constituents of the extract. When one attempts to get rid of these associated materials, one finds that their removal is accompanied by a progressive loss of enzymatic activity, and this sets a limit to the amount of purification possible.

The possible exception referred to is Sumner's urease.

9

Urease is an enzyme capable of converting urea to ammonium carbonate, and is found in the Soja bean and the jack bean. Sumner, by refrigeration of an acetone extract, prepared a crystalline product from jack bean meal, which he believes to be urease in pure form. He found that this product had the reactions of a globulin, and was so active as to be able to hydrolyse its own weight of urea in 1·4 seconds. Among other attempts to isolate enzymes in a pure state may be mentioned those of Willstätter and his co-workers on various enzymes. Some of their preparations gave protein reactions; others could be obtained free from protein reactions, though, when so freed, they were much less stable. Enzymatic activity is thus not invariably associated with the presence of protein, nor, for that matter, as far as known yet, with the presence of any particular chemical grouping.

A little more is known about the physical properties of enzymes. Their inability to diffuse through parchment or collodion membranes indicates that they are colloids, and, like other colloids, their particles will be electrically charged. Their activity is greatest at a certain optimum temperature, and they are probably optically active.

The tendency of an enzyme-containing extract to lose its activity on purification has led to such views as that of Arthus that enzymes are not chemical entities at all, but only properties assumed under certain conditions by chemical substances which, under other conditions, would exhibit no catalytic activity. However, such views have gained little acceptance, and the general belief is that advance in chemical technique will make it possible to isolate enzymes as definite chemical substances.

In the subsequent comparison of catalysts and enzymes, then, we are comparing substances of known chemical composition with extracts of living tissues, containing unknown quantities of unknown catalytic substances in more or less impure condition.

The true catalyst is found unchanged at the end of the reaction. This is exceptional with enzymes, and is simply an indication of their extreme instability.

As with catalysts, extremely minute quantities of the

enzymes can exhibit activity; and their activity is the more
astonishing when we recollect that the best extracts that can
be prepared are not all enzyme, but are very impure. One
part of rennet will curdle 400,000 times its own weight of
caseinogen, and a preparation of invertase has been obtained
of which one part will invert 200,000 parts of cane sugar.

As with chemical catalysts, the acceleration produced by an
enzyme is, in general, proportional to the quantity of enzyme
added. Nevertheless it has been shown that the smaller
quantities of some enzymes are proportionally much more
effective than the larger quantities, *e.g.* in the following
observations on trypsin :—

Relative Concentration of Enzyme	Time in Minutes required for equal amounts of Hydrolysis
8	41
5	48
4	55
2	81
1	144

(Bayliss)

These numerical relationships are similar to those found
to hold between adsorbent and adsorbed substance (p. 40)
when the concentration of the latter relative to the former is
varied. This is one of the grounds for the belief that the
process of adsorption plays some part in enzyme action.

In dealing with the chemical catalysts we have seen that the
course of a chemical reaction is represented by a logarithmic
curve, as in A, fig. 22. The presence of a catalyst does not
alter this logarithmic relationship, but only alters the value of
k, the velocity constant. What is the course of a reaction
accelerated by the presence of an enzyme? No universal
rule can be laid down, for there are great differences between
different enzymes; but in general the enzyme reaction tends
to be slower in the later stages than the logarithmic curve
predicts. Expressed in another way, the velocity constant

tends to fall, especially after the reaction has gone on for some time, as is shown in the following case of hydrolysis of lactose by lactase:—

Time from beginning of Reaction	Velocity Constant k.
1	0·0640
2	0·0543
3	0·0460
5	0·0310
24	0·0129

(Armstrong)

In addition to this general slowing, many enzymes show a rate greater than that theoretically expected in the very earliest stages of the reaction. The velocity constant in such rises

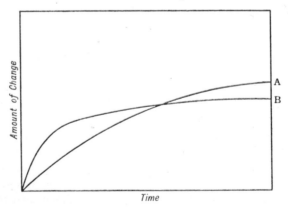

FIG. 22—A, Logarithmic curve of the inversion of cane sugar by acid
B, Curve of action of trypsin on caseinogen
(After Bayliss, *The Nature of Enzyme Action*)

for a brief period at the beginning of the reaction, this rise being followed by the general fall described above. The graph of an enzyme reaction showing both of these phenomena would therefore be something like curve B, A being the logarithmic curve of an ordinary chemical reaction, catalysed or uncatalysed (fig. 22).

What reasons can be assigned for these differences? The initial increased activity is readily accounted for on the hypothesis that adsorption plays a large part in enzyme action. At the beginning of the reaction there is an excess of substrate relatively to enzyme. More substrate is present than the enzyme particles can possibly adsorb, and, after the initially adsorbed substrate has been dealt with, there is a further supply of substrate ready to be adsorbed in its place. If the catalytic activity of enzymes is controlled by adsorption, the tendency during this early stage of excessive substrate will thus be for an equal amount of chemical change to occur per unit of time, and the graph of the reaction will tend to be a straight line. This effect of excess of substrate is illustrated by some experiments of Armstrong, in which a small amount of lactase was allowed to act on varying concentrations of lactose. When the lactose concentration was high (10 to 30 per cent.), the amount hydrolysed in a certain time was the same in the 30 per cent. as in the 10 per cent. solution. With low concentrations of lactose (1 per cent. and less) the amount hydrolysed in a definite time was the less the lower the original lactose concentration.

A second cause for an unexpectedly high activity of an enzyme during the early stages of its action is the production by the enzyme in many cases of a substance which either acts as a secondary catalyst for the reaction, or in some way, perhaps by changes in H^+ ion concentration, increases the activity of the enzyme itself. Thus a process analogous to 'autocatalysis' occurs.

The comparative slowness of the reaction in the later stages is much more constant than the excessive rapidity sometimes observed in the early stages, and is always due to inactivation of the enzyme. The causes of such inactivation are very various. In the first place, the accumulation of the products of the observed reaction will tend to produce a reverse reaction, and the enzyme will be partially diverted towards catalysing it. The magnitude of this reverse reaction will depend on the position of equilibrium, and on how far this equilibrium is altered by the presence of the enzyme. Again, the products frequently alter the hydrogen-ion concentration of the system, and, by so doing, either affect the enzyme directly by precipitating it, or indirectly by providing a medium comparatively unsuitable for its action (see hydrogen-ion concentration below).

Quite apart from the injurious effect of the products, however, enzymes show a spontaneous tendency to lose their activity. This loss is much smaller, though still existent, in the presence of their substrates, probably owing to the formation of a more stable adsorption compound between the two. That it is merely the adsorption that confers the stability, and not any chemical relationship between enzyme and substrate, seems probable from Bayliss's finding that trypsin is largely protected from spontaneous inactivation by adsorption to charcoal.

So far enzymes have been considered as accelerators for a reaction proceeding in one direction only, but their effect on reversible reactions must also be discussed. If they are capable of catalysing both directions of a reversible reaction, their biological importance will not be restricted to producing catabolic changes; but they will be equally important in biological syntheses. Now most of the enzyme reactions studied under laboratory conditions are reactions of hydrolysis such as

$$\text{Ethyl butyrate} + \text{Water} \rightleftharpoons \text{Butyric acid} + \text{Alcohol}.$$

Under the usual *in vitro* conditions of experiment such reactions are occurring in the presence of excess of water, and their equilibrium positions will therefore, by the law of mass action, be very near the point of complete hydrolysis; that is, in the case above, of complete change into butyric acid and ethyl alcohol. Any synthetic properties that the enzyme may possess are masked by the preponderance of its analytic activity. If, however, we arrange conditions so that the butyric acid and alcohol are in excess and the water is reduced to a minimum, we should expect the addition of an esterase to accelerate a synthetic formation of ethyl butyrate, and this it actually does, as was shown by Kastle and Loevenhart in 1900. Similar synthetic capacities under appropriate experimental conditions have been demonstrated for many other enzymes, *e.g.* by Croft Hill (1898) in the synthesis by maltase of iso-maltose from glucose, and by Kay in the synthesis of urea from ammonium carbonate by urease.

The control of the direction of a reversible reaction, whether catalysed by enzyme or not, by the relative concentrations of synthetic and analytic products, is a very important point, because it offers one explanation of the apparently automatic control of many reactions *in vivo*. For example, the animal stores its carbohydrate in the form of glycogen, and transports it in the blood in the form of glucose. A deficiency of glucose in the blood will lead to the reaction glycogen ⇌ glucose proceeding in the direction of the upper arrow, the deficiency being made good at the expense of the store; on the other hand, the presence of an excessive concentration of glucose in the blood will lead to the reverse reaction and addition to the store of glycogen.

Another point important to the biologist is that a reaction which, under laboratory conditions, is reversible with a definite equilibrium position may be a 'one-way' reaction in the living body if there are arrangements for the continuous removal of the products of the reaction. In the glycogen ⇌ glucose example, the constant withdrawal of glucose from the system would lead to a reaction confined solely to the direction of the upper arrow. This removal of products is easily achieved in the organism, most obviously by carrying them away in the blood- or lymph-stream, but by other methods as well, such as deposition in insoluble form. The relative dominance of the analytic and synthetic phases of an enzyme's action *in vitro* is thus no indication of its action *in vivo*.

The fact that enzymes catalyse both directions of a reversible reaction raises the question of their effect on the equilibrium position. In some cases this has been found to be unaltered, as with a true catalyst; in others, the equilibrium position is altered. Such an alteration of equilibrium is not very surprising when we consider that enzymes are apparently most unstable substances, and, moreover, can only be obtained for experimental purposes as components of more or less complex extracts. The enzyme itself may disappear before equilibrium is reached, or the position of equilibrium may be altered by reactions other than the enzymatic one under observation.

We may now consider one or two special features of enzymes which, generally speaking, are not exhibited by the chemical catalysts.

(1) *Optimum Temperature* – The activity of an enzyme increases with rise of temperature, up to a point, which for most enzymes is about 40°; with further rise of temperature their activity again diminishes. The explanation of this optimum temperature is simple. According to van't Hoff's Law, the rate of an enzyme action, like any other chemical reaction, should increase with rise of temperature, but countering this there is the injurious effect of heat on the enzyme itself, an effect probably due to coagulation or precipitation of the colloidal enzyme particles. The optimum temperature is the point at which the best balance is struck between these two opposing tendencies.

(2) *Optimum Hydrogen-ion Concentration* – The activity of enzymes is dependent to a great extent on the hydrogen-ion concentration of the medium in which they act, each enzyme having an optimum pH at which its greatest activity is manifested; *e.g.* pepsin acts best in a medium of pH 1·6, and trypsin in a medium of pH 8·3.

(3) *Specificity* – One of the remarkable features of enzymes, and one of the difficulties in any theory of their mechanism, is the highly selective nature of their action. The action of pepsin is limited to the breakdown of proteins, and it shows no action at all on either carbohydrates or fats; pancreatic lipase will split only fats and such related substances as simple esters, *e.g.* ethyl butyrate. On the other hand, the esterase extractable from the liver is highly active on ethyl butyrate, but almost entirely without action on the ordinary fats. The action of invertase is limited to cane sugar, and so on. Specificity reaches its highest degree in those enzymes, such as maltase and emulsin, which are found to act only (or at least very preferentially) on one of two stereoisomeric substances. Maltase, extracted from yeast, will hydrolyse maltose and α-glucosides, but not β-glucosides. Emulsin, from bitter almonds and other sources, hydrolyses only β-glucosides, such as salicin, and does not attack the α-form.

(4) *Co-enzymes* – There are cases in which the activity of an

enzyme is greatly increased by the simultaneous presence of another substance which is not itself an enzyme. Such a substance is called a co-enzyme. The classical example of a co-enzyme is the marked effect of bile-salts in increasing the activity of pancreatic lipase. Manganese acts as a co-enzyme for the oxidising enzyme, laccase, obtainable from Japanese lacquer. An extract from yeast contains a zymase which is active in converting sugar into alcohol and CO_2. By dialysing, it is possible to divide the extract into a portion containing enzyme and a portion containing co-enzyme, neither of which is active by itself. It will be observed that in two of the above examples the chemical composition of the co-enzyme, unlike that of the enzyme, is known; and, in fact, Magnus found that synthetic bile-salts were as effective a co-enzyme for lipase as the natural salts extracted from bile.

(5) *Zymogens and Activators* – Somewhat similar to the co-enzymes, but not identical, are the zymogen 'activators.' In many cases enzymes are secreted by the tissues in an inactive form, known as a zymogen. In this way digestion of the secreting tissue itself is prevented. The zymogen is then activated by some other substance on reaching its site of operation. For instance, pepsin is secreted by the cells of the gastric glands in the inactive form of pepsinogen, and only becomes active when it mixes with the HCl of the gastric juice; the product of the pancreatic cells is trypsinogen, which is activated in the intestine by the enterokinase secreted there. An activator is differentiated from a co-enzyme by the fact that activation of a zymogen is an irreversible change—the enzyme can never be obtained again in an inactive form—while the co-enzyme can be separated from its enzyme, the activity lost being restored as soon as they are again mixed.

(6) *Enzyme 'Poisons' and Anti-enzymes* – In common with some inorganic catalysts, enzymes can be rendered inactive by the addition of certain substances, such as various antiseptics, fluorides, and hydrocyanic acid. Some antiseptics are known, however, such as toluol, which, while preventing bacterial and other cellular growth, have little or no effect on enzyme activity, and hence are of value for preserving enzyme-containing extracts.

While the above substances have an anti-enzymatic action, the name 'anti-enzyme' is usually restricted to inhibiting substances of biological origin. In the case of many enzymes such inhibiting substances may be produced by injecting the enzyme into the blood-stream of an animal. The animal develops within a short period an 'anti-enzyme' which may be obtained from the serum of its shed blood. Bayliss has drawn attention to the fact that it has not been proved that the inhibiting properties of such sera are due to the presence of a true 'anti-body'; in some cases, at least, the action of the sera can be explained by their alteration of the hydrogen-ion concentration, or some other subsidiary influence. In addition to these sera, a number of naturally occurring 'anti-enzymes' are known, e.g. the anti-trypsin of parasitic intestinal worms, which prevents their destruction by the tryptic activity of the intestinal contents of their host. The presence in the gastric mucosa of an anti-pepsin, and in the intestinal mucosa of an anti-trypsin, have been postulated to account for the fact that these membranes are not attacked by the proteolytic enzymes in contact with them.

Mode of Action – So little is known of the nature of enzymes that any theory of their mode of action must be largely speculative. Since they are colloidal, their action presumably resembles that of the colloidal type of inorganic catalyst, such as spongy platinum, but this is as obscure as enzyme action itself. In both, adsorption no doubt plays a large part, because by adsorption a localised high concentration of re-actants will be set up around the colloidal particles of catalyst and, by mass action, the velocity of the reaction thereby increased. Evidence of adsorption as a probable factor in enzyme action has already been given in the variations of velocity that occur with different relative concentrations of enzyme and substrate, and, moreover, in certain cases definite adsorption compounds of enzyme and substrate have been isolated.

That adsorption will suffice as a complete explanation of enzyme action is, however, extremely doubtful. One great difficulty in accepting it as such lies in the high degree of specificity exhibited by enzymes. Though instances of selective adsorption are known, it is, on the whole, a non-specific process, and adsorption compounds may be formed not only between enzyme and substrate, but also between an enzyme and other substances on which it has no action (*e.g.* trypsin-charcoal mentioned above). Something more than mere adsorption would appear to be necessary to explain why an enzyme will act only on one substance or one particular group of substances. Of what that something is, biologists at present have no knowledge. It has been suggested that for catalytic action, adsorption must be accompanied by some definite molecular orientation between enzyme and adsorbed substance, and that with substances other than its substrate, though adsorption may occur, this molecular orientation is absent. Others believe that adsorption is only a preliminary process, and that it is followed by the formation between substrate and enzyme of an intermediate chemical compound, as is known to happen in many inorganic catalysts. On this view the specificity of enzymes offers no difficulty, but no evidence of such chemical compounds has ever been found. Further advance in our knowledge of enzyme action is unlikely until something more is known of their intimate nature.

In this connection Northrop's observations are of interest. Northrop has obtained evidence that certain enzymes are ionic in nature. He has also found that the action of pepsin and trypsin on protein is conditional on the protein being ionised. At the iso-electric point of the protein substrate, enzyme activity is almost nil, and the maximum activity is obtained at a pH at which the protein is most highly ionised. Further, pepsin is only active on a positively charged, and trypsin on a negatively charged, protein.

CHAPTER XI

THE CELL

As early as the second half of the seventeenth century observations had shown, with the low-power lenses then available, that plant tissues consisted of numbers of fluid-filled spaces surrounded by firm walls, which, from their likeness to honeycomb, were called 'cells.' However, the first comprehensive treatment of cells as the units of plant structure was only given in 1838 by Schleiden. One year later Schwann, in a paper on the "Similarity of Structure and Growth in Plants and Animals," first propounded the theory that animals also were built up of cells. All subsequent work has gone to confirm this view of the cell, not only as the structural, but also the functional unit in the organism. "Any given reaction of the whole body is the resultant of the reactions of the unlike cells of which it is composed" (Starling).

In the unicellular organisms there are combined in one cell the functions of

(1) Forming the structural basis of the organism;
(2) food-assimilation, with all the subsidiary processes of secretion of enzymes, etc., necessary for that end;
(3) food-catabolism and the excretion of the catabolic products;
(4) sensitiveness to change in environment, and mechanisms for co-ordinating the appropriate responses to such changes;
(5) movement;
(6) growth and reproduction.

In the multicellular organisms each of these functions is performed by organs, or systems of tissues, composed of cells very unlike each other in form, in physical properties, and in chemical constitution. All these unlike tissues have their origin from a single undifferentiated cell, the fertilised ovum, and theoretically every cell retains the potential capacity for performing all the functions of life, and generally does, in fact, in a more or less perfect manner, perform various subsidiary functions besides that service for which it is specially designed in the economy of the body.   The socialisation of innumerable cells into a complex community has required that function (4) should be served by a most elaborate nervous system, to respond to the external environment and to co-ordinate the internal environment created by the activity of the cells.   A further specialisation is seen in the endocrine organs, whose function is the regulation of the metabolism of the body as a whole.

The present chapter will deal with the physico-chemical aspects of the activities of cells in general.

Protoplasm – When the histologist examines an animal cell in the fixed and stained condition, he sees it as a mass of material differentiated into cytoplasm and nucleus.   The cytoplasm very frequently shows a reticulated appearance, and may contain granules, vacuoles, etc.   The nucleus is separated from the cytoplasm by a limiting membrane, and presents a network on which the chromatin is apparently held in granular form.   Just how far such observations can be taken to represent the condition of the living cell is problematical, for, in the histological processes of fixing and hardening, the colloidal protoplasm changes from sol to gel, and Hardy has shown that such changes, even in such simple colloidal solutions as egg-white and gelatin, may be accompanied by the production of a microscopically reticulate structure resembling that of the fixed cell.

The biochemist, on analysing protoplasm, finds it to be about three-fourths water, the remaining fourth being an extremely complex mixture, containing many organic compounds belonging to the groups of proteins, carbohydrates, lipides, etc., together with various inorganic salts.   But such analyses must be carried out on the dead material, and while they tell us the components of the living cell, they give little or no information as to the way in which such components are arranged in the living protoplasm.   Moreover, the constitution of the protoplasm is believed to be specific for every species of plant and animal, and still further, within one organism, the composition of the protoplasm of typical cells of different tissues differs widely. Finally, the protoplasm of even any one cell is not the same from one moment to the next, as anabolic and catabolic changes must always be altering its composition.

The observations of the histologist and the analyses of the chemist being thus limited to the dead condition, are there any properties which we can definitely attribute to living protoplasm?

In the first place it is, in general, liquid in nature, though dissection by the micro-dissecting needle has shown that the ectoplasm of amœbæ and the nucleus are solid structures. The generally liquid nature of protoplasm is shown by the fact that both the cell as a whole, and fluid droplets within the cell, assume shapes corresponding with the surface-tension forces acting at the interfaces between cell and surroundings, or droplet and enclosing cell.

Secondly, since, apart from water, it is chiefly composed of materials like proteins, which form colloidal solutions, protoplasm itself must be of the nature of a complex colloidal dispersion. There is also evidence for this in the Brownian movement visible in all living cells on ultramicroscopic observation. The existence of the Brownian movement is another proof that the colloidal protoplasm is in a liquid condition.

Thirdly, protoplasm is not simply a colloidal dispersion in *water*. Analysis shows also the presence of inorganic salts, and some of these are present free in the dispersion medium, others are adsorbed to the colloidal particles. The free salts and ions will be osmotically active; the adsorbed will have no osmotic activity, but will affect the degree of aggregation of the colloidal particles.

Fourthly, the components of the protoplasm, both colloidal and organic, must be incessantly changing with metabolic changes, not only within the cell itself, but also in its surrounding cells or bathing fluid. The diversity of metabolic processes which may occur within one single cell is so great that it must be supposed that they will often involve, not the cell as a whole, but only a part of it, and that different chemical processes may be proceeding in different parts of the same cell simultaneously. This demands a separation of the cell into still smaller functional units, in each of which certain changes may occur without interfering with simultaneous changes in a neighbouring region. This subdivision of the cell is probably effected, as Hofmeister first suggested (1901), by the formation throughout the cell of semi-permeable membranes. Such membranes may automatically form themselves as the result of adsorption of substances all round the zone of chemical change, the adsorption being produced by alterations in surface tension caused by the chemical action itself. In this way, semi-permeable dividing membranes will form and disappear within the cell where and when occasion demands.

Such considerations as these, and they might be greatly extended, will serve to indicate the complexity of the biological unit. Considering that there is such a complexity of structure within such small dimensions, it is not surprising that the biologist's knowledge of intracellular processes is rather meagre. Recent developments which are likely to become important are the determination of the pH and of the oxidation-reduction potential [1] in the interior of the living cell.

While little is directly known of what occurs within the cell, many observations have been made, and many inferences drawn, concerning the limiting membrane surrounding the cell.

The Cell-membrane – In the vegetable cell, the presence of a cell wall is quite obvious on microscopic examination. In animal cells, a visible differentiation of the outer layer of the cell is very often absent, though in some, e.g. amœba, the margin may be less granular and more highly refractile than the interior. Whether the margin of a cell shows optical differentiation or not, there is no doubt whatever that it is functionally differentiated to form a semi-permeable membrane. As evidence of the existence of such a membrane, it will be sufficient for the present to mention the two following points: (1) The cellular protoplasm is liquid, and therefore there would be nothing to limit its dispersion if no such membrane existed; (2) in the chapter on Osmotic Pressure, the experiments of de Vries on plasmolysis and similar experiments on blood corpuscles were described. Such osmotic interchanges between cell and surrounding fluids

[1] See Appendix, p. 154.

would be inexplicable without the postulation of a semi-permeable membrane surrounding the cell.

Allowing, then, that such a membrane exists, what functions are demanded of it?

(1) It must be impermeable to colloids, because only in this way can it limit the dispersion of the protoplasm.

(2) The passage of water across it must be permitted in either direction.

(3) It must allow of the free passage inward of nutrient material, and outward of excretory material. These are much more difficult conditions to fulfil, for the molecular magnitude of nutrients and excreta may be relatively large, while the results of hæmolysis and plasmolysis experiments show the membrane to be *impermeable* to substances of quite small molecular dimensions.

(4) The membrane must be such as to allow for cell growth.

This last requirement seems to demand either that the membrane should be an elastic one, thinning out as the cell grows, or that it is in some way formed from the cell contents themselves, so that, with every increase in the size of the cell, a more extensive membrane may be formed. All the evidence supports the latter view, and indicates also that the membrane is capable of being automatically and almost instantaneously re-formed in case of destruction. The classical experiment, of which there are many later variants, was performed by Nägeli in 1855. A rootlet of a water plant, *Hydrocharis*, was placed under a cover-glass in a solution of aniline blue. The root hairs are impermeable to this dye. By pressure on the cover-glass, the hairs were crushed at certain points, and at these points the protoplasm formed ball-like extrusions. The dye did not stain these extrusions, showing that the impermeable membrane, destroyed by the crushing, must have immediately re-formed upon them.

Now we have seen that the Gibbs-Thomson theorem propounds that substances which lower surface tension always congregate at the interfaces where such surface tension is manifested. From this proposition we should expect to find, at the interface between a cell and its environment (of water, plasma, lymph, or whatever it is), a congregation of the surface-tension lowering substances, derived both from the cell itself and from its immediate environment. The assumption that the membrane is composed, mainly if not entirely, of substances which have thus accumulated at the surface, would explain the cell's capacity for sudden re-formation of its membrane. Further, being a product partly of the cell and partly of its environment, a membrane formed in this way would vary with the variations of both; some such capacity for variation is necessary to explain the cell-membrane's varying properties of permeability.

Permeability – In previous chapters we have spoken of artificial membranes such as parchment, collodion, and copper ferrocyanide, which exhibit the property of semi-permeability to a greater or lesser degree. Strictly speaking, the term 'semi-permeable' applied to a membrane means that such a membrane is permeable to water alone, and allows no dissolved substance to pass through it. The term is often used, however, in reference to one particular substance or group of substances, a membrane being said to be semi-permeable to a substance A when it does not allow A to diffuse through it, but permits the passage not only of water, but of other substances as well. No artificial membrane hitherto prepared is semi-permeable in the strict sense of the term. Parchment is impermeable to colloids but permeable to crystalloids, and collodion membranes may be prepared with such a degree of impermeability as to prevent the passage of the larger-moleculed crystalloids. The artificial membranes approaching most nearly to true semi-permeability are those of copper ferrocyanide, originally prepared by Traube. Through such membranes, in addition to water, only a few of the smaller-moleculed salts, such as KCl, will pass.

Investigation of these artificial membranes has left practically no doubt that their semi-permeability is due to a sieve-like action, the pores being of such a size as to allow certain molecules to pass through, while retaining others. Biltz found that dyes whose molecules contained a number of atoms less than forty-five passed through parchment membranes rapidly;

dyes consisting of a larger number of atoms diffused through with increasing slowness until, when the number of atoms was greater than seventy, the membrane was quite impermeable to them. The same holds for the precipitation membranes, such as those of copper ferrocyanide. Walden investigated the permeability to various substances of a variety of membranes of this type, and obtained results explicable on the assumption that each particular membrane had a definite size of pore. Finally, Tinker, by ultramicroscopic photography, has given actual demonstration of the pores in a copper ferrocyanide membrane.

Comparing the cell-membrane with artificial membranes, we find in it a semi-permeability of an even higher order than that of copper ferrocyanide, but we find also that we are compelled to postulate a character not found in any artificial membrane—that is, a permeability to crystalloids which is adjustable over a considerable range. Let us now examine the grounds for this latter statement.

The membrane's general impermeability to crystalloids is demonstrated by abundant experimental evidence, which we may consider in three groups. First, there is the shrinkage or expansion, by passing out or in of water, which is seen when plant cells or red corpuscles are placed in hyper- or hypotonic solutions of crystalloids, even of those of quite small molecular size, e.g. NaCl. These osmotic effects cannot be accounted for unless the cell-membrane is impermeable to such solutes. Secondly, differences in crystalloidal content between cell and environment are found naturally, and are often of such magnitude that the only explanation must be a crystalloid-impermeable membrane. The following figures (Abderhalden) of the amounts of Na and K in the corpuscles and plasma of the rabbit show this :—

	Plasma	Corpuscles
K .	0·026 per cent.	0·523 per cent.
Na .	0·444 ,,	0·0 ,,

Although the Donnan equilibrium (p. 80) will account for

a certain difference in ionic concentration between plasma and corpuscle, it will not account for the plasma proteins retaining *all* the sodium. Thirdly, evidence for the general impermeability of the cell-membrane to crystalloids is found in the fact that the electrical conductivity of a circuit made up of a series of living cells is low, though the experiments of Höber have shown that the conductivity of the cell-substance itself is comparatively high. Since the passage of an electrical current through a solution depends on the transference of electrical charges by ions, these experiments indicate that the capacity for ionic movement through the cell-membrane is ordinarily very small.

In addition to these general considerations indicative of non-permeability to crystalloids, mention may be made of a few of the many specific instances of such impermeability.

(1) Most cell-membranes are impermeable, or very slowly permeable, to potassium chloride, a salt which even the most highly semi-permeable artificial membrane, copper ferro-cyanide, allows to pass.

(2) A piece of cut beet, washed and left lying in cold tap-water, allows neither the pigment nor the sugar to diffuse out.

(3) Many experiments indicate that the cell-membrane may be impermeable even to mineral acids and alkalis. One of the most interesting of these was performed by Bethe, who placed medusæ in sea-water to which some neutral red had been added. He noted the cells of the medusæ become coloured with the dye at its neutral tint. He then added HCl gradually, but no change of colour was induced in the indicator dye within the cells even up to the point of paralysis. Only after death did the cells become permeable and their colour alter. Corresponding results were obtained with NaOH.

Permeability and Lipoids – These facts taken alone would suggest that the semi-permeability of the cell-membrane is well-nigh perfect, that practically nothing but water can diffuse through it. On the other hand, there are substances to which it is known to be permeable. Overton, whose work on the cell-membrane is classical, came to the conclusion that its permeability to any substance depended on the solubility relations of that substance towards lipoids. Those substances which either formed solutions with lipoids, such as alcohol, chloroform, benzene, etc., or were soluble in lipoid solvents, such as urea, fatty acids, etc., gained entrance to the cell. Conversely, he found that non-lipoid-soluble sugars, amino-acids, inorganic salts, and mineral acids failed to penetrate. He found the same sort of thing to hold with aniline dyes. Basic dyes, in which the coloured part of the molecule was the cation of the salt, were lipoid soluble, and stained the cell; those known as acid dyes, in which the colour is associated with the anion, not being lipoid soluble, did not enter. Overton was thus led to the formulation of his well-known theory that the cell-membrane, to exhibit this behaviour, must be itself lipoid in nature.

Lipoid solubility cannot, however, be a complete explanation of the behaviour of the cell-membrane *in vivo*, because this would exclude materials such as the sugars, amino-acids, and inorganic salts, which, since they are known to be essential to the metabolism of the cell, must gain entrance to it somehow. Under the ordinary conditions of experiment it is quite true that the cell is found to be impermeable to these substances, so that the conclusion seems inevitable that the degree of permeability of the cell-membrane is not uniform or fixed, but can be in some way altered at times so as to permit their ingress and egress. There is, further, a great deal of direct experimental evidence in support of variable permeability, of which one or two instances may be mentioned. Thus, the electrical conductivity of the cells of the seaweed *Laminaria* increases markedly when their normal environment of sea-water is changed for one of pure sodium chloride of equivalent ionic concentration. Apparently, therefore, the presence of excess Na^+ without the other ions of sea-water increases the permeability of the *Laminaria* cells. The original condition can be restored if the subjection to NaCl is not too prolonged. Again, the section of beet does not lose its pigment when placed in cold tap-water, but if it is placed in pure isotonic sodium chloride, the pigment will slowly diffuse out. On addition of calcium chloride to the sodium chloride solution the cells' impermeability to the pigment is again restored. In general it may be said that a preponderance of Na increases permeability, while an excess of Ca diminishes it.

As a general summary of the properties of the cell-membrane, then, we may say that (1) it is always impermeable to colloids; (2) to crystalloids its impermeability is generally of very high degree, but is subject to considerable variation with the conditions of the environment; and (3) to those crystalloids of the lipoid-soluble class it is always permeable.

The cell-membrane is apparently, therefore, something much more complex than any artificial membrane, and we may now inquire further into the physico-chemical constitution of a structure which exhibits such wonderful properties.

In the first place, we have seen that the membrane is probably formed by an adsorptive accumulation at the cell-surface of materials from the cell-substance and from its environment. It follows that we must expect, as the constituents of the cell-membrane, substances which (1) are universal constituents of protoplasm, and (2) have a powerful action in lowering surface tension. The substances most nearly satisfying both of these conditions are those belonging to the group of lipoids. This presumption that lipoids are among the main components of the membrane fits in with Overton's experimental findings that lipoid solubility is a determining factor in permeability. Moreover, recent work of Leathes shows that lipoids would explain the variable permeability attributed to cell-membranes. Into this we must look rather more closely.

It has already been described how the fatty acids may form monomolecular films, in which the molecules are orientated with their polar groups towards the water, and the remainder of their long chains directed perpendicularly away from the water-surface. We also saw how these films could exist, according to temperature, in the solid, liquid, or expanded state, the difference between these states consisting in the extent of the lateral separation of the molecules from one another. While the substances forming such films are, in mass, impervious to water, in film form water readily passes through them, and the more expanded the film, the more permeable is it to water. Now the lipoids form similar monomolecular films. Leathes has shown that lecithin, the lipoid whose chemical constitution is best known, exists as an expanded film at temperatures as low as 5° C. Lecithin films, therefore, will be even more water permeable than fatty - acid films. This is because the part of the lecithin molecule with a high affinity for water, the polar group, is a glycerol-phosphoric acid-choline complex, and not a simple COOH group as in a fatty acid. The non-polar stems of the molecules in a lecithin film will therefore be further separated from one another by the large size of the water-attached 'roots.' Further, it is of special interest that the state of expansion, and hence the permeability, of these lecithin films is influenced by the presence of other substances. For instance, cholesterol, which itself forms a comparatively close film, will, if added to lecithin, diminish the area of the film formed by it, showing that the cholesterol has induced the lecithin molecules to pack more closely together. The effect of the simultaneous presence or absence of other substances on lecithin-film formation was shown by Leathes in another fashion. When a small mass of solid lecithin is brought into contact with a water-surface, the attempt of the lecithin to extend its surface area to form a film results in the outgrowth from its surface of what are called 'myelin forms.' These growths may be watched under a microscope, and it may be observed that their extent and shape are greatly modified by the presence of electrolytes, proteins, and other substances.

It is evident, then, that a membrane of lipoid composition would not only account for the permeability of cells to lipoid-soluble substances, but would have that capacity for varying its permeability which is so characteristic of the cell-membrane. There is, however, much evidence to show that the properties of the cell-membrane cannot be entirely explained by the presence of a membrane which consists of lipoid substances alone. It is more likely that the membrane consists of both lipoids and proteins, with possibly other components as well.

Although it is impossible, in the present state of physiological knowledge, to make any positive statement as to the actual composition of the cell-membrane, it is instructive to postulate that it is a lipoid-protein colloidal complex, and then to consider a few of the possibilities of permeability variation

which could be expected from the physico-chemical nature of
a membrane of this kind.

(1) The membrane being formed from the components of
the cell itself, will alter, if not in qualitative, at least in
quantitative composition, and also in the degree of
aggregation of its colloidal particles, with changes in
the composition of the cell. Changes in the degree
of aggregation will no doubt alter its permeability,
and so will changes of composition, in so far as it
shares the properties of lipoid films.

(2) Changes in hydrogen-ion concentration of either cell or
its environment will also influence the degree of
colloidal aggregation, and hence its permeability.

(3) The membrane as a whole, being colloidal, will carry
an electrical charge opposite to that of its environment, and this may in several ways promote or hinder
the diffusion of ions. For example, if the membrane
has a negative charge, it would presumably hinder the
diffusion of negative ions and favour that of positive
ions. On the other hand, the positive ions, though
attracted by the negative membrane, will be electrically
adsorbed to the colloidal particles of the membrane,
thus diminishing the size of its pores and, initially
at least, diminishing its permeability. Non-electrical
adsorption may, of course, act in a similar manner.

(4) Apart from these changes in the membrane itself, the
material which has to diffuse through the membrane
may undergo alterations, making it either more or
less diffusible. The first might be achieved by the
ionisation of a previously undissociated solute; while
an increase in the size of the particles of the diffusing
substance, as by a greater hydration or by adsorption
of some other substance, would hinder its passage
through the membrane.

(5) Finally, mention may be made of the theory of Clowes
that the cell-membrane is an emulsoid system in
which the two phases are lipoids and a watery solution
of proteins, these being interchangeable as dispersed

phase and dispersion medium, according to the conditions of the moment. When the membrane consists of a dispersed phase of protein in a continuous phase of lipoid, the membrane is permeable only to the lipoid-soluble substances. A reversal of the phases so as to make the continuous phase the watery protein solution, confers on the membrane permeability to water-soluble substances.

Permeability and Physiological Function – In conclusion, a few examples may be given of the relation of permeability changes in the cell-membrane to physiological function.

It is characteristic of all forms of excitation of living cells that their permeability is thereby increased. This offers an explanation of the production of the electrical currents which always accompany protoplasmic activity; it will be referred to again in dealing with the contraction of muscle and the action of nerve. Increased permeability being an accompaniment of excitation, the natural expectation would be that narcotics would diminish permeability. Experiment confirms this expectation, and while narcotics and anæsthetics are in general lipoid soluble, and hence are usually assumed to gain access to the cell, their narcotic or anæsthetic action may, at least in part, be due to their effect in diminishing the permeability of the cell-membrane, and not to an action on the cell itself.

Sherrington has put forward the theory that the two neurones forming a synapse are separated from one another by a synaptic membrane, and the degree of permeability of this membrane at the moment determines the transmission or non-transmission of the nerve-impulse across the synapse.

Bethe's experiments on medusæ, already described, showed that the addition of HCl to the sea-water caused at first abnormal activity of the animals, followed by paralysis, although the dye within the organisms indicated that the acid did not penetrate the membrane until after death.

It is a well-known fact in physiology that the activity of the isolated heart can be maintained only when the artificial perfusion fluid contains the proper balance of potassium, sodium, and calcium ions. A relative excess or deficiency of any one of these ions, even though the isotonicity of the solution is maintained, results in marked changes in rhythm and tone. In the case of the stoppage which occurs on deprival of the Ca ion, Straub has shown that the effect is so rapidly produced that an action on the surface layer only of the cardiac muscle cells can be held responsible, and it seems reasonable to suppose that the effect of inappropriate amounts of the other ions is similarly superficial. The main rôle of a proper ionic balance would thus appear to be the preservation of the correct degree of permeability in the cell-membranes of the cardiac muscle.

APPENDIX

Investigations of the oxidation-reduction potentials of living material seem likely to become increasingly important. The following brief sketch may help the student to gain some idea of their significance.

The term ' oxidation ' is applied not only to chemical changes in which there is a direct addition of oxygen or withdrawal of hydrogen, but also to changes involving an increase in the valency of an element, in which oxygen may have played no direct part. The transformation of ferrous chloride to ferric chloride by chlorine is an example. Similarly, ' reduction ' has been extended to include changes involving decrease in valency, though there may have been no direct withdrawal of oxygen or addition of hydrogen.

Iron is divalent in its ferrous compounds and trivalent in its ferric compounds, and the essential change in the transformation of a solution of $FeCl_2$ to one of $FeCl_3$ is that each Fe^{++} ion is deprived of one electron, thereby becoming a Fe^{+++} ion. Conversely, reduction of ferric ions to ferrous ions consists in the addition of an electron to each ion. The reversible oxidation-reduction action between ferrous and ferric ions might then be represented thus, e signifying an electron:

$$Fe^{+++} + e \rightleftharpoons Fe^{++}.$$

The trend of modern physical chemistry is to regard all oxidations and reductions from this point of view of electron transference, reduction being the addition and oxidation the withdrawal of electrons.

In Chapter VIII we saw that a difference of electrical potential exists between a platinum electrode laden with hydrogen and any solution containing hydrogen ions in which this electrode is immersed. We saw also that this difference of potential is related to the hydrogen-ion concentration of the solution. Though the point was not discussed in Chapter VIII, it is also dependent on the concentration of hydrogen atoms in the electrode, which in turn depends on the pressure of hydrogen gas surrounding the electrode. Now the reaction occurring between the hydrogen in the electrode and the hydrogen ions of the solution may be regarded as a reversible oxidation-reduction reaction, because the hydrogen atoms in the electrode, by losing an electron, may be ' oxidised ' to hydrogen ions, or, conversely, the hydrogen ions of the solution may, by gain of an electron, be reduced to atomic hydrogen. The difference of potential between platinum and solution is thus related to the concentration of the oxidised product (hydrogen ions) and to the concentration of reduced product (hydrogen atoms), and, in fact, is a function of the ratio between these concentrations.

Similarly, when a solution containing ferrous and ferric ions, or one of many other oxidation-reduction systems, is in contact with platinum or other noble metal, a difference of potential is set up between electrode and solution, the value of which, *at constant pH*, is a function of the ratio between the concentrations of ferrous ions and ferric ions, or, in general, the ratio $\frac{[\text{reductant}]}{[\text{oxidant}]}$. The limitation ' at constant pH ' is necessary because the pH of the system affects the ionisation of the oxidant and reductant.

Now, if the condition of constant pH is maintained and one measures the ' oxidation-reduction potentials ' obtained at varying values of the ratio $\frac{[\text{reductant}]}{[\text{oxidant}]}$, and graphs the potentials against the corresponding ratios expressed as percentage reductions, the form of the graph is similar to that for the variation of percentage dissociation with pH, which is given (for one of the pH indicators) in fig. 11. Moreover, just as different indicators have their graphs placed at different positions on the pH axis, so do the graphs of different oxidation-reduction systems occupy different positions along the potential axis. When a number of oxidation-reduction systems, such as $Fe^{+++} \rightleftharpoons Fe^{++}$, methylene blue $\rightleftharpoons$ methylene white, etc., are graphed in this way, we have them set out on a scale of electrical-potential units, and the position of systems on this scale indicates quantitatively their relative oxidation-reduction intensities. If the curve of one system falls in a range of potentials more positive than those of a second system, the first system will be oxidising with respect to the second, and the second reducing with respect to the first. Further, it is possible to place any system, however complex and obscure its component reactions, on this scale, provided that it will give a measurable oxidation-reduction potential, and so to compare its oxidation-reduction intensity with the intensities of known and relatively simple systems. Thus, it may be derived from such curves that, at a pH of 7·4, any system maintaining an electrode potential of —0·002 volt (the potential of the normal hydrogen electrode being taken as zero) will maintain a 50 per cent. reduction of methylene blue, a practically complete reduction of the indophenols, and a practically complete oxidation of indigo carmine. In statements of oxidation-reduction potentials the pH must be specified, for the reason already stated.

Determinations of oxidation-reduction potential need not be made electrometrically. Just as dyes which change colour with change in hydrogen-ion concentration may be used for the determination of pH, so may dyes which, *at constant pH*, change colour according to oxidation-reduction potential be used as indicators of the latter. Such dyes have been used for the determination of the oxidation-reduction potential of the living cell.

Oxidation-reduction intensities are sometimes expressed in what are known as rH units. The derivation of these units may be briefly indicated. In hydrogen-ion concentration measurements, the potentials measured are those between solution and platinum electrode when the latter is kept supplied with hydrogen gas at atmospheric pressure. Under these conditions the solution will be so highly reduced as to be in equilibrium with 1 atmosphere of hydrogen. In the measurement of oxidation-reduction potentials the electrode has, of course, no external hydrogen supply. Nevertheless, in any solution containing oxidation and reduction products in equilibrium there must be a corresponding oxidation-reduction equilibrium between hydrogen ions and hydrogen atoms, because these are themselves related as oxidant and reductant, and a platinum or gold electrode immersed in the solution will therefore theoretically be charged with hydrogen at some definite pressure. Though, in most systems, this hydrogen pressure is immeasurably small and is a calculated value, it may nevertheless be used instead of electrical potential to express the position of the system on the oxidation-reduction scale. Such immeasurably small hydrogen pressures are stated in rH units, these units being the negative logarithms of the hydrogen pressure in atmospheres. Thus an oxidation-reduction system of rH 19 is one in which the coexisting equilibrium between hydrogen ions and hydrogen atoms would theoretically produce a pressure of hydrogen $=10^{-19}$ atmospheres. rH units are analogous to pH units, which are the negative logarithms of hydrogen-ion concentrations.

CHAPTER XII

SECRETION

ALL cells elaborate what they need from blood-borne materials, and discharge waste and unwanted substances. The cells of glandular tissues, however, are specialised for the production of material which does not directly affect themselves but is transported outside the cell, often to a different part of the organism, there to excite or inhibit some other physiological process. The term 'secretion,' in its more restricted sense, denotes only this specialised function of glandular tissue. It is often loosely applied to rather similar processes, such as the kidney's transference of waste materials from blood to urine, in which the cells have no part in the formation of the materials which they extrude (with one minor exception).

Very little is known of the mechanism of true secretion, in spite of its great physiological importance. In the glands which discharge their secretion either on to the external surface of the body or into the alimentary canal, the secretion is apparently stored in the cell in a concentrated form, until an appropriate stimulus causes this stored secretion to be dissolved and washed out by a current of water (and salts) derived from the blood. The conception of such a double process has arisen mainly from the histological changes observed in gland cells during rest and activity, and also from some classical work of Heidenhain. Heidenhain found in the submaxillary gland, which has a double nerve supply, from the chorda tympani and from the sympathetic, that while stimulation of either of these nerves caused secretion, the characters of the secreted material differed. Stimulation of the chorda produced a copious watery secretion, while sympathetic stimulation produced a much scantier viscid saliva. From this observation Heidenhain surmised that there were two functional types of nerve fibres, the one predominant in the cranial nerves, and controlling the supply of water and salts in the secretion; these he called 'secretory' fibres. The other type he supposed tu predominate in sympathetic nerve and, in some way, to control protoplasmic growth as well as the formation of the specific secretory granules; hence he called them 'trophic' fibres. Although Heidenhain's views on trophic nerves in general have been much criticised, there is still a general belief in the dual nature of the secretory process and in the separate control of its two aspects, the elaboration of the product and its extrusion.

Concerning the histological evidence for the dissociation of these two aspects of secretion, the student will remember the appearance of the resting state of a pancreatic or salivary gland; how the protoplasm of the acinar cells is packed with granules; and how, when the gland is artificially excited to secrete, these granules break down as though dissolving, and pass into the lumen of the alveolus, so that, after prolonged activity, granules are only to be seen at the luminal border of the cell. This formation of granules is so general a phenomenon in glandular tissue that they are assumed to be either themselves the specific secretory constituents or, at least, their immediate precursors.

The formation of the special secretory constituents within the cell is, of course, only a specialised form of cellular metabolic activity. If we assume that the reactions by which they are formed are reversible, as many metabolic reactions are known to be, the control of their formation according to the varying activity of the gland is easily understood. Mass action would induce a further supply as soon as activity reduced the store, while accumulation would go on during inactivity only up to the point of equilibrium. The immediate source of the granules within the cell is unknown.

The other aspect of the secretory process, the production of a washing-out stream of solvent, cannot be explained as a mere filtration or seepage of water from the blood *via* the lymph, through cell to lumen. If the solvent were pure water, there is no driving force to make this water pass from the blood into the cell, because the average blood-pressure of 100 mm. or so is incomparably smaller than the osmotic pressure of the blood, which is of the order of 6000 mm. This argument is beside the point, however, because considerable quantities of inorganic salts derived from the blood are present in all secretions, and the pressure required to separate water with these salts in solution is much less, since the restraining osmotic influence of the blood is then more nearly that of its colloidal constituents alone. But even so, the pressure against which saliva is secreted may be much higher than the blood-pressure (Ludwig, 1851). By any process of filtration the secretion-pressure could never exceed the blood-pressure. There must therefore be some mechanism in the secreting cell itself to increase the hydrostatic pressure. Its nature is unknown, but it is usually supposed to be osmotic. The postulated mechanism, the basic idea of which was suggested by Pfeffer in his botanical work, may be most easily understood from the following model (fig. 23).

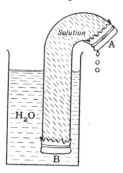

FIG. 23

Imagine a solution of some substance to be placed in a tube AB, of which the end A is covered by a membrane permeable to both water and the solute, and the end B with a membrane permeable to water but impermeable to the solute. Let the tube be immersed, B end downwards, in a vessel of water. In this model there will be an osmotic inflow of water from the vessel into the tube through membrane B, which is impermeable to the solute. The solution inside the tube, increasing in volume, will make its exit through membrane A, which has been supposed permeable to both solute and water. A continuous current will thus flow through the tube in the direction BA as long as the osmotic pressure inside the tube is higher than that of the fluid in the surrounding vessel. In this model the vessel of water represents the blood, or more correctly, the lymph, which is immediately adjacent to the secreting cell, the tube represents the cell itself, membrane B the surface of the cell farthest from the lumen, and membrane A the luminal margin, while the fluid issuing at A is analogous to the extruded secretion.

Applying the principle of this model to the living gland, we may suppose that the discharge of secretion would take place

somewhat as follows.   In response to stimulation, the osmotic
pressure of the cell-constituents would be somehow increased,
probably by the breakdown into smaller units of the complex
molecules of the secretory granules themselves.   By the rise of
osmotic pressure, water and some inorganic salts would be
drawn from the lymph into the cell, dissolving the secretory
granules.   Also, as a result of stimulation, there would be a
simultaneous increase of permeability in that part of the cell
which abuts on the alveolar lumen, allowing the secretory
constituents, which are now in solution, to pass out and be
discharged through the duct of the gland.   Notice that this
hypothesis requires two kinds of energy expenditure from the
gland cell: the chemical work of preparing its specific secretion,
and, during extrusion, the osmotic work of maintaining the
osmotic potential above that of the blood.   The increased
oxygen consumption observed during the functioning of a
gland is evidence of this work (p. 268).

There is no direct evidence that such osmotic changes do
actually take place in the cell, but there is a certain amount of
experimental evidence that the permeability of the cell alters
during secretion.   The student is already familiar with the
fact that atropine has an inhibitory, and pilocarpine a stimulant,
action on secreting cells in general.   Garmus has shown that
the cells of the mucous glands in the nictitating membrane of
the frog are more readily and rapidly stained by dyes when
excited by pilocarpine than when treated with atropine.
Again, the action-currents of nerve and muscle are generally
believed to be due to changes in permeability in the cells of
these tissues, and similar variations of electrical potential have
been observed in secreting glands.   In 1885 Bayliss and Bradford showed that the watery secretion of saliva, which flows
in response to stimulation of the chorda tympani nerve, is
accompanied by a difference of potential between the gland
duct and that part of the cell-surface farthest from the lumen,
the degree of potential difference varying approximately as the
rate of salivary secretion.   They found a smaller variation to
accompany the more viscid and scantier secretion produced by
stimulation of the sympathetic, but while during chordal stimulation the hilus of the gland was positive to the surface, the

potential difference on sympathetic stimulation was of the reverse sign. The intimate relationship of these electrical changes to the secretory process is indicated by two other observations. First, atropine inhibits both chordal and sympathetic secretion, but the former more than the latter; its relative effects on the two electrical variations is similar. Secondly, in the cat, where both chorda and sympathetic produce a watery secretion, the signs of the electrical variation are also similar.

These observations lent considerable support to Heidenhain's view of the existence of two types of nerve fibres, and Bayliss and Bradford concluded that the electrical variation obtained when the chorda was stimulated was associated with the flow of water and salts through the cell, and the reversed electrical variation on sympathetic stimulation was in some way connected with the formation of the specific secretory constituents.

On the theory outlined above, the electrical variation during chordal stimulation, when the cell is actively discharging fluid, is readily explained, and is itself evidence for the postulated change of permeability. The highly permeable cell-lumen interface provides a passage to both positively and negatively charged ions, so that the electrode on the hilus of the gland is virtually in contact with the interior of the secreting cells. Between it and the other electrode one is therefore detecting the difference of potential which exists between the interior and surface of all cells. The variation of opposite sign during sympathetic stimulation, which is supposed to be associated with the preparation of secretory material within the cell, is much more difficult to explain, and any suggestions so far offered are quite speculative.

The electrical changes observed by Bayliss and Bradford have been found in various glands by other workers: by Gesell, who made a more detailed investigation of the effect of chordal stimulation on the submaxillary gland; by Hermann on the skin and tongue glands of the frog and the sweat glands of cats; and by Anrep and Daly on the pancreas. The experiments of the last-named workers are of particular interest, because the pancreatic secretion was brought about by the chemical stimulus, secretin. The consequent difference of potential was like that of chordal stimulation in the salivary glands, the duct becoming positive to the surface of the splenic end of the pancreas.

It is an interesting point that, though the majority of electric organs in fishes are developments of skeletal muscle, in one species, the electrical cat-fish, this organ is a modified gland in which the secretory are subservient to the electrical effects.

The postulated mechanism just described seems a reasonable theoretical process by which a gland might function, and it receives a fair amount of support from the experiments of Garmus and the existence of the electrical changes, but it must be freely admitted that the evidence for it is far from conclusive. It is also uncertain that the mechanism is the same in different types of glands.

Finally, mention must be made of some observations by Macallum on the surface-tension conditions in gland cells, as indicated by the distribution of potassium in them. By applying the cobaltinitrite test intracellularly, Macallum demonstrated that the greatest concentration of potassium is to be found at the cell border adjacent to the lumen of the gland, and least at the margin next the blood supply. Since the concentration of potassium will be greatest where the surface tension is least (Gibbs-Thomson principle, p. 38), the surface tension in the secreting cell must be relatively high at the cell-lymph interface and relatively low at the cell-lumen interface. Whether these changes are causal or incidental to the secretory process is doubtful, but it is an interesting point that the cells of the intestinal villi through which *absorption* takes place show just the reverse distribution of potassium, and hence surface-tension conditions opposite to those of the secreting cell.

CHAPTER XIII

BLOOD

In the present chapter we shall confine our discussion to two of the most important functions of blood, the mechanisms of which have been elucidated almost entirely by the application of physico-chemical principles. These two functions are (1) the transport of the gaseous metabolites, oxygen and carbon dioxide; and (2) the preservation, within narrow limits, of an optimal hydrogen-ion concentration in the body as a whole.

The Transport of Oxygen – Before attempting this chapter the student would be well advised to re-read the first few pages of Chapter V on Solutions, in which the meanings of the terms 'partial pressure,' 'tension,' and 'coefficient of solubility' are explained.

The coefficient of solubility of oxygen in water at body temperature is 0·024; 100 c.c. of water at this temperature would contain, therefore, 2·4 c.c. (measured at N.T.P.) of dissolved oxygen. For blood the solubility is even less, about 2·2 c.c. of oxygen per 100 c.c. of blood. In the mixed arterial blood, where we may take the tension of oxygen to be approximately 11 per cent. of an atmosphere, the amount of oxygen in solution in 100 c.c. would be 0·24 c.c. Actually, as determined by experiment, between 17 and 18 c.c. are present per 100 c.c. of blood. It is evident, therefore, that the oxygen must be largely present in a combined form; it is combined, in fact, with the red colouring matter of the blood, hæmoglobin, as oxyhæmoglobin. The extent to which the hæmoglobin takes up oxygen is nevertheless dependent on the partial pressure of oxygen to which the blood is exposed, though not directly proportional to it, and the 'dissociation curve' is simply a graph relating the degree of this uptake of oxygen to the oxygen tension to which the hæmoglobin is subjected. To make this clear, we may consider the principles of the

preparation of such a dissociation curve for a solution of pure
hæmoglobin (fig. 24).   Imagine five vessels into each of which
is placed an amount of the hæmoglobin solution.   The space
above the solution is filled with a gas mixture containing
oxygen at different partial pressures in each vessel.   The closed
vessels are then rotated in a horizontal position, the hæmoglobin solution spreads out into a thin film, and equilibrium

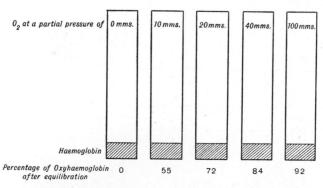

FIG. 24—Determination of dissociation curve of hæmoglobin
(From data in Barcroft, *The Respiratory Function of the Blood*)

between the oxygen of the gas mixture and oxygen in the hæmoglobin solution is soon attained.   When equilibration is complete, the gas mixture in each vessel is analysed for its percentage content of oxygen, and the partial pressure calculated.
The percentage amount of hæmoglobin existing as oxyhæmoglobin is also directly determined in each case.

    If the partial pressures are those recorded in the upper part
of the diagram, then the percentage oxyhæmoglobin, or, as it
is usually called, the percentage saturation of the hæmoglobin,
in each of the five solutions, will be the corresponding ones
given in the lower part of the figure.   Now if we take these
figures and graph them, placing the partial pressures of oxygen
as abscissæ and the percentages of oxyhæmoglobin as ordinates,
we shall obtain a curve like the upper one in fig. 25.   This is
the dissociation curve of a solution of hæmoglobin in water.

    Such a curve has exactly the form, viz. a rectangular hyper-
bola, that would be expected from the application of the law
of mass action, provided that the formation and dissociation

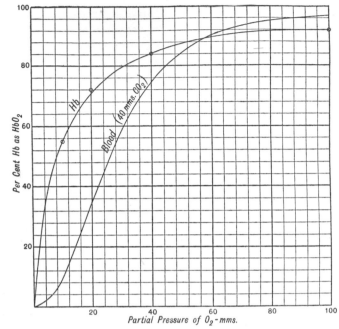

FIG. 25—Oxygen dissociation curves for (1) an aqueous solution of
hæmoglobin, and (2) blood at a CO_2 tension of 40 mm.

(Redrawn from Barcroft, *The Respiratory Function of the Blood*)

of oxyhæmoglobin were represented by the simple reversible
reaction:
$$Hb + O_2 \rightleftharpoons HbO_2.$$

Hüfner, who first considered this question from its theoretical
aspects, constructed such a curve on theoretical grounds, and
then tested its accuracy experimentally on a solution of hæmoglobin crystals. He was gratified to find a good agreement
between the two curves (1890). Hüfner's curve did not agree
well, however, with some rough measurements which had been
made about twelve years previously by Bert, using not a
solution of hæmoglobin, but the whole blood. In 1904 the
matter was taken up by Bohr, who made the interesting discovery that the dissociation curve as obtained from whole
blood is not the same as that obtained in a watery solution
of hæmoglobin, but is of a curious S-shape (fig. 25, lower
curve). Shortly afterwards Bohr, with his fellow-workers,

Hasselbalch and Krogh, found that the form of the curve varies according to the tension of carbon dioxide present with the oxygen in the gas mixtures to which the blood is exposed. The higher the tension of CO_2, the more does the curve move towards the right of the graph, at the same time apparently altering in shape (fig. 26).

Five years later Barcroft and his associates began the researches which have not only cleared up the question of the divergence between the Hüfner and the Bohr curves, but have given us an extensive knowledge of the nature and behaviour of this most important substance, hæmoglobin. As a result of these investigations it was shown:

(1) That the rectangular hyperbola is valid for salt-free hæmoglobin solutions.

(2) That the lower curve (fig. 25) is equally valid for whole blood, but, if the blood is dialysed, so as to rid it of its electrolytes, then the curve obtained is again, at least approximately, a rectangular hyperbola.

The cause of the curious S-shape lies, therefore, in the salt content of the blood.

The effect of CO_2 on the oxygen dissociation curve was also more thoroughly investigated and the following important relation established. When a series of curves for blood under various CO_2 tensions are compared, it is found that the effect of altering the CO_2 tension is, so to speak, to alter the O_2 pressure scale on which the curve is drawn. For example, in the curves as represented in fig. 26, if we drew the 90 mm. CO_2 tension curve on an abscissal scale two-fifths that of its present one, it would lie exactly superimposed on the 3 mm. CO_2 tension curve, as drawn to the original scale. This effect is not specific to CO_2, but is shown by any acid, and is therefore due essentially to a rise in hydrogen-ion concentration, and is exactly proportional to the rise in hydrogen-ion concentration produced. Thus the curves in fig. 26 might equally well be the oxygen dissociation curves of blood at various pH's. We shall return to these effects of CO_2 and electrolytes in a moment, but meantime we may consider the general biological advantages of the modifications introduced by electrolyte and acid.

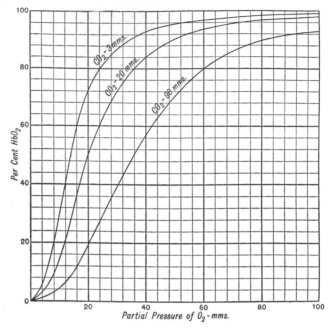

FIG. 26—Effect of varying CO_2 tension on the oxygen dissociation
curve of blood

(Redrawn from Barcroft, *The Respiratory Function of the Blood*)

For the first, comparison of the two curves of fig. 25 shows
that the electrolyte-containing blood is better adapted for
parting with oxygen at low tensions, while it is just as fully
saturated with oxygen at high tensions as the pure hæmoglobin
solution. The uptake of oxygen in the lungs, where the
partial pressure of oxygen is high, is thus not interfered with,
while the giving off of oxygen to the tissues, where the tension
is low, is considerably aided.

For the second, the physiological advantage of the CO_2
(acid) effect may perhaps best be appreciated from the following purely hypothetical example. Suppose A (fig. 27) is an
actively metabolising tissue, such as a muscle, which, in spite
of its activity, maintains a constant oxygen tension of 40 mm.,
but evolves sufficient CO_2 to raise the tension of that gas in
the blood from 20 mm. on its arterial side to 90 mm. on its

venous side.   By this change alone, as we may see by referring
to the curves in fig. 26, the percentage saturation of the hæmoglobin would be reduced from 84 per cent. to 57 per cent.
Oxygen would thus be made available in the tissue without
any alteration in oxygen tension at all.   It must be clearly

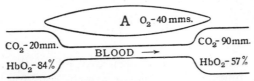

FIG. 27—Hypothetical illustration of the effect of increased CO_2
tension in aiding desaturation of the hæmoglobin

understood, of course, that this is a purely imaginary illustration.   Under actual *in vivo* conditions carbon dioxide and
oxygen tensions change simultaneously, and such wide variations in CO_2 tensions as have been supposed never occur.

Naturally, physico-chemical explanations of the 'salt' and
'acid' effects on the dissociation curve have been sought.   In
a reversible reaction like

$$HbO_2 \rightleftharpoons Hb + O_2$$

an equilibrium is reached such that

$$\frac{[Hb][O_2]}{[HbO_2]} = k \qquad . \qquad . \qquad . \quad (1)$$

where k is the equilibrium constant (p. 70).   Let this formula
be converted into terms of percentage oxygenation of the
hæmoglobin.   If y=percentage extent to which the hæmoglobin exists as oxyhæmoglobin, then $100-y$=the percentage
amount existing as reduced hæmoglobin, and

$$\frac{[Hb]}{[HbO_2]} = \frac{100-y}{y}.$$

Substituting in equation (1) we have

$$\frac{100-y[O_2]}{y} = k.$$

Now the concentration of oxygen is proportional to the partial pressure of oxygen in the gas mixture with which the hæmoglobin is in equilibrium. Therefore we might introduce, instead of the concentration of oxygen $[O_2]$ in the above equation, the partial pressure of oxygen (x), altering the value of the constant k accordingly. The equation would then become

$$K_1 = \frac{(100-y)}{y}x.$$

The above relationship has been evolved on the assumption that each unit of hæmoglobin which combines with one molecule of O_2 acts individually. If, however, the hæmoglobin molecules are aggregates of more than one such unit, then we may have reactions of the following type occurring:—

$$Hb_2 + 2O_2 \rightleftharpoons Hb_2O_4,$$
$$Hb_3 + 3O_2 \rightleftharpoons Hb_3O_6,$$

according to the number of units in each Hb aggregate, and, in general,

$$Hb_n + nO_2 \rightleftharpoons Hb_nO_{2n}.$$

The relationship holding in the last general case is

$$k = \frac{[(Hb)_n]\,[O_2]^n}{[(HbO_2)_n]},$$

or, putting in terms of percentage oxygenation,

$$k = \frac{100-y}{y}[O_2]^n,$$

and, altering the constant, so as to introduce $x =$ the partial pressure of oxygen,

$$K_2 = \frac{100-y}{y}x^n.$$

Putting $K = \frac{1}{K_2}$, we have

$$K = \frac{y}{(100-y)x^n};$$

i.e.

$$Kx^n(100-y) = y,$$

or

$$100Kx^n = y + yKx^n$$
$$= y(1 + Kx^n).$$

$$\therefore \quad y = \frac{100Kx^n}{1 + Kx^n}.$$

Now this equation (Hill's equation) may be used to *calculate* the possible dissociation curves of blood under varying conditions of aggregation of the Hb units, *i.e.* varying values of n. When n is assumed to be 1, the calculated curve has the form (rectangular hyperbola) experimentally found in salt-free solutions of hæmoglobin. When higher values are given to n, the calculated curve shows the S-shape characteristic of the experimental findings in blood; and, in fact, by choosing a value for n of approximately 2·5 and a value for K depending on the CO_2 tension, the experimental curves obtained for blood can be reproduced very closely. Moreover, many other curves obtained experimentally for hæmoglobin solutions under varying conditions can be matched by the calculated curves of Hill's equation, provided that suitable values are assigned to n and K.

Thus A. V. Hill pointed out (1910) that the difference between the dissociation curves of a salt-free solution of hæmoglobin and one containing salts (*e.g.* blood) could be explained by aggregation of the Hb units. In the pure hæmoglobin solution there was no aggregation, and oxygenation occurred by the union of single Hb units with single molecules of oxygen:

$$Hb + O_2 \rightleftharpoons HbO_2.$$

The curve, in accordance with this reaction, was a rectangular hyperbola. In blood and other salt-containing solutions, however, many of the Hb units aggregated, and aggregated in varying degree so that the hæmoglobin molecules were a mixture of single Hb units and aggregates such as Hb_2, Hb_3, etc. In such solutions the curve was therefore an S-shaped one. The fact that the blood curve could be fitted by an equation in which $n = 2·5$ indicated that the *average* value of n, *i.e.* the average degree of aggregation in blood, was 2·5.

The recent researches of Adair on the osmotic pressure of hæmoglobin solutions have shown that Hill's theory, in its original form, is inadequate to explain the difference between the dissociation curves of a pure hæmoglobin solution and of blood. When hæmoglobin unites with oxygen, combination occurs in the proportion of one molecule of oxygen to each atom of iron in the hæmoglobin. According to Hill's theory, therefore, hæmoglobin in the simple unaggregated form in which it was assumed to exist in salt-free solution must consist of molecular units each containing one atom of Fe. Such a unit would have a molecular weight of approximately 17,000. Adair's osmotic pressure measurements show, however, that the molecular weight of hæmoglobin in dilute solution is 67,000, and this figure has been confirmed by Svedberg, who used an entirely different method of determination. Each molecule of hæmoglobin in such solutions must thus contain four Fe atoms.

In solutions of hæmoglobin, therefore, the reaction with oxygen would be:
$$Hb_4 + 4O_2 \rightleftharpoons Hb_4O_8,$$

and the corresponding form of Hill's equation,

$$y = \frac{100Kx^4}{1 + Kx^4}.$$

The curve calculated from this equation is not only not a rectangular hyperbola, but is one in which the S-shape is even more accentuated than in the curve for blood.

Summarising these facts, we have that—

(1) The curve experimentally obtained in a hæmoglobin solution is in actual fact the graphical expression of the equation,
$$y = \frac{100Kx}{1 + Kx}.$$

(2) The curve of a hæmoglobin solution should be the graphical expression of
$$y = \frac{100Kx^4}{1 + Kx^4}.$$

(3) The curve for blood is in actual fact the graphical expression of
$$y = \frac{100Kx^{2\cdot5}}{1 + Kx^{2\cdot5}}.$$

There is as yet no experimentally verified explanation which will reconcile these apparent discrepancies.

With regard to the acid effect, it is found that the change in position of the oxygen dissociation curve that occurs when the CO_2 tension is altered can be accounted for if the n of the equation is kept constant and K is varied according to the CO_2 tension. Now the K of the above equation is simply the equilibrium constant (k) altered to allow of the introduction of partial pressures in place of oxygen concentration. The effect of alterations in the CO_2 tension is therefore to alter the equilibrium of the reversible reaction $(Hb)_n + nO_2 \rightleftharpoons (HbO_2)_n$, which is simply another way of expressing what we saw before, viz. that increase of CO_2 tension has the effect of extending the horizontal scale to which the graph is drawn. For example, on referring to the curves in fig. 26, the reader will find that under 20 mm. CO_2 tension, hæmoglobin exists as 40 per cent. oxyhæmoglobin and 60 per cent. reduced hæmoglobin when the oxygen tension is 17·5 mm.; under a tension of 90 mm. CO_2, however, the same equilibrium between the oxy- and reduced condition is reached only when the oxygen tension becomes 30 mm. The same relative difference of oxygen tension will be found for any other two points of corresponding saturation equilibrium on these curves. A similar relation is found in hæmoglobin solutions, though, in these, the effect of CO_2 in altering the curve is slightly more complicated.

The Transport of Carbon Dioxide – Carbon dioxide is a much more soluble gas than oxygen, having a coefficient of solubility in water of 0·55. In blood it is slightly less soluble than in water, the corresponding figure being 0·51. One hundred c.c. of blood would, therefore, carry in solution at atmospheric pressure 51 c.c. of CO_2. Taking the partial pressure of CO_2 in the blood to be 42 mm., and allowing 47 mm. for the tension of aqueous vapour at body temperature, the amount of CO_2 in solution in the blood would be $\dfrac{42}{760-47} \times 51$, or approximately 3 c.c. per 100 c.c. blood. In actual fact the blood carries a quantity of about 50 c.c. CO_2 per 100 c.c. blood. Obviously, therefore, as in the case of oxygen, the CO_2 is present largely in a combined form.

What is the nature of this combination? The fact that the CO_2 is entirely removable from blood, either by subjection to a vacuum or the addition of acid, suggests that it must be a bicarbonate. Further, the fact that the acids other than CO_2 present in blood are too small in amount to combine with all the sodium found, suggests that the combined CO_2 must be mainly in the form of sodium bicarbonate.

Now just as a dissociation curve may be drawn for the combination of oxygen with hæmoglobin, so we may construct a dissociation curve in which the total amount of CO_2 (dissolved CO_2+CO_2 combined as bicarbonate) in a solution or in blood is graphed against the tension of CO_2 to which that solution or blood is exposed. Fig. 28 shows such curves obtained from (1) a solution of sodium bicarbonate in water, (2) 'separated' plasma, (3) 'true' plasma, and (4) whole blood. The significance of the terms 'separated' and 'true' plasma may be gathered from the methods by which their respective curves are obtained. In the first case the plasma is obtained by centrifuging in the ordinary way. It is then exposed to various CO_2 tensions and the corresponding amounts of absorbed CO_2 determined. The amount of CO_2 that enters into combination as $NaHCO_3$ is thus entirely dependent on reactions within the plasma itself. In the preparation of the true plasma curve the following procedure is adopted. The exposure to various CO_2 tensions is carried out with the whole blood, and the blood afterwards centrifuged under paraffin to prevent contact with the atmosphere and, hence, alteration of the CO_2 tension. The plasma is then withdrawn and analysed with every precaution to avoid alteration of its CO_2 tension during the analysis. The curve in this case gives the correspondence between CO_2 tension and total CO_2, when reactions may occur not only between the CO_2 and plasma substances but between the CO_2 and substances in the corpuscles as well.

Returning now to a comparison of the four curves, we see that exposure to a vacuum ($CO_2=0$ mm.) only liberates about half of the CO_2 in the aqueous bicarbonate solution. On the other hand, we know that treatment of such a solution with an acid like HCl will liberate all the CO_2. This is because exposure to a vacuum alters the bicarbonate only to carbonate

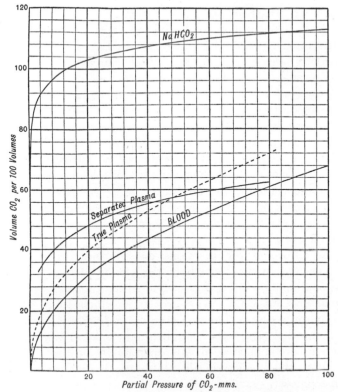

FIG. 28—CO$_2$ dissociation curves for (1) a 0·0484N solution of sodium
bicarbonate, (2) separated plasma, (3) true plasma, and (4) blood
(Redrawn from Lovatt Evans, *Recent Advances in Physiology*)

while the mineral acid unites with the base and evolves all
its combined CO$_2$, in accordance with the following equations:

$$2NaHCO_3 \longrightarrow Na_2CO_3 + CO_2 + H_2O,$$
$$2NaHCO_3 + 2HCl \longrightarrow 2NaCl + 2CO_2 + 2H_2O.$$

Looking now at the curve for separated plasma, we find that
it is similar in shape to that of the bicarbonate solution.
Moreover, separated plasma behaves towards exposure to a
vacuum and treatment with acid much as the bicarbonate
solution does, except that, *in vacuo*, rather more than half of
its CO$_2$ is liberated.

The curves for true plasma and whole blood are quite

otherwise. In their case, diminution of the CO_2 tension to zero leads to a complete evolution of CO_2 from the bicarbonate which they contain. In these two instances there must be some mechanism which assists in displacing the CO_2 as its tension falls. This mechanism must be mainly associated with the corpuscles, since it is only in the true plasma and the whole blood that the corpuscles have any influence. That the mechanism belongs mainly to the corpuscles can be confirmed by adding corpuscles to separated plasma after as much as possible of its CO_2 has been removed by evacuation, when a further amount of the gas is given off. While mainly associated with the corpuscles, the mechanism must be present to a very slight degree in the plasma, because separated plasma on evacuation evolves, as we have seen, rather more than half of its total CO_2.

The nature of the reactions constituting this mechanism are depicted in fig. 29, where the effects of increasing CO_2 tension (blood becoming more venous) are indicated by the full-line arrows, while the reverse reactions which occur when the CO_2 tension lessens (blood becoming more arterial) are shown by the dotted arrows. Though for the sake of simplicity the reactions are indicated in this diagram by ordinary chemical formulæ, the reader should think of them rather as ionic transferences.

The pH of the blood is normally about 7·4, *i.e.* it is just on the alkaline side of neutrality. It is still farther on the alkaline side of the iso-electric points of both plasma proteins and hæmoglobin. Therefore within the corpuscle the hæmoglobin will be attached to cations, and, in fact, mainly to potassium. The plasma proteins will similarly be associated mainly with the cation sodium. The first has been indicated in the diagram as 'KHb,' and the second as 'Na protein.' To both of these cations, it may be remembered, the corpuscle wall is impermeable, though permeable to hydrogen ions and to anions. Hæmoglobin and the plasma proteins being weak acids, their combined K and Na may be readily displaced by any stronger acid. This happens if the blood becomes less alkaline (say, by increased CO_2 tension) and the position of the base is taken by the H^+ ions of the acid. Further, since the ionisation of the protein is at the same time reduced, much of the hydrogen taken up by it will be transferred to an undissociated form; in other words, the proteins, including Hb, act as buffers.   There are also present, in both corpuscles and plasma, bicarbonates and phosphates.   The latter, at the blood pH, will be mainly in the form of K_2HPO_4 (corpuscle) and Na_2HPO_4 (plasma).   The buffering effect of salts of this type we have already discussed.   The plasma contains also considerable quantities of NaCl.

Let us now see what will happen when the blood is in the neighbourhood of an active tissue where the CO_2 tension is high.   The high CO_2 tension leads to an increase of dissolved $CO_2(H_2CO_3)$ in the plasma, and the cH of the blood will tend to rise.   This rise is minimised, and simultaneously the carriage of the CO_2 provided for, by the following reactions :—

The excess H_2CO_3 is in small part taken up by the plasma proteins, the base of the latter being displaced by the H^+ ions of the H_2CO_3.   The HCO_3^- ion, associating with the Na^+, raises the bicarbonate concentration of the plasma.   Most of the H_2CO_3, however, is taken up by the following reactions. (1) It passes into the corpuscle, displacing base from the KHb and K_2HPO_4, so increasing the bicarbonate concentra-

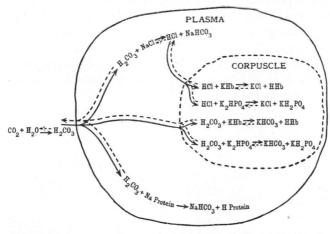

FIG. 29—To illustrate uptake and release of CO_2 by the blood

tion within the corpuscle. (2) It exchanges ions with the plasma NaCl, the Cl⁻ ions (and the H⁺ ions) passing into the corpuscle to take up base (and anions). Reaction (2) is better considered as a return to the plasma of some of the HCO_3^- ions dissociated from the intracorpuscular $KHCO_3$ formed in (1); these HCO_3^- ions and the Cl⁻ ions change places, the Cl⁻ passing into the corpuscle to associate with the K⁺ which the HCO_3^- has left. Reaction (2) is known as the chloride shift. Note that, by it, the H_2CO_3 again avails itself of the base of the corpuscles, though indirectly through the medium of the Cl⁻ ions.

As a result of all these reactions, (a) the extra CO_2 is held in the blood with only slight rise in cH; (b) the concentration of bicarbonate in both plasma and corpuscle rises; (c) the chloride concentration falls in plasma and rises in corpuscle; and (d) the total ionic concentration within the corpuscle is increased. As a result of (d), the corpuscular volume increases owing to the osmotic inflow of water.

When the blood reaches the lungs, the same reactions will occur in the reverse direction, the reversed hæmoglobin, phosphate, and plasma protein reactions driving the CO_2 out of the blood. As two of these reactions are inherent in the corpuscle and one in the plasma, we now see the explanation of why blood and true plasma give off all their CO_2 when the tension of that gas is reduced to zero, and why separated plasma, though somewhat superior to a bicarbonate solution in this respect, is yet not the equal of whole blood.

The distribution of those ions which can diffuse through the corpuscle wall will be controlled by the Donnan equilibrium (p. 80) in such a way that

$$\frac{[\text{anions in corpuscle}]}{[\text{anions in plasma}]} = \frac{[\text{cations in plasma}]}{[\text{cations in corpuscle}]}.$$

Taking, for example, the chlorine and hydrogen ions,

$$\frac{[Cl^-]_{[\text{corpuscle}]}}{[Cl^-]_{[\text{plasma}]}} = \frac{[H^+]_{[\text{plasma}]}}{[H^+]_{[\text{corpuscle}]}}.$$

The ratio in the above equation is known as the Donnan ratio, and it is evident that it too will alter with, and in proportion to, the changes in CO_2 tension.

Now Hb in its oxygenated condition is a more acid substance than reduced Hb. Referring again to fig. 29, let us consider what this means. The oxyhæmoglobin, being more strongly acid, will give up its base less readily, and the corpuscular reactions involving displacement of base from Hb will therefore not be so effective for indirectly taking up the CO_2. In other words, the more oxygenated blood is, the less CO_2 will it hold, and *vice versa*.

When, therefore, we plot the dissociation curves for CO_2 in blood, different curves are obtained according to whether oxygenated or reduced blood is used. The portions of these two curves within the limits of the physiological variations of CO_2 tension are shown in fig. 30.

Now, it is evident that neither of these two curves can represent the *in vivo* relations between CO_2 pressure and quantity of CO_2 in the blood, because, in the body, when the CO_2 tension rises, the oxygenation of the blood simultaneously falls, and the CO_2 curve as a whole moves (upwards in the graph). Since, therefore, in the lungs or tissues variations in CO_2 tension are accompanied by simultaneous changes in oxygen tension, the graph which will represent the *physiological* variation of blood CO_2 with CO_2 tension is neither of these curves but a line joining them, the slope of the line depending on the relative rates of CO_2 and O_2 change, *i.e.* on the respiratory quotient. The line drawn in the figure is that for an R.Q. of 0·8. Further, since in the body the hæmoglobin is never completely reduced, only a part AV of this physiological CO_2 curve is applicable to *in vivo* conditions.[1]

The alteration in the position of the CO_2 curve with oxygenation of the blood is useful in two ways:

(1) Suppose that the blood, in passing through the tissues, has to take up 5 vols. of CO_2, so increasing its CO_2

---

[1] The CO_2 cycle of the blood is not quite accurately represented by an oscillation along the line AV. The changes during absorption of CO_2 in the tissues would be described by a point moving from A to V along a path with a slight downward convexity, and the release of CO_2 in the lungs by a movement from V to A along a path with a slight upward convexity.

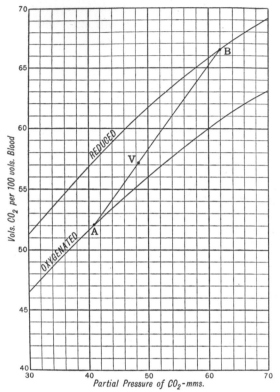

FIG. 30—CO_2 dissociation curves of (1) reduced, and (2) oxygenated, blood. AVB—physiological dissociation curve

(Christiansen, Douglas, and Haldane, *Journ. Physiol.*, 1914. Redrawn)

content from 52 to 57 vols. To do this without simultaneous reduction would involve a rise of CO_2 tension from 41 to 53 mm. With partial reduction, the rise in CO_2 tension is only from 41 to 48 mm.

(2) Variations in pH are minimised.

To understand the reason for (2), we must consider the physico-chemical relations which govern the pH of a solution containing both a weak acid and one of the salts of that acid. In Chapter VII we saw that an acid was so dissociated that

$$\frac{[H^+] \times [A^-]}{[HA]} = k, \text{ the dissociation constant.}$$

Transposing,

$$[H^+] = k \frac{[HA]}{[A^-]} \qquad . \qquad . \qquad . \qquad (1)$$

If in such a solution there is also present a salt of the acid, which we may represent as BA, then this salt will also give rise to anions A^- by dissociating as follows:—

$$BA \rightleftharpoons B^+ + A^-.$$

Now most salts are so completely dissociated that, in a mixture of a weak acid and one of its salts, the anions may be regarded as being supplied entirely from the dissociation of the salt BA. Equation (1) might then be written:

$$[H^+] = \frac{k[HA]}{[BA]} \qquad . \qquad . \qquad . \qquad (2)$$

Even supposing that the dissociation of BA is incomplete, if it nevertheless supplies almost entirely the anions, $[A^-]$, equation (2) will still hold, provided the constant k is altered to allow for the degree of dissociation (a) of BA; thus:

$$[H^+] = \frac{k[HA]}{a[BA]}. \quad \text{Let } \frac{k}{a} = k_1, \quad \text{then} \quad [H^+] = k_1 \frac{[HA]}{[BA]}.$$

In general, therefore, the hydrogen-ion concentration of any solution containing a weak acid and one of its salts will be proportional to the ratio between the concentration of free acid and the concentration of its salt.

Applying this to blood, we see that the pH of the blood will be proportional to the ratio of free carbonic acid to bi-carbonate, *i.e.* $\frac{[H_2CO_3]}{[BHCO_3]}$ (BHCO$_3$ representing carbonic acid combined with any base). In normal blood this ratio is approximately $\frac{1}{20}$ and the corresponding pH 7·4.

Reverting to the two dissociation curves in fig. 30: since on the abscissa are placed the CO_2 tensions (to which the free H_2CO_3 is proportional), and on the ordinate, the CO_2 content (which will be determined by the amount of BHCO$_3$ present), it is evident that each point on the curves will re-present a definite pH. By joining points of corresponding pH in each of the two curves, we obtain a series of lines along each of which the pH is the same. These lines, which are known as pH isopleths, all coincide at the zero-point of the graph (fig. 31). From this graph the advantage of the CO_2 curve's change with oxygenation of the blood is very apparent. If we follow the physiological CO_2 curve, A to V, we see that

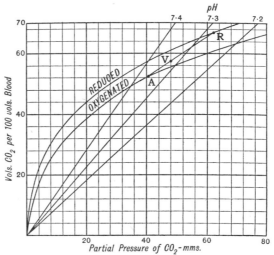

FIG. 31—CO_2 dissociation curves with three pH isopleths added
(Lovatt Evans, *Recent Advances in Physiology*. Redrawn, slightly modified)

the pH changes less for any defined alteration in CO_2 tension than if we follow either the 'reduced' or 'oxygenated' curve.

We may now summarise these interrelated changes which occur in blood during its transformation from the reduced to the oxygenated condition, or *vice versa*, as follows:—

(1) Changes in O_2 tension cause an alteration in the CO_2 dissociation curve.

(2) Changes in CO_2 tension cause an alteration in the O_2 dissociation curve.

Also, as a result of changes in CO_2 tension, alterations will occur in:

(3) The concentration of bicarbonate in both plasma and corpuscle.

(4) The distribution of chloride between plasma and corpuscle.

(5) The pII.

(6) The Donnan ratio.

(7) The corpuscular volume.

The interrelationship between these seven variables, and also between others dependent on them, is such that, if in any particular sample of blood the values of any two are known, the values of the remainder will be fixed according to the laws of physico-chemical equilibrium. Several graphical methods of representing the interdependence of these variables have been introduced, the most comprehensive being the alignment charts (d'Ocagne nomograms) of L. J. Henderson. An example of one of these charts drawn for the seven variables just discussed is given in fig. 32. By adding other scales the nomogram can be extended to include other related variables. In these charts the variables are scaled on lines in such a way that, by joining the points corresponding to the two known variables by a straight line, the remaining values can be read off from the points of intersection of this straight line with the other scales. The scales in the diagram reading from left to right are as follows:—

(r) The Donnan ratio, which indirectly is a measure of the chloride interchange between plasma and corpuscle;

(Vol.) the corpuscular volume, expressed as a percentage of their volume at an oxygen tension of 80 mm. and a CO_2 tension of 39 mm.;

(Total CO_2), the total CO_2 held by the blood;

(CO_2 tension);

(pH_s), the pH of the serum;

(O_2 tension);

(HbO_2), the percentage saturation of the hæmoglobin.

Such a graph gives a convenient composite picture of the various interrelated physico-chemical changes which occur during the oxygenation of the blood in the lungs and its reduction in the tissues.

Before leaving this subject it may be well to stress again the fact that the two processes, carriage of oxygen and carriage of

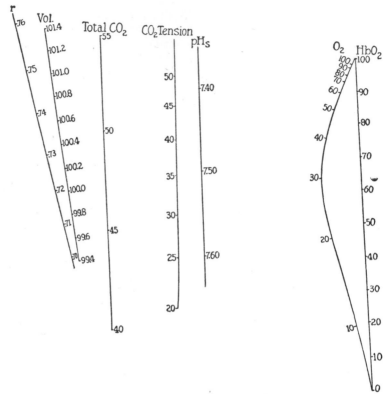

FIG. 32—Alignment Chart for the Blood of A. V. B.

Conditions in the arterial blood of this individual are given by a straight line drawn through 40·3 mm. CO_2 tension and 96 per cent. HbO_2; conditions in the venous blood during moderate exercise by a straight line through 47 mm. CO_2 tension and 65 per cent. HbO_2

(L. J. Henderson, *Lectures on Certain Aspects of Biochemistry*)

CO_2, are mutually interdependent. This may best be done by giving the following superficial summary of the changes occurring during the circuit of the blood.

When the oxygen of the alveolar air diffuses into the blood, the reaction hæmoglobin ⟶ oxyhæmoglobin takes place. Oxyhæmoglobin being a stronger acid than hæmoglobin is more able at a given pH to combine with cations, and thus the available base of the blood is diminished, and the equilibria, combined $CO_2 \rightleftharpoons$ dissolved $CO_2(H_2CO_3) \rightleftharpoons$ gaseous CO_2, are displaced towards the right. The taking up of the oxygen by the blood therefore facilitates the removal of the CO_2. Exactly the reverse process takes place in the tissues where the dissociation of oxyhæmoglobin to hæmoglobin and oxygen, by liberating available base, favours the uptake of CO_2 by the blood and its removal from the tissue. If there were no simultaneous reduction of oxyhæmoglobin to hæmoglobin in the tissues, and no simultaneous oxygenation of hæmoglobin in the lungs, the blood would be only about 20 per cent. as efficient in absorbing and giving off CO_2 as it actually is. In these gaseous interchanges we have a very fine example of how, in the economy of the living organism, the delicate adjustment of complex physico-chemical equilibria ensures the alternation of cycles of activity.

The Preservation of Neutrality – Sufficient has been said in the chapters on Enzymes and Colloids to indicate how important it is that the reaction of the tissues and body fluids should be kept within certain narrow limits. . Such a constancy of pH has to be maintained despite (1) an intake of food whose aggregate acidity or alkalinity may be very variable, (2) an intermittent supply to the alimentary canal of digestive secretions of very varying hydrogen-ion concentration, and (3) the fact that much of our normal metabolism results in the production of acids. For instance, CO_2, that universal product of tissue activity, is itself an acid; the metabolism of the phosphorus and the sulphur of the protein molecule produces phosphoric and sulphuric acids; and muscular activity is attended by the production of lactic and phosphoric acids. On the alkaline side of the metabolic balance we can place only the production of ammonia from amino-acids. This is not sufficient to neutralise the greatly preponderant acid production, and, even though it were, we have no guarantee that metabolic acid production and metabolic alkali formation would be, from moment to moment, and in each locality, so balanced as always to preserve the optimal reaction. It is evident, therefore, that the organism must possess some defensive mechanism against alterations in pH.

This mechanism is partly resident in the blood itself and partly in the tissues. In the case of the blood, the buffering mechanism is primarily that of the $NaHCO_3$ contained in its

plasma. By the action of acid on this salt, the free H_2CO_3
of the plasma will be increased at the expense of some of the
bicarbonate. From this change alone the acidity will be
reduced by the bicarbonate supplying HCO_3^- ions to unite
with the free H^+ ions of the acid; in other words, by the
$NaHCO_3$ exerting its physico-chemical action as a buffer salt.
But this is not all. The increased H_2CO_3 may be largely taken
up by all the reactions of fig. 29; in fact, the blood will react
towards increase of cH from any cause just as it does towards
the particular case of CO_2.

Further, we have seen that the hydrogen-ion concentration
of the blood is proportional to the ratio $\dfrac{[H_2CO_3]}{[BHCO_3]}$. Though
the effect of the acid will be lessened by the physico-chemical
buffer actions of the blood, still there will be some increase
in the hydrogen-ion concentration as the numerator in the
above fraction is increased and the denominator diminished.
But by the effect of the increased hydrogen-ion concentration
on the respiratory centre, hyperpnœa sets in until the free
H_2CO_3 is reduced to correspond with the diminished $BHCO_3$
and the normal pH is restored. To the purely physico-
chemical action of the buffers of the blood in minimising the
existence of H^+ ions in the free state, there is added the physiological action of the respiratory centre in ridding the blood
of the excess of CO_2, thus completely, or almost completely,
restoring the original pH. The plasma bicarbonate has been
named by van Slyke the 'alkaline reserve' of the blood.

Behind this lies a second line of defence constituted by the
combined action of tissues and kidneys. The tissues contain
phosphates of the type K_2HPO_4 and Na_2HPO_4. These also
will act as protective buffers, the hydrogen ions of the acid
being taken up by the alteration of the B_2HPO_4 to BH_2PO_4,
and finally removed from the body altogether by the excretion
of the latter type of salt by the kidney.

Yet another line of defence exists in the presence of NH_3
as a product of the NH_2 groups of amino-acids. During
normal metabolism, the greater part of this NH_3 is converted
to urea, only a slight amount appearing in the urine as ammonium salts. If the need arises for neutralisation of acid,

the greater part of the NH_3 may be diverted towards combining with acid radicals, and correspondingly less allowed to follow the course of conversion to urea.

As the main changes resulting from the excessive production of acid within the body, or its introduction from without, we thus have:

(1) A diminution of plasma bicarbonate with a temporary increase of free CO_2, until this is removed by the lungs.

(2) Subsidiary changes in the distribution of chlorides and other diffusible ions in the blood.

(3) An increased excretion of phosphoric acid by the kidney, the urinary phosphates becoming more of the NaH_2PO_4 and KH_2PO_4 type, with a rise in the hydrogen-ion concentration of the urine.

(4) An increased excretion of acid anions by the kidney in the form of ammonium salts and a corresponding diminution in the excretion of urea.

The effect of introduction of alkali or its excessive metabolic production will be a reversal of these changes.

By these mechanisms, then, the organism maintains its blood pH within narrow limits, and so compensates for the disturbances of hydrogen-ion concentration that must be constantly occurring as the result of its extremely complex metabolic processes.

The wider variations that might be expected and actually do occur in pathological conditions are compensated in an exactly similar fashion. A blood pH of less than 7 or more than 7·5 or 7·6 is incompatible with life. Although this range seems numerically small, it must always be remembered that the pH notation is logarithmic, and a change from 7·4 to 7·1 means a doubling of the hydrogen-ion concentration.

The pathological disturbances of blood reaction may be grouped into those in which the tendency is towards a more acid condition of the blood (acidosis), and those in which the hydrogen-ion concentration tends to fall (alkalosis). Each of these is again of two types, according to whether the condition is primarily due to a change in the free CO_2 of the blood or in its bicarbonate content, *i.e.* whether the initial alteration occurs in the numerator or the denominator of the ratio

$$\frac{[H_2CO_3]}{[BHCO_3]} \propto [H^+].$$

I. *Acidosis from Increased Free* CO_2 – Such a condition may arise clinically from respiratory obstruction or insufficiency (asphyxia, morphia poisoning, emphysema), or be produced experimentally by breathing air mixtures rich in CO_2. The hydrogen-ion concentration of the blood is primarily raised owing to the excessive H_2CO_3, the bicarbonate concentration being normal. Compensation is brought about partly by increased breathing lessening the free CO_2, and partly by the kidney excreting less base than normally, so as to provide for a greater concentration of $BHCO_3$ in the blood; the urine thus becomes more acid. After compensation has been established, though the pH is restored, both plasma bicarbonate and free CO_2 are abnormally high.

II. *Acidosis from Excessive Production or Retention of Acid* – This is the type of most clinical interest, for it occurs in the diabetic from excessive production of β-hydroxybutyric acid, and in certain types of nephritis from defective elimination of the acids of normal metabolism. The hydrogen-ion concentration of the blood tends to rise owing to diminished bicarbonate and excess of free CO_2. Compensation is achieved by hyperpnœa reducing the free CO_2 concentration to a level commensurate with that of the bicarbonate, and by the kidney excreting phosphoric and other acids and also abnormally large quantities of ammonium salts, the urea excretion diminishing. Compensation is secured and normal pH restored at the cost of a low plasma bicarbonate, and therefore the blood of such a patient is less capable of resisting further acid change. If the pathological condition progresses so far that the compensatory changes fail to maintain the blood at normal pH, the acidosis is said to be uncompensated. In such cases coma quickly supervenes.

III. *Alkalosis from Addition of Alkali* – Such a condition may occur from the administration of large quantities of carbonates, bicarbonates, or alkaline phosphates, and also in cases of high intestinal obstruction (*e.g.* pyloric stenosis). The hydrogen-ion concentration of the blood tends to be lowered by the increase in its bicarbonate. Compensation is brought about by diminished breathing, by the kidney excreting less acid and more base than normally, and by NH_3 being transformed almost entirely to urea. The urine thus tends to become alkaline, contains much urea, and very little ammonium salts. Extreme alkalosis of this type gives rise to the symptoms of tetany.

IV. *Alkalosis from Removal of Free* CO_2 – This interesting type of alkalosis is usually the result of stimulation of the respiratory centre by oxygen want. It occurs in unacclimatised persons at high altitudes. The respiratory centre, stimulated by the oxygen deficiency, becomes over-active, and the resulting hyperpnœa leads to an abnormal washing-out of CO_2. The hydrogen-ion concentration of the blood becomes too low owing to the diminution of its H_2CO_3 and the consequent *relative* excess of bicarbonate. Compensation is achieved by the same means as in Case III, but a normal pH is obtained at the cost of a low bicarbonate, and therefore the subject is in a position similar to that of Case II : his blood has now less buffering action towards *acid*. It is during the stage of compensatory change that the symptoms of mountain sickness occur.

While in all these disturbances of blood reaction the compensatory changes have been described as restoring the blood pH to normal, this normal signifies only the absence of an abnormality sufficient to be detected by our methods of estimation. It must be remembered that the stimulus for these compensatory changes is itself the abnormal pII of the blood, and if the pH were completely restored to the normal, all stimulus for their continuance would cease. The so-called restoring of the blood pH in a pathological condition is only a restoration within the limits of detectable change, and, in actual fact, must be incomplete so long as compensatory symptoms persist. The division of acidosis into 'compensated' and 'uncompensated' is thus an arbitrary one, the boundary line between them depending on the accuracy of the method used for determining the pH.

As a means of judging the condition of a patient suffering from one of these pathological conditions, the blood-data of interest are obviously the free CO_2, the plasma bicarbonate, and the blood pH. As the pH is a function of the $\dfrac{[H_2CO_3]}{[BHCO_3]}$ ratio, the determination of any two of these factors is sufficient, since the third can be computed from the other two.

The free CO_2 may be obtained by analysis of the patient's alveolar air, or by determining, from the CO_2 dissociation curve for his blood, what tension of CO_2 corresponds to the CO_2 content of his arterial blood.

The plasma bicarbonate may be estimated directly by separating the plasma from a sample of blood, equilibrating it against alveolar air, and then determining the amount of CO_2 expelled by acidification and evacuation. An easier procedure is to obtain it indirectly by a simple calculation from the CO_2 content of the whole blood.

The pH of the blood may be calculated from these data as follows:—

$$[H^+]=k\frac{[H_2CO_3]}{[BHCO_3]},$$

where k is a constant. Taking the negative logarithm of both sides,

$$pH=pK+\log\frac{[BHCO_3]}{[H_2CO_3]},$$

where $pK=-\log k$. This is the important Henderson-Hasselbalch formula. $[BHCO_3]$ is known from the plasma bicarbonate. $[H_2CO_3]$ can be obtained from the alveolar CO_2; if the partial pressure of CO_2 is p, and a is the coefficient of solubility of CO_2 in the plasma, the concentration of H_2CO_3 in vols. per cent. is $\dfrac{p}{760}\times100a$.

The pH of the blood may be determined directly by the Dale-Evans method or by electrometric methods, using either the glass or quinhydrone electrode.

Valuable information may also be gained from an analysis of the urine for (1) its ammonia and urea content, (2) its relative

acid excretion, and (3) its total titratable acidity. The second
may be determined by a method such as that of Leathes,
where the relative amounts of the monobasic and dibasic
phosphates are estimated together with the total phosphoric
acid excretion. The third is determined by titrating the urine
to a definite alkaline pH with N/10 NaOH. Alternatively the
acid excretion by the kidney may be gauged by an 'alkali-
tolerance test,' *i.e.* by the amount of sodium bicarbonate which
it is necessary to administer to the patient to change the
reaction of the urine from acid to alkaline. The validity of
these urinary estimations is, of course, dependent on the
normal functioning of the kidneys.

CHAPTER XIV

EXCITABILITY

EXCITABILITY in the sense of a response to stimulation is a character of all protoplasm. As ordinarily used, however, the term is applied particularly to muscle and nerve, in which the responses are at once most rapid and most striking. This chapter will deal primarily with excitability as exhibited by nerve.

As a result of stimulation of an end-organ, some change travels up a sensory nerve and produces either an alteration in our consciousness, or, by a reflex action, an appropriate adjustment of the body to the stimulus; or it may cause both. When an outgoing nerve is stimulated, some change occurs in the nerve, which is rapidly transmitted to the effector organ: to a muscle, where it results in contraction, or to a gland, where it causes secretion. The evidence is now fairly complete that the transmitted change in both ingoing and outgoing nerves is of the same nature, the different effect being simply a matter of their terminations, the cortex cerebri or other synapse for the ingoing, and the effector organ for the outgoing impulse.

Similarly, in stimulation of the sensory nerves, the nature of the sensation produced is dependent on the cortical centre to which that sensory nerve goes, and is entirely independent of the way in which the nerve is stimulated. For example, stimulation of the optic nerve, however caused, always results in a sensation of light. These facts were summarised in Johannes Müller's doctrine of 'specific nerve energies.' He supposed that every sensory apparatus had its own 'specific energy,' and that this energy was evoked by any stimulus which was effective.

The change in the nerve itself during its functioning, the so-called nerve impulse, we may then presume to be fundamentally the same in all nerves.

Although the real nature of the nerve impulse is not yet clearly understood, experiment has brought to light a number

of phenomena characteristic of its transit. A nerve impulse
can be produced by a variety of stimulations—mechanical,
chemical, and electrical. Since the last is most easily controlled, it is generally used for studying the impulse under
laboratory conditions.

General Phenomena of Electrical Stimulation – The
student is familiar with the experiments which show that
electrical nerve excitation causes a disturbance originating in
the cathodal region, and self-propagating along the nerve with
a definite velocity. In the frog, the rate of propagation
averages about 30 metres per second, and in man about 120
metres per second. The velocity varies considerably, however,
with different nerves in the same organism, and also in the
component fibres of any one nerve.

When the motor nerve to a muscle is electrically stimulated,
contraction of the muscle occurs only at the making and
breaking of the circuit. During the intervening period when
the electrical current is *flowing* along the nerve, provided that
the strength of the current does not vary, no visible change
occurs in the muscle. Nevertheless, there is evidence that
the nerve itself is not in the same condition as when no current
is passing. This alteration shows itself as a state of sustained
hyper-sensitivity around the cathode (catelectrotonus), and a
state of depressed sensitivity in the region of the anode
(anelectrotonus).

Along with these effects on the sensitivity of the nerve to
stimulation, the constant current produces electrical changes in

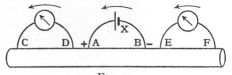

Fig. 33

the substance of the nerve, of which the so-called electrotonic
currents are the result (fig. 33). A constant current from a
battery X is passed through a portion of the nerve, A being the
anode and B the cathode, the direction of the current in the
external circuit being shown by the arrow. If leads are taken
from points C and D, and E and F, on either side of the

constant current circuit to two galvanometers, these galvanometers will indicate currents flowing in their circuits in the
same direction as that of the circuit AXB.   These electrotonic
currents are due to polarisation effects (accumulation of anions
at anode and cations at cathode) produced in the interior of
the nerve by the battery circuit AXB.

The Refractory Period – A nerve is not able to transmit
impulses with unlimited frequency.   When a single impulse
has been set up in a nerve fibre there follows a short period
of 1 to 3σ,[1] during which a second stimulation of the nerve
produces no effect.   This is known as the 'absolute refractory
period.'   This is followed by a 'relative refractory period' of
about 10σ, during which the nerve transmits impulses with
diminished intensity.   For a further period of about 16σ the
nerve is hyperexcitable, and will respond to stimuli which, in
its normal state, would be subminimal.

The refractory state is not merely a local effect at the point
of stimulation, but is present throughout the whole extent of
the nerve.   It must therefore be associated with, and caused
by, the propagation of the impulse.   The state of hyper-
activity which follows the refractory period is also present
throughout the whole track of the impulse.

Summation – A nerve may be induced to respond to stimuli
normally subminimal for it by repeating these stimuli with
suitable frequency.   This effect, which is known as summation,
is limited to the point of excitation; that is, the stimuli must
be repeated on the same portion of the nerve.

All or Nothing Law – There is every reason to believe
that a single nerve fibre, if excited at all, responds by transmitting an impulse of maximal intensity; it either functions
to its full extent, or not at all.   This is known as the 'All or
Nothing Law.'   The original evidence for it was that, when
a muscle is stimulated *via* its motor nerve by stimuli of different
strengths, the grades of response of the muscle are never more
numerous than the number of fibres in its motor nerve.

Decrement – The intensity of an impulse propagated along
a nerve may be reduced in various ways, *e.g.* by cooling or by

---

[1] $\sigma = \frac{1}{1000}$ second.

treatment with anæsthetics, such as alcohol or chloroform. Now the interesting point about this reduction in intensity is that, if the narcotisation or cooling is limited to a stretch of nerve short enough for the reduced impulse to be propagated through it at all, the maximal intensity is regained on re-entering a normal portion of nerve. This precludes the possibility of regarding the nerve impulse as in any way similar to the conduction of an electrical current along a wire, for there the potential falls proportionately to the length and resistance of the conductor. On the contrary, the propagation of the impulse must be one from segment to segment of the nerve, the excitation process in one segment leading to a similar process in the next, and so on. Keith Lucas has given an apt analogy in the transmission of fire along a train of gunpowder, the narcotisation of the nerve being similar to a slight damping of the fuse. In the moistened portion the flame will travel more slowly, and the temperature rise will be less, but the original intensity of combustion will be regained when the flame again reaches a dry part of the fuse.

Fatigue – Nerve fibres cannot be rendered inactive by repeated stimulation, however prolonged. This absence of the phenomenon of fatigue, coupled with the fact that it had proved very difficult to show that nerve activity was accompanied by either increased O_2 consumption or CO_2 output, led to one of two conclusions : either that the transmission of a nerve impulse was unassociated with any consumption of material at all, *i.e.* was not a metabolic process ; or, that the metabolic changes were so small that the products of metabolism were never allowed to accumulate in measurable quantity. The existence of the refractory period indicated that some time was necessary for recovery, and favoured the latter view. Moreover, a certain amount of experimental evidence did exist that nerve activity was accompanied by at least an extra production of CO_2, though, because the amounts to be measured were extremely small, the data were variable and unsatisfactory.

However, the recent researches of A. V. Hill on the heat production of nerve, and those of Gerard and Meyerhof on its chemical changes, leave no doubt that there is a small

13

amount of metabolic change during the transmission of nerve impulses.

Heat Changes – Hill has been able to measure the extremely minute production of heat by an adaptation of his thermopile and galvanometer method.

A thermopile is an electrical conductor made up of alternate segments of two different metals (or alloys). The junctions between the two metals are arranged to fall alternately on the two sides of the pile, so that the set of junctions on one side can be exposed to a source of heat from which the other set is shielded. When this is done, a difference of potential is set up between the two ends of the conductor. The amount of the difference of potential is dependent on the number of junctions and upon the difference of temperature between the two sides of the pile. Owing to the ease and accuracy with which minute amounts of electrical energy can be measured, a thermopile and galvanometer can be made to record very minute changes of temperature, and, by suitable calibration, can be used to measure the heat changes responsible for these temperature changes. Hill had already applied such a technique with conspicuous success to the heat changes in muscle contraction before he achieved the much higher sensitivity in both thermopile and recording apparatus necessary to measure the exceedingly minute heat changes in nerve.

Briefly, the method adopted for nerves is this. The thermopile itself is constructed by winding, with suitable precautions for insulation, a rectangular frame with a continuous length of constantan wire (fig. 34). The flat coil so formed, consisting of over 200 turns, is then electroplated with silver over one-half of its circumference and the whole coil coated with an insulating varnish. Provision is made for the connection of the two ends of the coil to galvanometer leads. In this way

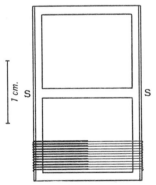

FIG. 34—Thermopile element. Shown partially wound and electroplated over one-half
(Downing and Hill, *Proc. Roy. Soc.,* 1929)

there are formed over 200 'hot' junctions down the middle
of one face of the thermopile, and an equal number of 'cold'
junctions down the middle of the opposite face. This thermo-
electric element is mounted on supports held in a rubber bung,
the supports conveying through their hollow interiors (1) leads
from the thermopile to the galvanometer system; (2) leads to
electrodes for stimulating the nerve; and (3) leads for calibrating
the thermopile and for recording the action-current of the nerve
if desired. A cylindrical glass vessel is placed over both element and supports, so forming a chamber through which moist
oxygen or nitrogen may be passed. In use, several nerves are
laid side by side along the 'hot' junctions of the element.
Along the line of the 'cold' junctions is applied either a similar
set of nerves which are not stimulated, or an equal bulk of wet
filter-paper. Any heat changes in the stimulated nerves will
produce a difference of temperature between 'hot' and 'cold'
junctions and generate an electrical current in the coil of the
element.

Although such thermopiles, owing to their careful design
and large number of junctions, are extremely sensitive, the
currents produced are still so minute that great difficulty was
experienced in obtaining a sufficiently sensitive galvanometer
which yet would remain unaffected by the external electrical
and mechanical disturbances of an ordinary laboratory. The
system finally adopted was as follows. The thermopile was
connected to a moving-coil mirror galvanometer of quite
ordinary sensitivity. The reflected beam from this galvanometer was projected on a thermocouple, consisting of a
central manganin strip joined laterally to two pieces of constantan. To this thermocouple was connected a second
galvanometer. In the zero position of the first galvanometer
its beam fell exactly on the middle spot of the central manganin
strip of the thermocouple. Each of the manganin-constantan
junctions was thus equally heated, and no current passed in
the circuit of the second galvanometer. When, however,
there was any deflection of the first galvanometer, the light
beam moved towards one manganin-constantan junction and
away from the other, so producing a magnified deflection in
the second galvanometer. By this arrangement a current of

2×10^{-12} amperes flowing in the nerve thermopile would cause a deflection of the light beam of the secondary galvanometer of 1 mm. at a distance of 1 metre. In spite of the sensitivity of this apparatus, it was necessary to produce many impulses per second in the nerve to obtain reliable results, and to deduce indirectly from such data what happened during the transmission of a single impulse.

Hill's more important findings may now be summarised. Just as in muscle, the heat produced by a nerve in action may be divided into an *initial* evolution of heat, coincident with the action-current (see below), and therefore presumably the accompaniment of the actual transmission of the nerve impulse, and a *delayed* heat, lasting for a relatively long period, and associated with the recovery of the nerve. While the initial heat lasts only a few σ, the delayed heat may extend over ten minutes. The initial heat coincides, therefore, with the period of absolute refractoriness. The quantitative relation between the amounts of initial heat and the total heat evolved from the moment of stimulation to the return of resting heat production is approximately as 1 : 10. In this the nerve differs greatly from muscle, where the corresponding relation is as 1 : 2. This would suggest that chemically the process of recovery in nerve is quite different from that in muscle. Further evidence of such a difference is that, in nerve, the deprival of oxygen depresses both initial and delayed heat alike; in muscle, deprival of oxygen leaves the heat associated with the contraction phase unaltered, but cuts out entirely the evolution of heat that accompanies the recovery process.

The amounts of heat produced by nerve action are, as expected, extremely small; for one impulse traversing 1 cm. of a single nerve fibre, it was calculated that the initial heat would be about 10^{-13} calories and the delayed heat about $8 \cdot 5 \times 10^{-13}$ calories.

Metabolic Changes – The definite observation of heat changes associated with nerve activity made it certain that consumption of oxygen and production of CO_2 must also occur. The extent of these changes has been recently investigated by Gerard and by Meyerhof. Their results agree, on the whole, with those to be expected from the heat changes. The resting respiratory quotient of nerve was found to be 0·77. During activity the oxygen consumption might rise as high as four times its resting value, and the respiratory quotient rose to 0·97. The latter figure cannot be taken, however, as in muscle, to indicate a carbohydrate type of metabolism, for nerve has been shown to produce a certain amount of ammonia from protein, and this metabolic process by itself has a theoretical respiratory quotient of 0·95. Moreover, in nerve, lactic acid does not accumulate during anaerobic activity as it does in muscle. The metabolic processes underlying nerve action await further elucidation.

The Action-current – Another phenomenon which accompanies the transmission of nerve impulses is the action-current.

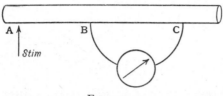

FIG. 35A

From a study of it a great deal of information has been gained about nerve action in general. It may be brought into evidence in two ways. First, an uninjured nerve may be stimulated by a cathode at A (fig. 35A), and galvanometer leads placed on the nerve at B and C. As the impulse passes point B, the surface of the nerve there will be found to become electrically negative to the inactive parts of the nerve. A current will therefore flow through the galvanometer from C to B. When the impulse reaches C, that portion of the surface will become negative to the rest, and a current will pass through the galvanometer in the opposite direction, *i.e.* from B to C. Since the current flows, first in the one direction and then in the other, this phenomenon is called the diphasic variation. The presence of the impulse at any point in a nerve is thus accompanied by a negative condition of the *surface* of the fibre at that point.

The second method by which the action-current may be shown is by the diminution of the demarcation-current, or current of injury.   If a nerve fibre is cut across and two galva-nometer leads are attached, one to the injured end, and the other to the uninjured surface of the fibre, the galvanometer will indicate a current flowing in the galvanometer circuit from uninjured to injured portion of the fibre (fig. 35B).   The direction of this current of injury shows that the *surface* of the uninjured portion is positive relatively to the injured part.   Now, if such a fibre is stimulated, as the impulse passes the galvanometer lead which rests on the uninjured portion of the fibre, the positive condition there will be reduced by the negative condition associated with the impulse, and the galvanometer will therefore show a diminished deflection

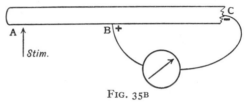

FIG. 35B

while the impulse is passing this point.   After the impulse has passed, the previous intensity of the current of injury will be restored.   On reaching the injured end of the fibre, the impulse does not add to the negative condition already existing there, because the structure of the fibre is destroyed.   The deflection of the galvanometer obtained in this case is in one direction only, hence it is called the 'monophasic variation.' The monophasic and diphasic variations have thus essentially the same cause, but in the former the results are modified by the simultaneous presence of the constantly flowing current of injury.

The phenomena of the monophasic and diphasic variations, and of the current of injury, may be explained on a physico-chemical basis in the following way.   As we have already seen, not only is every cell surrounded by a semi-permeable mem-brane, but there is reason to believe that the interior of the cell is also divided up into compartments by such membranes. Each of these, owing to its permeability to some ions and impermeability to others, will exhibit a difference of potential between its two sides.   The nerve fibre will be no exception to this rule, and if we assume (an assumption with some experimental justification) that there is within it a longitudinally disposed membrane or series of membranes, whose outer surface is positively charged and inner surface negatively charged, the injury- and action-currents may be readily explained. To take first the current of injury, AC (fig. 36A) is a nerve fibre injured at C. By the injury, the membrane structure of the fibre is destroyed, and hence there will be no potential difference between surface and core at this point. At any uninjured portion B the surface positive potential will still exist, hence the injured part will be negative relatively to the normal part B.

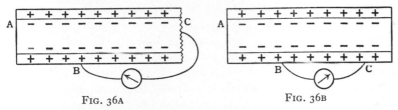

FIG. 36A   FIG. 36B

Now suppose an impulse is propagated from A towards the injured part. In Chapter XI it was noted that a general effect of activity in any tissue is an increase in permeability. But increased permeability at B will remove the very conditions which are responsible for the surface positive potential. Thus, when the impulse passes B, the positive potential is lessened, and the current of injury diminished or abolished altogether.

Take now the uninjured fibre (fig. 36B). This will present a positive potential all along its surface. When, however, the permeability of any portion of it is increased by the presence of the impulse at that point, the difference of potential will be diminished. That portion will, therefore, be negative relatively to the remainder, which still retains its superficial positive charge. In this way may be explained the wave of negativity that produces the diphasic variation in an uninjured fibre.

The starting of the impulse in response to electrical stimulation is generally believed to be due to changes in the distribution of the ions in the fibre, a theory first introduced by Nernst, and since elaborated by others. The nerve, as we saw, is believed to be divided up into compartments by membranes which, except in the refractory condition, are impermeable to certain ions, and, according to these theories, stimulation induces an increased concentration of cations on the cathodal side of the membranes in the immediate neighbourhood of the cathode. The excitation wave is started when this concentration rises above a certain minimal value. A simple explanation is thus offered of the failure of high-frequency alternating currents to produce any excitation, because, with such currents, the direction in which the ions will tend to move is so frequently reversed that the necessary minimal concentration of cations can never be reached. Explanations of various other phenomena associated with nerve action are also afforded. For instance, electrical stimulation is only effective when a certain strength of current is passed for a certain length of time, because the strength and duration have to be sufficient to produce the necessary minimal concentration of ions. Again the refractory period is simply the brief persistence of the increased permeability which is assumed to accompany a nerve-impulse; while this increased permeability exists it is impossible for a second stimulus to produce the necessary ionic concentration for a second excitation, and this condition will last until normal semi-permeability is restored.

To account for the propagation of the impulse, it may be supposed that the electrical disturbance produced at any one part of the fibre is sufficient to excite the next, and so on. An experiment of Lillie provides an interesting analogy. He found that an iron wire placed in concentrated nitric acid becomes coated with a film of a higher oxide. If it is then removed to a more dilute solution of nitric acid, the presence of this film of oxide makes it immune to the action of the dilute solution. If, however, a point on the wire is made the cathode of an electrical circuit, the dilute acid attacks it at that part, forming a lower oxide. As a result of the chemical action a current passes from the attacked to the neighbouring passive part of the wire, setting up a similar chemical action there, while the part first attacked again becomes passive. This process repeats itself until the disturbance has passed right along the wire. The iron wire model shows another interesting parallel with nerve action, in that each active part of the wire exhibits a refractory period after its activity.

For the proper registration of the currents of action two points are essential in the recording apparatus. The first is that the moving system of the recorder must have as little inertia as possible, so that it may follow the extremely rapid variations of the action-current. A capillary electrometer or string galvanometer may be used, but more suitable instruments with which much of the recent work has been done are the cathode-ray oscillograph, described below, and the Matthews' oscillograph. The latter is essentially a moving-iron loud-speaker unit with a small mirror fixed to the vibrating armature. The oscillations of a beam of light reflected from this mirror are recorded photographically. As both types of oscillograph are comparatively insensitive, the action-currents have to be amplified by thermionic valve amplifiers before being applied to the recorder.

The second is that the electrodes by which the recorder leads are brought into contact with the nerve should be of a non-polarisable variety. As these are used in all electro-physiological work, we may explain their principle here. Let us suppose, for the sake of simplicity, that, instead of the variety of ions that are present in a nerve (or other tissue), there are only Na^+ and Cl^-, and that two metallic (*e.g.* platinum) electrodes are placed on the nerve. As soon as any current flows in a circuit of which these electrodes and the intervening portion of nerve are a part, the positively charged Na^+ ions will accumulate at the negative electrode, and the negatively charged Cl^- ions at the positive electrode. The initial potential difference between the two electrodes will thus progressively diminish since each is accumulating ions of opposite sign to itself. Because of this polarisation the recorder will only register correctly at the instant at which the current begins to flow, and subsequent indications will be progressively too low.

Polarisation may be avoided by using as electrodes a metal in contact with a solution of one of its salts, *e.g.* Zn in $ZnSO_4$. One type of such non-polarisable electrodes, shown in fig. 37, consists of a tube plugged at the bottom with a kaolin plug moistened with isotonic saline, and filled with $ZnSO_4$ in which a Zn rod is immersed. By laying the nerve or other tissue across the kaolin plug, direct contact of the tissue with the $ZnSO_4$ is avoided. When current flows in any circuit including these electrodes and the intervening portion of nerve, the Zn^{++} ions will travel to the negative electrode, but, on reaching it, they will deposit as zinc metal, losing their charge.

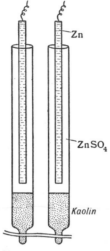

Similarly, though the $SO_4^=$ ions tend to accumulate at the positive electrode, they become associated there with Zn^{++} ions formed by solution of the metal of the electrode, the only result being an increase of the zinc sulphate concentration of the solution at this region.   By this arrangement, the opposing e.m.f. of accumulated ions at each of the electrodes is avoided. Another combination, more frequently used nowadays, consists of a silver rod, electrolytically coated with silver chloride, and dipping into isotonic saline solution.

We have said that the instrument for recording action-currents must have as small an inertia as possible.   This condition is most completely fulfilled by the cathode-ray oscillograph, in which the recording element is essentially a stream of electrons.   The electron stream is liberated in a tube, rather like a large wireless valve (fig. 38), but with a tubular anode, so that the electron stream can pass through

Fig. 37—Zn—ZnSO₄ non-polarisable electrodes

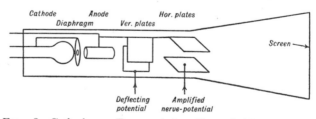

Fig. 38—Cathode-ray (Braun tube) oscillograph (diagrammatic)

the anode and produce a spot of light on a fluorescent screen at the end of the tube.   Surrounding the path of the stream and in front of the screen are four metal plates, two horizontal, placed one above and one below the electron path, and two vertical, one on either side of the path. A progressively increasing difference of potential is applied from a battery to the two vertical plates, causing the spot of light to travel laterally towards the more positively charged plate. The potential variations of the action-current obtained from the nerve, magnified many times by a thermionic valve circuit, are applied to the plates above and below the electron stream. The spot of light therefore moves up and down in response to the potential variations of the action-current, these movements being superimposed on a continuous sideward movement of the light spot. By rapid repetition of synchronised action-current and lateral deflection, the potential variations of the former can be projected as a standing wave on the screen, and photographic records can be made.

By the use of this instrument, Gasser and Erlanger have obtained, for various nerves, extremely accurate records of the action-current. They found, if the action-current was led off from a point on the nerve as far distant as possible from the point of stimulation, that the recorded variations were evidently composite ones made up of more than one action-current. These results led them to the interesting conclusion that the action-currents, and hence also the excitation waves in the different fibres of a nerve trunk, did not travel at the same rate. Individual nerve fibres could be classified according to the velocity with which they propagated the impulse. In general it was found that the larger the diameter of the fibre, the more rapidly did the impulse pass along it. Evidence was also obtained that the fibres with different velocities subserve different physiological functions.

Action of Nerves in the Body – All our attention has been focussed so far on the observations made when a nerve is artificially stimulated by a single electrical shock, and nothing has been said of the way in which they function when stimulated naturally in the living body, where the stimulus may be of much longer duration.

The refractory period indicates that nerves cannot be continuously in action; even though the stimulus is a continuous one, the excitation of the nerve is automatically interrupted.

Taking the absolute refractory period as 2σ, it is evident that continuous stimulation can never give rise to more than 500 impulses per second, and even at rates approaching this each successive stimulus would be falling in the early part of the relative refractory period of the preceding one. On theoretical grounds, therefore, we should expect this frequency to be certainly a maximum, and probably a maximum never reached.

Voluntary contractions of intact muscle resemble very closely the tetanic contractions produced in excised muscle by rapidly repeated electrical stimulation, which suggests that the passage of a prolonged excitation in (at least) motor nerves is actually not continuous but is a rapid train of impulses. Piper found (1907), by the use of the string galvanometer, that the voluntary contractions of muscle *in situ* were accompanied by action-currents recurring with a frequency varying in different muscles from about 40 to 100 per second. This supported the view of the discontinuity of normal nerve excitation, if one assumed that each muscle action-current corresponded with a single nerve action-current. This assumption has been proved valid by simultaneously recording action-currents from both nerve and muscle, as first done by Dittler and Garten in the phrenic nerve and diaphragm muscle. Modern work, mostly on the phrenic nerve and diaphragm and on various reflex actions, has shown that the action-current records of a motor nerve are composites of the responses in its many fibres, and that the discharge in a single fibre is a regular succession of impulses of constant magnitude, but varying in frequency with the degree of muscular response produced.

There seems no reason to expect a different mechanism in sensory nerve, but investigation of the sensory nerve is often more difficult. In the first place, the sensory fibres are often mixed with motor fibres in the same nerve trunk, and, secondly, when the end-organs of the sensory nerves are artificially stimulated, it is difficult to set in action more than a few of the fibres connected with it, and the action-currents are correspondingly small. Nevertheless Adrian, by using a valve-amplifier to magnify the action-current potentials and by recording the amplified potential variations with a capillary electrometer, has recently been able to make an extensive investigation of the response of various sensory nerves to normal stimulation. The first experiments were made on the response of a frog's sciatic nerve to the stretching of its gastrocnemius muscle. It was found that such stimulation caused a rapid succession of electrical oscillations to be recorded by the capillary electrometer. Although the records were apparently composite curves, made up of the combined action-currents of many fibres, they showed evidence that the greater the stimulation of the muscle, the more frequent the impulses. This relation of intensity of stimulus to frequency of impulse was better brought out by using the sterno-cutaneous muscle of the frog, which is supplied by a nerve containing only 12 to 25 fibres. Strips of the muscle were removed until eventually a small piece was obtained whose stretching stimulated only one end-organ. With this preparation it was found that stretching produced a succession of regular impulses, whose frequency varied from 5 to 100 per second, according to the tension exerted on the muscle, the amplitude remaining the same whatever the strength of stimulus applied. Similar results have been obtained by Adrian and his colleagues with many other sensory nerves, e.g. those conveying sensations of pressure, touch, and pain, the depressor nerve from the heart, the vagus, and the optic nerve. The response of a sensory nerve fibre to stimulation of its end-organ is thus a series of nerve impulses, always of the same intensity, an intensity which we may assume to be maximal. The nerve in vivo, therefore, obeys the 'all or nothing' law, and differences in strength of stimulation are transmitted by the nerve as differences in frequency of the impulses.

If the maximum frequency of nerve impulses in any one sensory fibre is 100 per second, one nerve impulse can never encroach on the refractory period of the preceding one. Apparently the frequency is determined by the end-organ's refractory period, which is so much longer than the nerve's refractory period that the transmitting powers of the nerve can never be overtaxed.

It is a familiar fact that our sensory organs are stimulated only by a change in the environment. When a stimulus has persisted at constant intensity for a certain length of time

we cease to be aware of it. So it is found that the trains of
impulses set up in a sensory nerve fibre by prolonged stimulation cease after the stimulus has lasted for a certain period,
the period varying with the particular type of sense organ
involved. For example, prolonged stimulation of the neuro-
muscular spindles (the proprioceptive end-organs) produced
by continuous stretching of a muscle gives rise to a long train
of impulses, while impulses from the receptors of light pressure
and touch cease very rapidly. It is interesting that the former
are concerned mainly in the postural reflexes, where prolonged
action is to the advantage of the organism, while the latter are
concerned principally with reflexes where the reaction to the
sensation is frequently a very rapid one.

Excitability of Muscle – Muscle shows many of the
features that we have just described for nerve. When it is
stimulated either through its motor nerve or by placing electrodes directly upon it, a wave of excitation is set up and
propagated through the muscle. As with nerve, the origin
of this excitation is in the cathodal region. Muscle also
exhibits a refractory period; the all or none principle is equally
applicable; and an action-current of similar form to that of
nerve accompanies the passage of the excitation wave. The
velocity with which the wave travels is, however, much slower
in muscle, and the refractory period is longer. The theory
that the passage of a nerve impulse is accompanied by increased
permeability changes in the nerve, gains some support from
more direct evidence of a similar occurrence in muscle. For
example, it has been shown that the electrical conductivity
of stimulated muscle is higher than that of muscle at rest,
and increased conductivity is an indication of a greater ionic
permeability. It has also been shown directly that muscle is
more permeable to KCl during stimulation than at rest.

In exhibiting all these phenomena, muscle is, therefore,
very similar to nerve. But the excitation-wave in muscle is
followed, after a latent period, by a phenomenon which has
no counterpart in nerve, namely, contraction; this will be
dealt with in the next chapter.

The Electrocardiograph – It seems appropriate in this
place to consider the very practical clinical use which has been

made of the action-currents of the heart muscle in the electro-cardiograph. The excitation-wave of the heart, it will be recalled, begins at the sino-auricular node, involves the auricles, and passes to the auriculo-ventricular node, from which it is distributed over the two ventricles. If, therefore, two elec-trodes are placed, one on the base of the heart and the other on its apex, and leads are taken from them to a string galva-nometer, the galvanometer will record the potential variations due to the passage of the excitation-wave over the different parts of the heart. While, in animals, it is quite possible to place the electrodes actually on the heart, we have to be content, in the human subject, with leading off the current by non-polarisable electrodes applied to either (1) the right arm and left arm, (2) the right arm and left foot, or (3) the left arm and left foot. The moist tissues of the limbs and trunk then complete the circuit between the heart and electrodes. All three pairs of leads are used, the type of electrical variation differing slightly in detail, though remarkably little in its general features, according to which leads are used.

The principle of the recording apparatus is as follows. A powerful beam of light from an arc lamp is concentrated by a condensing lens on the string of the galvanometer. The shadow of the string, magnified by a microscope, is focussed by a cylindrical lens on a photographic plate, which is enclosed in a light-tight box provided with a slit through which the light-beam passes. The plate is moved at constant velocity by a clockwork movement across the path of the beam. The lens is ruled with lines at millimetre distances, and these cast shadows on the plate and record the horizontal lines seen in the tracing (fig. 39). The sensitivity of the instrument is so adjusted that each of these horizontal lines indicates a potential variation of one-tenth of a millivolt. The vertical lines mark off intervals of time (usually one twenty-fifth of a second), and are obtained by arranging a toothed wheel so that its periphery rotates in the path of the light-beam. As each tooth passes, it momentarily cuts off the light from the moving plate.

A typical record of the changes in one normal cardiac cycle is shown in fig. 39. The connections to the instrument are so arranged that all deflections above the zero line indicate a negative condition at the base of the heart, and those below the line a negative condition at the apex.   The various points in the tracing are designated P, Q, R, S, and T.   Of these the most important are the P and Q waves, P being the potential variation caused by the auricular contraction and Q marking the beginning of ventricular contraction.   The ventricular

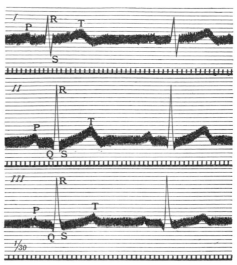

FIG. 39—Three electrocardiograms from a young and healthy subject

I. Leading from the right arm to the left arm
II. Leading from the right arm to the left leg
III. Leading from the left arm to the left leg

(Lewis, *The Mechanism and Graphic Registration of the Heart-beat*)

contraction, because the excitation-wave is rapidly conducted all over it by the Band of His, takes place almost simultaneously all over the ventricular surface.   Hence it gives rise to a complex disturbance, the QRS waves, the interpretation of the individual parts of which is still somewhat controversial.   The T wave, the exact cause of which is also doubtful, occurs almost simultaneously with the second heart sound, and marks the end of active contraction in the ventricle.

The electrocardiogram enables the clinician to determine with accuracy the interval between the auricular and the beginning of ventricular contraction (P–Q interval in the record), and also to analyse any disturbance in the normal sequence of cardiac action. Thus, an appearance in the record of P waves, not succeeded by the ventricular QRS complex, will indicate either that the auricle is contracting so frequently that some of the impulses transmitted from it to the ventricle reach the latter during its refractory period, and therefore are not followed by ventricular contraction; or, that the conduction of the impulse through the Band of His is defective (heart-block).

Measurement of Excitability – Excitability is a general property of living cells exhibited in most striking fashion by the tissues of muscle and nerve. From what has been already said, it is plain that the excitability of these two tissues is widely different in degree, though qualitatively of the same type. Further, visceral muscle is much slower in its action than voluntary muscle, and some voluntary muscles are much more rapid in their action than others. Similarly in nerve, there are variations in the duration of the refractory period and in the velocity of propagation of the impulse.

It is evident that some means of measuring excitability would be of great value both for experimental research and for clinical diagnosis. Such a method should, preferably for the former, and of necessity in the latter, be applicable to nerves and muscles *in situ* in the body. Because of the ease with which electrical stimuli can be controlled and measured, it is natural that the means of estimating excitability should have been sought in the response of a tissue to electrical stimulation.

Formerly, the most usual method was to place one electrode on the skin, either directly over the muscle, or over the point at which its motor nerve entered it (according to whether the excitability of the muscle itself or of its nerve were under investigation), and a second electrode on some indifferent portion of the body. These two electrodes formed part of an electrical circuit containing means of varying and measuring the intensity of the current passed through it. The excitability of the tissue was then determined by finding the least amount of current which would just cause a contraction of the muscle, when the circuit was made and broken.

This method suffers from certain defects. The electrical stimulation of a tissue is not only dependent on the intensity of

14

the current used for excitation, but on the *time* during which that intensity of current is allowed to act.   In the second place, the stimulation of the tissue depends on the current flowing through the actual tissue itself, and not on any portion of the electrical disturbance which may have spread to the tissues surrounding the muscle or nerve under investigation.   Now, in the method described above, it is impossible to know what proportion of the current is actually traversing the nerve and muscle and exciting it, and what proportion is being diverted. Moreover, when observations are made on the same muscle or nerve in different persons, or in the same person on different occasions, the electrical resistance of the tissues between the electrodes will almost certainly not be the same on each occasion.   It is also impossible to be certain that the stimulating electrodes are placed on exactly the same spot at each investigation.   These factors and others will vary the strength of current required for excitation, and hence the results obtained will not be truly comparable.

In the modern method of estimating excitability by the 'chronaxie,' not only is the time-factor taken into account, but difficulties due to alteration in resistance, electrode position, size of electrodes, etc., are largely obviated.

The significance of the term 'chronaxie' may be briefly explained as follows.   It has been said that the excitation of a tissue is dependent on the intensity of the current used for stimulation, and the duration of its action.   Now this is true only within limits.   If the intensity of a stimulating current is progressively reduced, the period during which it must flow through the tissue in order just to excite becomes progressively longer, until a certain limiting intensity is reached.   A current of intensity below this limiting value will not excite the tissue at all, however long it acts, while a current of exactly the limiting intensity would require theoretically an infinite time to cause excitation.   In any particular observation, the voltage which produces an intensity as near this theoretical minimum as can be observed practically, is called the 'rheobase.'   As just stated, when the intensity of the current is increased by raising the voltage above this rheobase value, the duration necessary for excitation becomes shorter and shorter, and the 'chronaxie' of a tissue is the minimal *time* during which the current produced by *twice* the rheobase voltage must act in order just to produce excitation.

The reason for the choice of this particular multiple, twice the rheobase voltage, may be briefly indicated. Let us suppose that the minimal intensity of current which will excite at infinite duration is *b*. As the intensity is increased above this value, the minimal duration for excitation diminishes, and Weiss showed that if the relation between intensity (or, equally, voltage, if the resistance of the circuit is a constant one) and minimal time is graphed, the curve is a rectangular hyperbola [1] (fig. 40). From the definition

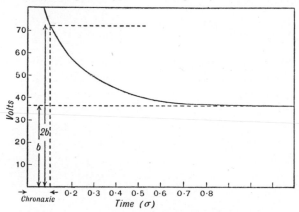

FIG. 40—Chronaxie
(Adapted from Bourguignon, *La Chronaxie chez l'Homme*)

of *b* it is evident that one of the asymptotes [2] of this hyperbola is a line parallel to the time axis placed at a level *b* units of intensity above it.

Now this curve is the graphical expression of the relation that the excess over the limiting value *b* of current intensity necessary for excitation is inversely proportional to the time of the current's action, in symbols:

$$i - b = \frac{a}{t} \quad \text{or} \quad i = \frac{a}{t} + b,$$

where *a* is a constant.

---

[1] A rectangular hyperbola is a curve expressing the relation between two variables, of which the one varies as the reciprocal of the other ; the two limbs of the curve approach nearer and nearer to, but never touch the axes.

[2] Asymptote—a line which approaches continually nearer to the curve, but does not meet it at finite distance.

Further, since quantity of current=intensity of current × time of its flow, the minimal *quantity* of electricity lasting for time t which will excite is:

$$Q = it = a + bt.$$

Weiss suggested that the ratio $\frac{a}{b}$, which is in time units, since it is a quantity $\div$ an intensity, is a characteristic of the excitability of the tissue. This ratio, the ' chronaxie ' of Lapicque, can be obtained experimentally by measuring the time required for excitation when the exciting current has an intensity of twice the minimal value b, since, substituting $2b$ for i in $i = \frac{a}{t} + b$, we get $\frac{a}{b} = t$. Hence, since the rheobase voltage produces a current of intensity b, estimation of t when twice this rheobase voltage is used gives the chronaxie.

The practical value of the chronaxie lies in the fact that, though the rheobase value may, and does, vary with the experimental conditions of tissue resistance, etc., the chronaxie is remarkably constant. This is shown by the following figures, which are the chronaxies for stimulation of the rabbit's rectus femoris as estimated (1) *in situ*, and (2) when the skin had been removed and the motor nerve was directly stimulated at its point of entry into the muscle. In spite of the difference in the rheobase figures, the chronaxies are identical.

	Rheobase	Chronaxie
Skin surface . .	34	0·074 σ
Exposed muscle .	8	0·074 σ

(Bourguignon)

The practical determination of the chronaxie consists in (1) the application of (non-polarisable) electrodes in the way before described, the cathode being used for stimulation and the anode being a large indifferent electrode; (2) the estimation of the rheobase voltage by finding the lowest voltage which will just stimulate; and then (3), without moving the electrodes, the estimation of the time during which the current produced by exactly double this voltage must flow, in order to cause the least visible response of the tissue.

Now, as chronaxies may be of the order of one σ or less, it is obviously impossible to measure them directly. Advantage is taken of the fact that the time-course of the discharge of a condenser, discharging through a known resistance, is calculable from the capacity of the condenser in farads. If a series of several condensers of different known capacities are charged up to double the rheobasic voltage, and these condensers discharged one by one through the tissue, the chronaxie can be calculated from the capacity of the condenser which will just excite the tissue. Stage (3) of the determination of chronaxie, therefore, consists of finding this appropriate condenser.

A great deal of information has accrued from a study of the chronaxies of different muscles and nerves. Lack of space precludes even a summary of these, but the following points of general importance must be mentioned. Chronaxies from hundredths of a σ to 15,000 σ (pigment cells of frog's skin) have been observed. In nerves the shortest chronaxies are found in those which have the shortest refractory periods, and in which there is the most rapid propagation of the impulse. In muscles, the speed of contraction and the chronaxie are related to one another; the shorter the chronaxie, the more rapid is the muscle in its action. Under normal conditions the chronaxie of a muscle and the motor nerve belonging to it are identical, or nearly so. Lapicque believes that this condition of 'iso-chronism' between muscle and nerve is an essential for the proper transmission of the excitation from the nerve to the muscle, the transference of the excitation becoming less efficient the more this relationship is disturbed, and that when the difference between the two chronaxies is 100 per cent. or more, transference fails altogether.

The student will recollect that when a nerve-muscle preparation is 'fatigued' by repeated stimulation through its motor nerve, the muscle still responds to electrical stimuli applied directly to it, an experiment long held to show that the 'fatigue' affected some intermediate substance between the nerve and muscle. In such a preparation, it can be shown that the progressive weakening of the muscle response is accompanied by an ever-widening discrepancy between the muscle and nerve chronaxies, due to an increase in the former, and the muscle ceases to act when its chronaxie is double that of the nerve. If the muscle is allowed rest, its chronaxie diminishes, and activity is restored when its value is again less than twice the value of the nerve chronaxie. Similar disturbances of chronaxie have been shown to be produced by certain drugs such as curare, veratrine, strychnine, etc., which have been known for a long time to affect muscular contraction.

CHAPTER XV

MUSCLE

OUR muscles are the engines by which the chemical energy derived from our food-stuffs is converted into kinetic energy for doing mechanical work. Like other conversion machines, they lose as heat a certain amount of the energy fed to them. The mechanical efficiency of the muscular motor is thus never 100 per cent., and, in fact, is rarely more than about 25 per cent. But while the degraded energy in an inanimate machine is a dead loss to the engineer, it is hardly so with muscle. One of the broad evolutionary advances in the higher vertebrates has been the maintenance of a temperature above that of the environment, a change which has been advantageous because, by the acceleration of all metabolic activity, the organism as a whole has become more active. The maintenance of this higher temperature demands a constant production of heat within the body, and the heat evolved by muscular activity is by far the greatest contributor to this end. From the standpoint of biological utility, therefore, muscle is much more than 25 per cent. efficient.

Even in their inactive, *i.e.* non-contracting, condition, the muscles contribute largely to the heat output and consequently to the temperature maintenance of the body. This they do for the simple reason that 'inactive' as applied to the non-contracting condition of muscle is a misnomer. There is no such thing, in a living muscle with normal nerve connections, as a completely inactive condition. When they are not contracting in response to stimuli, muscles are in a constant state of greater or lesser tension, which is called 'tone.' Of the physical and chemical causes underlying the maintenance of this tone, physiologists, unfortunately, have very little information.

Much more is known about the alterations in tension which are the muscle's response to stimulation, alterations which produce the visible phenomena of contraction and relaxation. Largely as the result of the researches of Hill and his associates on the physical aspects, and of Fletcher and Hopkins, and of Meyerhof, on the chemical side, a remarkable insight has been obtained into the more intimate phenomena of muscular action.

Structure – In structure, a voluntary muscle is composed of a large number of cylindrical muscle fibres, each enclosed within its sarcolemma. Each fibre is in turn composed of large numbers of fibrils and a variable amount of intervening sarcoplasm. The fibrils are all similar in structure and run lengthwise in the fibre.

On microscopic examination with ordinary illumination the fibril is seen to be marked off into alternate dark and light bands. When the fibril is microscopically examined by polarised light by placing it between crossed Nicol prisms (p. 274), it becomes evident that the dark and light bands are of different physical structure. The dark bands now appear bright, showing that they are doubly refracting or anisotropic, while the light bands are isotropic and now appear dark. During contraction the anisotropic parts apparently increase in volume at the expense of the singly refracting portions, the fibril as a whole changing its shape, becoming thicker and shorter. Nothing is known of the significance of this alternation of anisotropic and isotropic material except that it indicates some definite molecular arrangement within the substance of the fibril.

Theories of Contraction – Of the immediate cause of the contraction equally little is known with any certainty. There are various hypotheses: (1) That during stimulation, substances of small molecular weight are produced within the fibril, causing an osmotic influx of fluid from the surrounding sarcoplasm, with resulting increase of tension within the fibril; (2) that the increase in hydrogen-ion concentration following upon stimulation increases the imbibition properties of the colloidal components of the fibril, with resulting ingress of water and consequent swelling and shortening of the fibril; and (3) that substances produced by stimulation so alter the conditions of surface tension at the surface of the fibril or at the surfaces of its structural elements as to produce the necessary changes in shape directly. All these are little more than guesses, and the intimate physical processes underlying the shortening of muscle are still unknown.

Whatever may be the physical or physico-chemical interpretation of the shortening, it has been generally accepted until very recently that the chemical change within the muscle which causes contraction is the production of lactic acid; that relaxation follows when this acid is neutralised in the muscle by protein-combined base and by alkaline salts (*e.g.* K_2HPO_4); and that muscular fatigue, with its accompanying loss of power to contract, is due to an over-accumulation of lactic acid within the muscle substance. This view has been the basis of a great deal of experimental work on muscle, experiments from which have been drawn many valuable conclusions which in themselves are no doubt correct. In the following brief sketch, the intimate relation between lactic acid and the mechanism of contraction is assumed; but it must be stated that there is now a very strong tendency to regard the changes in the creatine-phosphoric acid compounds of muscle as being more closely concerned than lactic acid with the contractile mechanism.

Hill has shown that, if lactic acid is accepted as the chemical instigator of contraction, the surface-tension theory in its simplest form is untenable, because the amount of lactic acid produced by a contracting muscle is insufficient, even in a monomolecular layer, to account, by surface-tension change, for the force which a muscle can exert. Garner introduced a surface-action theory of contraction which avoids this difficulty. His hypothesis is that the anisotropic segments contain liquid crystals of long-chain carbon compounds orientated with their chains in a direction parallel to the axis of the fibril, and the liberation of lactic acid causes the formation of a solid film at the surface of these segments with consequent shortening of the fibril. A similar theory has been put forward by Clark in America. Certainly the existence of the anisotropic condition in segments of the fibril indicates some form of molecular orientation, and a structure such as that postulated by Garner would explain a number of the phenomena which are exhibited by muscle because of its elastic and yet viscous nature.

Maximum Theoretical and Realisable Work – When a

muscle is stimulated it develops within it a state of tension. Because of this tense state, the muscle possesses potential energy, but just how much of this energy can be converted into mechanical work depends upon the conditions under which it has to shorten.   If the two ends of the muscle are fixed so that shortening is impossible (isometric contraction), the energy of its tense state is entirely converted into heat; if shortening is allowed (isotonic contraction), then a variable part, but never the whole, of the tension energy is transformed into mechanical work.   A most important datum to obtain would thus be the potential energy of a maximally stimulated muscle; this would be the maximum theoretical work of which the muscle was capable, and could be compared with the work actually obtainable from it under varying experimental conditions.   The maximum theoretical work may be derived from a 'tension-length' diagram.

The nature of a tension-length diagram and its use as a measure of work may be gathered from the following illustration.   Consider the work done by a stretched elastic band which shortens through a distance represented graphically

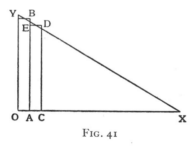

FIG. 41

by OX (fig. 41).   The tension or force exerted by the band when first stretched may be represented by OY.   Now, as the band shortens, its tension progressively diminishes until it is zero at the point X, but if we divide up the total shortening into a series of small steps, we may, with negligible error, consider the tension to remain constant within each step.   Let the first of these fractional shortenings be represented by OA; the work done during this period = force × distance = OY × OA, and is therefore represented by the area OABY. During the next fraction of shortening the tension will have fallen, say, to AE, and the work done will be given by the area ACDE, and so on.   Thus, if the fractional shortenings are taken as infinitesimally small, it is evident that the work done during the total shortening OX will be the area OXY, that is, the area included between the tension-length curve YX and the two axes.

If a tension-length diagram be constructed for an isolated muscle by maximally stimulating it, measuring the tensions which, at various lengths, it can exert under this stimulation, plotting these tensions against the corresponding lengths, the area of the graph obtained measures the maximum work of which the muscle is theoretically capable. By experimental investigations of this type, Hill found that there is a constant relation in muscles generally between the maximum theoretical work and the product of the length of the resting, unloaded muscle and the tension that it can develop at that length. For frog's muscle, the maximum theoretical work (W_0) is about one-sixth of the tension-length product—in symbols, $W_0 = \dfrac{Tl}{6}$.

A similar relation is found to hold between the 'initial heat' (see below) and the tension-length product.

The maximum *realisable* work which can be obtained from a muscle is always less than the maximum theoretical work as deduced from a tension-length curve, even under the best experimental conditions. In order to obtain as much external work from a muscle as possible, the experimental conditions must be such that the muscle can contract to the full extent of which it is capable, and at every stage of its contraction it must be opposed by as great a resistance as it can just overcome. These conditions can obviously not be achieved by making the muscle lift a constant weight, because the force of the muscle varies·from a maximum at the beginning to zero at the end of its contraction. With a light load much of the initial force of the muscle would be wasted, while heavy loading would prevent the muscle from shortening to its full extent. Optimal conditions can be attained, however, by opposing the contractile tension of the muscle to the inertial reaction of a mass. The reaction of the mass then adjusts itself exactly to the action exerted upon it by the muscle, and, by varying the mass, the observer can indirectly adjust the time occupied in shortening, so as to obtain as extensive a contraction as possible. An apparatus embodying these principles, devised by Hill for isolated frog's muscle, is shown diagrammatically in fig. 42. The two large masses M are placed equidistant from the fulcrum F, and are therefore balanced. The light weight w keeps the muscle extended to a definite length, which can be varied by the stop S. The effective inertial mass applied to the muscle can be varied by altering either the distances of the masses from the fulcrum, or the distance of the muscle attachment from the fulcrum. In experimenting with this apparatus, one changes the effective mass and the weight w until the maximum work, as measured by the

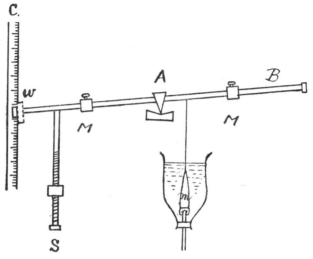

FIG. 42—Inertia lever for frog's muscle
(Doi, *Journ. Physiol.*, 1920)

distance through which the small weight is raised, is obtained from the muscle.

The results with this apparatus gave, for frog's isolated muscle, a maximal work output which was only one-third to one-quarter of the maximal theoretical work as estimated from the formula $W_0 = \dfrac{Tl}{6}$. A considerable amount of the available tension energy was therefore being wasted, in spite of the optimal conditions of loading given by the inertia lever. The cause of this energy loss lies in the viscosity of the colloidal muscle substance. The muscle, though elastic, will resist a sudden deformation of its shape during either contraction or relaxation, and this viscous resistance will increase as the speed of shortening rises.

A number of experiments by Hill and others have stressed

the importance of this viscous-elastic nature of muscles.   For
instance, muscles show the phenomenon of after-extension to
a high degree; that is, they recover from stretching rapidly
at first, and then very slowly during the final stages of recovery.
Again, a muscle kept in tension by a maintained stimulus
does not immediately, when its tension is partially released
by sudden approximation of its two ends, take up the new
tension appropriate to its lessened length.   Or again, the
thermal changes occurring during passive stretching of a
muscle, or during its release from a stretched condition, are,
on analysis, divisible into a part due to the actual stretching
or recovery, and a part due to the overcoming of its viscous
resistance.

Effect of Speed of Contraction on Realisable Work –
Into these experiments we shall not enter in further detail,
but we may mention rather some investigations of Levin
and Wyman, which showed very strikingly the relation of the
wastage of energy through viscous resistance to the speed of
shortening.   These workers devised an ingenious apparatus
which would automatically record the actual work done by
a contracting muscle.   The muscle was stimulated by a
continued maximal stimulus.   When its tension had reached
a maximum, the stimulus still being maintained, the muscle
was allowed to shorten by a given length at a constant pre-
determined speed.   As the muscle shortened it pulled upon a
recording device, which automatically wrote a tension-length
curve upon a smoked surface.   The work done could then be
obtained as usual from the area of this tension-length diagram.
Records obtained with this apparatus showed that the greatest
areas were enclosed by the slow curves, and, as the contractions
became more rapid, the areas enclosed were less and less.

Most work is thus obtained from a muscle when contracting
slowly, and least at rapid speeds.   If we call the realisable
work W and use W_0 as before for the maximum theoretical
work, the energy dissipated on shortening, expressed as a
fraction of the maximum theoretical work, *i.e.* $\dfrac{W_0 - W}{W_0}$, is
shown by these experiments to increase with the speed of
contraction; in other words, it varies inversely as the time

involved in contraction. If this time be t, we may therefore say that

$$\frac{W_0 - W}{W_0} = \frac{k}{t},$$

where k is a constant varying with the viscosity of the muscle substance. Rearranged, this formula becomes

$$W = W_0 \left(1 - \frac{k}{t} \right).$$

The longer t, the nearer does W approach W_0.

Hill has shown that this relation also holds for the contraction of human muscles *in situ*, by using the inertia principle as in the apparatus previously described for frog's muscle.

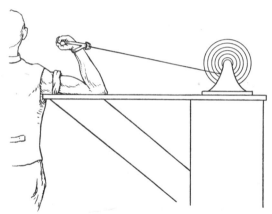

FIG. 43—Inertia flywheel for human muscle
(Drawn from photograph in Hill, *Journ. Physiol.*, 1922)

This human muscle apparatus is diagrammatically shown in fig. 43. The subject rested his arm on a board at a convenient height, and, by bending his elbow, pulled on a string which was wound around one of the pulleys of a wheel of considerable mass, this wheel rotating almost frictionlessly on ball-bearings. The string was so attached that, as soon as it had been drawn out to its full extent, it dropped off the pulley and left the wheel rotating. The work done was estimated by the kinetic energy imparted to the wheel. The effective inertial mass against which the muscles acted could be increased or diminished by placing the string on a smaller or larger pulley, thus increasing or diminishing the leverage.

Hill carried out a large number of experiments with this apparatus. Fig. 44 is the graph relating speed of contraction

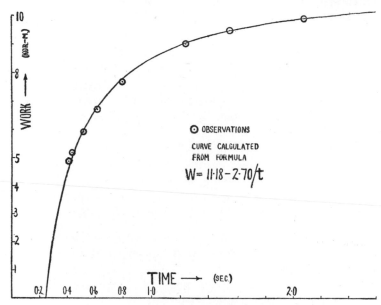

FIG. 44—Relation between maximum work and duration of contraction
(Hill, *Journ. Physiol.*, 1922)

and work done for a powerful subject on whom many observations were made. The same dependence of W, the realisable work, on the duration of shortening, t, is brought out, and, in fact, the relationship $W = W_0 \left(1 - \dfrac{k}{t} \right)$ held with great accuracy. In the curve given above $k = 0.24$, and the value of W_0, estimated from the curve, was 11.18 kg.-mt. If we assume that the general relation $W_0 = \dfrac{Tl}{6}$ holds for human muscles, as it does in frog muscles, we are led to the remarkable conclusion that the maximal tension which the human arm muscles could develop if they were prevented from shortening would be:

$$T = \frac{6W_0}{1} = \frac{6 \times 11 \cdot 18}{0 \cdot 15 \, ^1} = \text{approx. 450 kg.-mt.}$$

These experiments furnished also some interesting data of the relations between efficiency and speed of muscular movement, but these it will be well to leave until we have examined briefly another side of Hill's work, his myothermic investigations.

Heat Changes during Isometric Contraction – By devising sensitive thermopile and galvanometer systems (p. 194) and adapting them for use with isolated muscles, Hill was able to measure the minute heat changes occurring during the various stages of isometric muscular contraction. It must be remembered that, as these were isometric contractions, no mechanical work was done, and all the energy evolved in the various phases of the muscle's activity appeared as heat.

Of the many valuable results obtained by the application of this method, the following are the most important for our present purpose. The heat evolution of a muscular contraction may be divided into the following four phases:—

(a) An amount of heat associated with the development of increased tension in the isometrically contracting muscle—1 (fig. 45).

(b) An amount of heat associated with the process of relaxation of this tension—3 (fig. 45).

(c) A prolonged and relatively large amount of heat evolved after the tension changes in the muscle are completed, and evidently associated with the muscle's recovery of its original condition—4 (fig. 45).

(d) Depending on the duration of the contraction an amount of heat—2 (fig. 45)—associated with the maintaining of the muscle in a tense condition.

Phase No. 2 would be absent altogether if the contraction were short enough; that is, if it were of the order of a twitch. In ordinary muscular action, no external work is done during this phase; the muscle is merely maintained in a contracted condition, so that, from the standpoint of mechanical efficiency, this maintenance energy is a dead loss to the muscle.

---

[1] Length of muscle in metres.

Another important finding was that the heat energy evolved
in Stages 1 and 3—that is, excluding maintenance and recovery
heats—is the exact equivalent of the potential mechanical
energy of the tense muscle, or, in other words, of the theoretical
maximum work, W_0. In a twitch, then, these two phases,
taken alone, are 100 per cent. efficient. Further, the recovery
heat evolved in Stage 4 was found to be, on the average, almost
exactly equal to the combined heat of Stages 1 and 3. Thus,
even if the maximum theoretical work could be obtained from

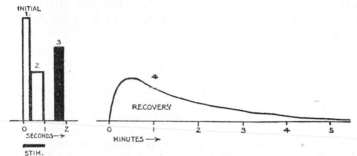

FIG. 45—Diagram of stages of heat production of muscle in
contraction and recovery

(Lovatt Evans, *Recent Advances in Physiology*)

the muscle, the efficiency of the whole process of muscular
action would never be more than 50 per cent., since the total
energy liberated $=2W_0$.

Chemical Changes – The importance of these phases in
the liberation of heat energy was only fully appreciated when
they came to be quantitatively matched against the heats of the
chemical reactions occurring during contraction. The chemical
changes were being elucidated at the same time by Meyerhof
and his pupils in Germany. Without going into details, we
may sum up their scheme of the chemical changes as follows:—

On stimulation, a certain amount of glycogen is split up into
lactic acid. The lactic acid is assumed to produce in some
way the state of tension in the muscle, which causes it to
shorten if it is allowed to do so. As soon as any lactic acid
is formed, its neutralisation by the protein-combined base or
alkaline salts in the muscle begins, and this neutralisation,
if effective, is accompanied by the relaxation of the contracted

15

fibrils. If, therefore, the muscle has to be maintained in a state of contraction, a constant production of lactic acid is necessary, hence the maintenance heat (2, fig. 45) in any but the shortest contraction. When contraction and relaxation are both over, we have a muscle in which a certain amount of the glycogen has been converted into lactates. During recovery, *i.e.* after the visible changes of muscular action are over, approximately four-fifths of the lactate is reconverted to glycogen, the energy for this reconversion being obtained at the expense of the oxidation of the remaining fifth. These changes, expressed per gram of lactic acid, may be tabulated as follows:—

Contraction, 0·9 grm. glycogen ⟶ 1 grm. lactic acid.
Relaxation, Neutralisation of the lactic acid.

Recovery,   1 grm. lactic acid $\begin{cases} \text{0·79 grm. reconverted to glycogen.} \\ \text{0·21 grm. oxidised to } CO_2 \text{ and } H_2O. \end{cases}$

Oxygen is therefore not directly necessary for muscular action, but is necessary after contraction to restore the muscle to its previous chemical condition.

Let us now compare Hill's actual measurements of the heat evolved during isometric contraction with the theoretical heat changes (given in brackets) of the various chemical reactions. This has been done in the table on opposite page, where both are again expressed per gram lactic acid.

Considering the great technical difficulties, the agreement was good enough to be a decided support of the actuality of the chemical processes postulated. Attention has already been drawn to the ratio given in the last column, and to its significance in limiting the maximum theoretical efficiency of the whole process.

Mechanical Efficiency and Speed of Contraction – Returning now to the experiments with the inertia flywheel on the arm muscles, we may consider the efficiency of the work so performed. We have seen that the realisable work (W) is given by

$$W = W_0 \left(1 - \frac{k}{t} \right).$$

Phase of Muscular Action	Chemical Change	Theoretical Heat	Heat Found	Ratio of Contraction and Relaxation Heat to Recovery Heat
Contraction . Relaxation .	Formation of 1 grm. lactic acid from glycogen (+235 cals.). Neutralisation of lactic acid (+105 cals.).[1]	340	385	1·0
Recovery .	Reformation of 0·79 grm. lactic acid into glycogen (−269 cals.). Oxidation of 0·21 grm. lactic acid (+734 cals.).	465	412	1·07

Note.—The data given in the last two columns of this table were obtained from isometric twitches. In tetanic contraction the figures differ from the above, the ratio of contraction and relaxation heat to recovery heat being as 1 : 1·5.

We saw also that the total energy evolved in a *brief* muscular contraction is approximately twice the energy evolved during the stages of contraction and relaxation, and this, for a twitch, is equal to W_0, the maximum theoretical work obtainable from the muscle. In a *prolonged* contraction we have to add an amount of energy for maintenance of the contraction, an amount which will increase proportionately to the time, t, during which the contraction is maintained. This extra fraction of energy may be expressed as bt, b being a constant. In a contraction longer than a twitch, such as was involved in these arm-muscle experiments, the total energy liberated will be therefore

$$2W_0(1+bt).$$

---

[1] This figure is the heat of neutralisation of lactic acid as determined by actual experiment on the muscle itself. If the lactic acid were neutralised by alkali-protein alone, the theoretical heat of neutralisation would be 140 calories per grm. lactic acid; if by salts like K_2HPO_4, 19 calories. Apparently neutralisation in the muscle is carried out mainly by the proteins.

The efficiency which is the ratio between the realisable work and the total energy expended will then be

$$E = \frac{W}{\text{total energy}} = \frac{W_0\left(1 - \frac{k}{t}\right)}{2W_0(1+bt)},$$

where E=efficiency and W=actual work done.

Now, with increasing t, the numerator of this fraction, $W_0\left(1 - \frac{k}{t}\right)$, will increase from zero to a theoretical maximum at which $W = W_0$. On the other hand, as t increases, the denominator will go on increasing indefinitely. Note that this is quite independent of the value of b. Whatever value is given to b, the efficiency must rise from zero to a maximum and then fall again as the duration of the contractions increases. In other words, there is an optimum rate of contraction at which the efficiency is highest.

Now, for the man whose curve was given on p. 223, k was 0·24, and W_0 was 11·18 kg.-mt. If the value of b were known, it would be possible from the formula to obtain actual values for the efficiency of various rates of contraction. b has been directly determined, but, without direct experiment, it may be given a probable value of 0·5. The use of this value in the equation gives a maximum efficiency of 26 per cent., which accords with the best efficiencies obtained for muscular work in trained subjects, when the cost of the work is estimated from the oxygen consumption. With this value of 0·5 for the constant b, the graphical expression of the formula is as shown in fig. 46.

This graph illustrates two interesting points in the dependence of efficiency on the speed of muscular contraction. First, the optimum duration of contraction for these muscles is just over 1 second, and, secondly, there is less loss in efficiency when the muscles are working at a rate slower than the optimum than when they are working at a rate correspondingly quicker than the optimum. These relations, though worked out specifically for the muscles of the arm, are, no doubt, generally applicable to all types of muscular movement.

Practical Applications – We may now turn from these somewhat theoretical discussions to their more practical applications, and consider particularly how the amount of muscular effort of which a man is capable is limited by the chemical processes involved. We have seen that the actual contraction of muscle has as its chemical basis a non-oxidative process, viz. the production of lactic acid from glycogen, and

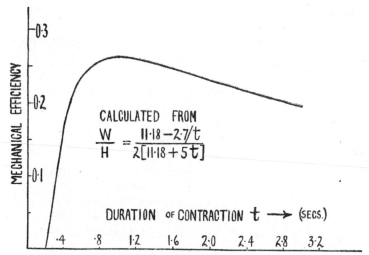

FIG. 46—Relation between mechanical efficiency and duration of contraction
(Hill, *Journ. Physiol.*, 1922)

the oxidations which supply the energy for the contraction occur in a recovery phase after the actual shortening is past. In continued muscular action, therefore, the oxidation processes are always, so to speak, a step behind the contraction processes for which they are supplying energy. Now the actual contraction, being a non-oxidative process, can go on even in the absence of oxygen, but it can go on only up to a point, because the accumulation of lactic acid in a muscle produces fatigue, and when its concentration reaches approximately 0·3 per cent. the muscle is completely fatigued, and cannot contract any longer. In a muscle or set of muscles *in situ*, oxygen is being constantly supplied by the blood, but this supply is limited by the capacity of the lungs to oxygenate the blood, by the capacity of the heart and blood-vessels to supply blood to the muscles, and by the capacity of the blood to provide oxygen to the tissues by dissociation of the oxyhæmoglobin. These factors in combination limit the supply of oxygen to the body to a maximum of about 4 litres per minute. A group of muscles can go on working without accumulating lactic acid up to a point at which as much lactic acid is being produced as their oxygen supply can deal with. But it can go beyond this limit, because the blood not only brings oxygen to the muscle, but may carry away lactic acid to other tissues where it may be dealt with by their oxygen supply. The greater part of the total oxygen supply of the body is thus available for any group of muscles, and they could produce lactic acid without its accumulation up to practically the full oxidation capacity of 4 litres of oxygen per minute.

But for short periods of activity, the working capacity of a muscle is not even limited by the current supply of oxygen. Contraction being a non-oxidative process, the muscles may go on producing lactic acid and accumulating it right up to the fatigue limit of 0·3 per cent., and leave the accumulated excess to be dealt with by oxygen taken in after the exercise is over. Therefore we can undertake short spells of very violent exercise, producing far more lactic acid than we can simultaneously resynthetise to glycogen and oxidise to CO_2 and H_2O, and thereby running into an 'oxygen debt' which is only paid off after the exercise is over. This oxygen debt may accumulate, in normal healthy subjects, to about 100 c.c., and in athletes to about 150 c.c., per kilogram of body-weight.

The differences between moderate exercise which may be kept up for a long time, and a severe exertion which can only be maintained as a short bout, are illustrated in fig. 47.

In the diagram on the right are represented the conditions during a period of moderate exercise, which is shown in the diagram as lasting only three minutes, but which could be continued indefinitely as far as muscular fatigue is concerned. The dotted rectangle represents the total oxygen required for the exercise (in the example approximately 3 litres per minute for three minutes or a total of 9 litres). The continuous line shows how the subject actually obtains this oxygen. He does not

develop his full oxygen intake coincidently with the beginning
of the exercise, but gradually the intake rises to a point at
which it equals the oxygen requirement.   During this period
the lactic acid concentration in the muscles rises but does not
reach 0·3 per cent.   From this point onwards, the subject is
in a 'steady state,' *i.e.* he is oxidising and resynthetising his
lactic acid as fast as it is formed by the contracting muscles.

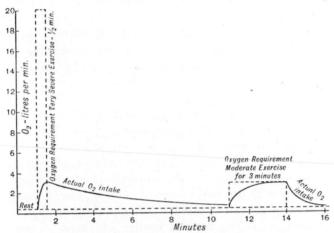

FIG. 47—Oxygen requirement and oxygen intake in severe and
moderate exercise

(After Hill, Long, and Lupton, *Proc. Roy. Soc.*, 1924)

When he comes to the end of the exercise period there is a lag
in the fall of the oxygen intake to its pre-exercise value.   During
this period the 'steady state' concentration of lactic acid is being
reduced to zero.

Compare with this the diagram on the left.   Here the
subject has undertaken an exertion so violent that the fatigue
concentration of lactic acid was rapidly reached and he was
unable to keep it up for more than half a minute.   The oxygen
requirement for this half-minute's activity (dotted rectangle)
was 10 litres.   His oxygen intake in one half-minute, of
course, could not approach this amount, in fact, it had not
even risen to its maximum.   Let us suppose that, in the half-
minute, the subject had managed to take in $1\frac{1}{2}$ litres O_2; the
remainder of the requirement, $8\frac{1}{2}$ litres, is an oxygen debt

which stands over for repayment when the exercise is finished. It is then repaid by a prolonged maintenance of the oxygen intake above the resting level, this period of excess intake lasting for as long, perhaps, as two hours after the cessation of the activity.

A healthy man's ability to take violent exercise is controlled, therefore, less by the capacity of his circulatory system to supply a large immediate oxygen intake than by his ability to contract an oxygen debt.

The ability of the muscular machine to perform work for short periods out of all proportion to its immediate oxygen supply is clearly a mechanism of great biological value. The following calculation shows what enormous amounts of power may thereby be developed over a short period. A trained sprinter covered a distance of 130 yards in 13 seconds. For this purpose his oxygen requirement (actual oxygen intake +oxygen debt contracted) was 6·3 litres, or at the rate of 29 litres per minute. Now 1 litre of oxygen used in the body for oxidising carbohydrate, the muscular fuel, produces 5·05 calories. The 29 litres of oxygen would represent an energy expenditure at the rate of 146·5 calories per minute or 13·7 h.p. This, however, is the rate of energy liberation if muscular action and recovery went on simultaneously, which is not so, because practically all the recovery occurs after the sprint is over. As we have seen, the energy of the contraction and relaxation phases is only half that of the whole process. But, even so, assuming that no recovery changes at all occur during the short period of the actual sprint itself, the rate of energy liberation during the sprint is $0·5 \times 13·7$; that is, approximately *seven horse-power*.

Fenn Effect – The conclusions referred to in the earlier parts of this chapter have been chiefly drawn from a study of the isometric contraction of muscle. It has been stated that the maximum work theoretically derivable from a muscle is the equivalent of the heat energy evolved during the phases of contraction and relaxation. If, as in an isotonic contraction, the muscle were allowed to shorten and do mechanical work, it might be expected that the energy represented by this work would be deducted from the amount appearing as heat. Fenn, however, made the discovery that a muscle when allowed to shorten frequently liberated a greater amount of total energy (heat evolved + work done) than it did under isometric conditions, when its energy was evolved entirely as heat. It seemed as though the shortening of the muscle provided a further stimulus, causing it to liberate more energy.

This Fenn effect was later investigated by Hartree and Hill. They confirmed the occurrence of the extra liberation of energy in isotonic tetani, but failed to find it in isotonic twitches. Quite recently, Hill has shown that this statement must be amplified. In isotonic twitches, the energy liberation may be greater, equal to, or less than the energy liberated during isometric contraction. The particular result obtained depends on the degree of extension of the muscle fibres, and hence on their loading. With heavy loads the Fenn effect is obtained; with light loads the reverse effect. In tetani, the Fenn effect predominates because the loading with which the reverse effect is got is so light and covers so narrow a range that the experimental conditions for its exhibition are rarely attained.

This disagreement between the energy liberated by a muscle during isometric and isotonic contraction makes it doubtful in how far the conclusions derived from a study of isometric conditions can be applied to ordinary muscular contractions in which shortening occurs. For instance, the theoretical maximum work derived from a tension-length curve or from the isometric heat changes does not necessarily represent the total potential energy which a shortening muscle has at its command. How far previous ideas will have to be modified has still to be worked out.

CHAPTER XVI

ENERGY EXCHANGES IN THE ANIMAL ORGANISM

PREVIOUS chapters have indicated something of the diversity of energy transformation which takes place in living tissues. All forms of energy arise in the animal's body from the potential chemical energy of its food, which is derived directly in herbivorous animals, or indirectly in carnivora, from the material of plant tissues. The potential chemical energy of the food is, in the first instance, radiant solar energy which, absorbed by the chlorophyll, enables the plant to synthetise its carbohydrates, fats, and proteins, substances of high energy content, from the simple materials of the soil and the carbon dioxide of the air. The sun is thus the source of energy for all biological processes, and life as we know it entirely depends on the plant's ability to appropriate this energy.

In animals, though the internal energy transformations are most varied, energy is finally given out almost entirely in two forms only, heat and muscular work. The estimation of this energy liberation in a living organism is not only interesting for its own sake, but since it is possible to apportion the energy liberation to each of its sources in proteins, carbohydrates, and fats, it is one of the few ways by which we can gain an insight into the chemical changes occurring within the living body. Moreover, since it has been demonstrated that the law of conservation of energy holds for living creatures, the measurement of both intake and output of energy, and the striking of a balance between the two, will provide valuable information of the fate of the food ingested—whether it immediately undergoes metabolism or is temporarily retained in store. The principles of the methods for estimating energy intake and output are therefore worth understanding.

Measurement of the Energy Intake – When a chemical change occurs in any system, it is invariably accompanied by either absorption or evolution of energy. Though we have no knowledge of the actual energy content of the system either before or after the reaction, it is quite possible to determine the *change* in energy which occurs during the reaction. These changes, which are often actually thermal, and, in any case, can always be expressed in heat units,[1] are constant for any particular chemical reaction, provided that the amounts of the reacting substances and the temperature are defined. They are known as 'heats of reaction,' and are usually expressed as per gram-atom or gram-molecule of the reacting substances. As the molecular weight of many substances of physiological importance is unknown, their heats of combustion are expressed per gram of material.

These heat changes are conveniently stated by equations like the following:—

$$C(s.) + O_2(g.) = CO_2(g.) + 94 \cdot 4 \text{ Cals.}$$

Such thermochemical equations show not only the proportions in which the elements combine, but also the amount and direction of the heat change which accompanies their combination. Reactions are called exothermic when heat is evolved, and endothermic when heat is absorbed. Though there is some diversity of custom in the matter, the exothermic nature of a reaction is usually indicated by the prefixing of a positive sign to the number of calories, and heat absorption by the use of the negative sign.

Changes of the physical state of substances, such as fusion, vaporisation, solution, a change into an allotropic form, are also accompanied by energy changes. It is therefore necessary in a thermochemical equation to define the physical state of the reacting substances and the products, as has been done above—(s.)=solid, (g.)=gas. To be still more precise, the actual form of the carbon, whether charcoal, graphite, or diamond, should be specified, as in each the heat of reaction

---

[1] It may be well to remind the student of the units in which amounts of heat are expressed. The small calorie (spelt with a small *c*) is the amount of heat required to raise 1 grm. of water 1° C., or, more precisely, from 14·5°–15·5° C. As this unit is too small for many purposes, the kilocalorie or large Calorie (spelt with a capital C) is also used. The large Calorie is equivalent to 1000 small calories.

is slightly different. These differences correspond with the heat absorbed or evolved in the transformation of carbon from one allotropic form to another.

In a reaction in which a compound is formed from its constituent elements, the heat evolved or absorbed is spoken of as the 'heat of formation'; for example, the heat of formation of carbon dioxide is 94·4 Cals. The 'heat of combustion' is another special type of heat of reaction; it is the amount of heat evolved during the complete oxidation of a substance. The 'heat of neutralisation,' a third type, signifies the thermal change which is always found when an acid is neutralised by a base. Provided that one is dealing with a strong acid and a strong base, both in dilute solution and therefore almost completely ionised, and provided that the salt formed is also highly ionised, this thermal change is a constant one of 13·7 Cals. per gram-molecule, and is independent of the specific base and acid. This is to be expected, because the reaction is, in all such cases, essentially a combination of hydrogen ions and hydroxyl ions to form water. Thus:

$$NaOH + HCl = NaCl + H_2O.$$
$$(Na^+ + OH^- + H^+ + Cl^- = Na^+ + Cl^- + H_2O.)$$

If, on the other hand, the acid or base is a weak one, that is, one which is only partially dissociated at the beginning of the neutralisation, the thermal change due to the combination of the hydrogen and hydroxyl ions will be complicated by the thermal change due to further dissociation of the base or acid during the reaction.

The law of Hess (p. 18) states that the heat changes in a chemical reaction are dependent only on the initial and final states of the reacting system, and are not influenced by the way in which the reaction occurs. For example, starting with 1 gram-molecule of ammonia and 1 gram-molecule of HCl, and an indefinitely large amount, say 100 litres of water, all under certain conditions of temperature and pressure, it is possible to prepare a dilute aqueous solution of ammonium chloride in two ways. First, the two gases may be combined— during this reaction 42·1 Cals. are liberated; the solid NH_4Cl produced may then be dissolved in water, its solution being attended by an absorption of 3·9 Cals. The total heat developed is thus $42·1-3·9=38·2$ Cals. The solution of NH_4Cl could equally well be prepared by dissolving the ammonia in part of the water and the HCl in the remainder of the water, and then mixing the two solutions. The heat of the solution in the case of the ammonia is 8·4 Cals., and 17·3 Cals. in the case of the HCl. Mixing of the two solutions is accompanied by a further development of 12·3 Cals. The total heat change when the reaction is carried out by the second method is thus $8·4+17·3+12·3$ or 38·0 Cals., which, within the limits of experimental error, is the same as the figure obtained in the first method.

Expressed as thermochemical equations these two methods might be stated as follows:—

(a) $NH_3(g.)+HCl(g.)=NH_4Cl(s.)+42·1$ Cals.
       $NH_4Cl(s.)=NH_4Cl(aq.)-3·9$ Cals.

(b) $NH_3(g.)=NH_3(aq.)+8·4$ Cals.
       $HCl(g.)=HCl(aq.)+17·3$ Cals.
       $NH_3(aq.)+HCl(aq.)=NH_4Cl(aq.)+12·3$ Cals.[1]

The law of Hess is extremely important. It justifies the indirect determination of heats of reaction which cannot be found directly. The heat of formation of most organic compounds is arrived at in this way by determining the difference between the heat of combustion of the compound and the aggregate heats of combustion of all its component elements. Thus, the heat of combustion of benzoic acid (C_6H_5COOH) per gram-molecule is 772·2 Cals. From the following,

$$C+O_2=CO_2+94·4 \text{ Cals.,}$$
$$H_2+O=H_2O+68·4 \text{ Cals.,}$$

we find that the seven atoms of carbon in benzoic acid, if uncombined, would yield, in combustion, 660·8 Cals., and the six atoms of hydrogen 205·2 Cals. The carbon and the hydrogen of the benzoic acid, if oxidised in the free state, would thus yield 866 Cals., whereas 1 gram-molecule of the

[1] The bracketed ' aq.' indicates that the substance is in solution so dilute that further dilution would cause no heat effect.

compound gives only 772·2 Cals. The difference of 93·8 Cals. must then be the heat evolved during the formation of benzoic acid from its elements.

The law of Hess also justifies the assumption that the heat produced by the proximate principles of the food during their metabolism within the body is the same as their heats of combustion when burned outside the body, provided always that the end-products are the same, though these end-products may have been reached by quite different intermediate stages.

Determination of Heats of Combustion – Heats of combustion are experimentally determined by burning the substance in an atmosphere of compressed oxygen, under such conditions that the heat produced will be absorbed as completely as possible by a known mass of water. The determination is carried out in a bomb calorimeter. The bomb portion of the apparatus is a heavy-walled steel vessel provided with a screw-on gas-tight cover, having in its interior a crucible supported on two electrodes with external connections. The calorimeter portion consists of an inner vessel containing a measured amount of water and provided with a stirrer and a Beckmann thermometer. This inner vessel is surrounded by a double-walled outer vessel containing water which serves as a heat insulator. The procedure of determination is briefly as follows. The substance under examination is compressed into a tablet, the tablet weighed and placed in the crucible. A small spiral of iron wire is stretched between the electrodes and so arranged as just to touch the tablet. The cover is then screwed on to the body of the vessel, and, through valves in the cover, the bomb is charged with oxygen to a pressure of several atmospheres. The external terminals are then connected through a switch to an accumulator and the bomb immersed in the water within the inner vessel. When the temperature conditions have stabilised the switch is closed, and the iron wire, heated by the current, burns. It ignites the tablet, which, under the high oxygen pressure, burns rapidly and completely. The heat given out by the burning substance is obtained from the mass of water in the inner calorimeter vessel and its maximum rise of temperature. A correction has to be made for the heat contributed by the iron wire. As with all other calorimetric observations, corrections have also to be applied for the water-equivalent of the apparatus, and for the slight amount of heat gained or lost by radiation from or to the surroundings.

Heats of Combustion of Physiologically Important Substances – The following table gives the heats of combustion, determined in the bomb calorimeter, of some substances important in nutrition and in physiological calorimetry :—

Substance	Heat of Combustion per gram
Starch	4·183 Cals.
Glucose . . .	3·743 ,,
Cane sugar . . .	3·955 ,,
Lactose . . .	3·952 ,,
Tissue fat . . .	9·461 ,,
Olive-oil . . .	9·442 ,,
Butter-fat . . .	9·230 ,,
Flesh	5·631 ,,
Casein	5·850 ,,
Legumin . . .	5·793 ,,

It may be observed that, in spite of slight individual differences, there is a calorific similarity in the members of each of the three classes of food-stuffs— proteins, carbohydrates, and fats.

Now, by the law of Hess, since carbohydrates and fats are burned in the body to the same end-products, viz. CO_2 and H_2O, as are produced during their combustion in a bomb, the heat given out in a calorimetric determination will also be their heat value to the body. This is not true of the proteins. They undergo complete combustion in the bomb, but in the body combustion is not complete, for a certain part of the protein ends up as urea, uric acid, and other nitrogenous products of both urine and fæces. The calorie value of protein in metabolism will therefore be lower than the bomb determination by the amount of the heats of combustion of such urinary and fæcal end-products. Rubner (1885) first

made valid estimates of the physiological heat value of protein
by feeding an animal with meat protein whose heat of combustion had been determined, and then deducting therefrom
the calorific value of the urine and fæces excreted by the
animal.   An example of this type of calculation will be given
shortly, but meantime we may note that Rubner's experiments
led him to conclude that the following were the physiological
calorie values of meat protein, vegetable proteins, and casein :—

Substance	Physiological Calorie value per gram (Cals.)
Ash-free meat . .	4·233
Vegetable proteins . .	3·96
Casein	4·4

From these figures Rubner considered that the average
calorie value of 1 grm. of protein in an ordinary mixed diet
might be taken as 4·1.   Similarly he adopted 9·3 Cals. per
gram as an average figure for the fat of a mixed diet, and
4·1 Cals. per gram for the carbohydrates.   This last figure,
4·1, was taken for carbohydrate because of the large preponderance of starch over other carbohydrates in the diet.

These figures are known as Rubner's standard values.   By
their use the total energy content of any diet, and hence the
energy intake of a person, may be computed from the total
weights of protein, carbohydrate, and fat in the diet, the weight
of each being multiplied by its appropriate factor.   Evaluations
of the energy content of diets are much simplified by the use
of food-analysis tables, in which are given the content of
protein, fat, and carbohydrate, and the calorie value per
kilogram of all the common articles of diet.

Measurement of the Energy Output – Attempts at the
measurement of animal heat were made by Crawford in
Glasgow and Lavoisier in Paris in the latter part of the
eighteenth century, but it was not until about 1890 that an
accurate apparatus for the direct calorimetry of animals was
devised by Rubner.   Rubner had established his standard

values before this, and he was now able to show that the amount of heat given off by a dog, measured directly by his calorimeter, was equivalent within the limits of experimental error to the energy calculated to be derivable from the metabolic changes within its body. This was the first demonstration that the law of the conservation of energy was as valid for living organisms as for the inorganic world. All subsequent work on animals and the human subject amply confirms it.

At about the time Rubner was publishing his experiments with this calorimeter, Atwater, with the physicist Rosa, had

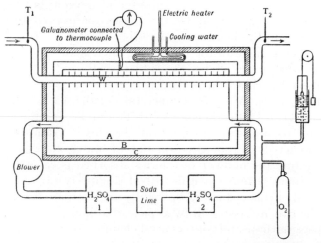

FIG. 48—Schematic diagram of a respiration calorimeter

begun to devise a calorimeter which could be used for the direct determination of the heat output of human subjects. This was the prototype of the modern respiration calorimeter.

The respiration calorimeter is the same in principle as other calorimeters; the evolved heat is taken up by a known mass of water, heat interchange between the calorimeter and its environment being in this case either entirely prevented or at least brought to a negligible amount. A diagrammatic scheme of the apparatus is given in fig. 48. It consists of an air-tight metal chamber A, sufficiently large to accommodate a man, and often, in addition, a folding-bed, chair, and table, and an ergometer (a machine on which muscular work may be done

16

and measured). The air in this chamber is freed from the subject's CO_2 by being pumped round an external air-circuit through (a) a bottle of H_2SO_4, which absorbs the moisture eliminated in the sweat and breath of the subject; (b) a vessel containing soda-lime to absorb the CO_2; and (c) a second bottle of H_2SO_4, which absorbs any water carried over by the air from the moist soda-lime; from this it is returned to the chamber. A spirometer bell and an oxygen cylinder are connected as side-branches on the air-circuit. The spirometer bell descends as the volume of the whole air-system is diminished by the subject's utilisation of oxygen, but periodically this is made good by the release of oxygen from the cylinder until the bell regains its original height. In this way the oxygen content of the circulating air is maintained.

The heat given off by the subject within the chamber is absorbed by cold water flowing through a series of heat-absorbing coils, W. The temperature of the water is taken at entry and exit by the thermometers T_1 and T_2, and the amount of water passing through the heat-absorbing system is accurately metered. From this amount of water and its rise of temperature the number of calories absorbed is calculated.

The inner chamber just described is entirely surrounded by a second metal chamber, B, slightly larger than the first, so that the two are separated by a space of still air. Another dead air space separates this outer metal chamber from a well-lagged external casing, C. In the space between the external casing and the outer metal chamber are run pipes conveying cooling water and electrical heating wires. By adjusting the current flowing through the heaters, the cooling effect of the water circulators can be more or less antagonised. The cooling and heating appliances are divided up into separately controlled segments, each serving a certain area of the chamber. In the walls of both outer and inner metal chambers are set thermo-electric junctions connected in series, so that any temperature difference between the walls of the two chambers will produce an electric current, which can be detected on galvanometers outside the apparatus. The distribution of the thermo-electric junctions corresponds with the arrangement of the cooling and heating appliances between external casing and outer metal chamber. When, over any area of the cabinet, a difference of temperature begins to show between outer and inner walls, it is recorded as a deflection on the galvanometer for that area, and an observer, by adjusting the current in the appropriate heating wires, immediately brings that section of the outer wall to the temperature of the inner wall. By constant adjustment the outer metal casing can thus be kept at a temperature identical with that of the inner chamber, and so heat loss from the latter is entirely prevented.

With this arrangement, if the temperature of the chamber is the same at the end of an experiment as it was at the start, all the heat given off from the subject by radiation and conduction is readily calculated from the mass of water which has passed through the absorbing system and its rise of temperature. If the final temperature of the chamber walls differs from the initial temperature, a correction has to be applied, because the whole apparatus has gained or lost heat. The heat so calculated does not, however, represent the total heat output of the subject, for approximately one-quarter of his metabolic heat has been utilised in the vaporisation of sweat, and of moisture in the expired air. An estimate of this heat is obtained by weighing No. 1 sulphuric acid bottle before and after the experiment, and allowing 0·586 cals. for each gram of water collected.

Indirect Determination of the Energy Output – The energy output of an animal or human being can also be determined by an indirect method. While the energy content of the food actually eaten measures a man's initial intake of energy, not all this energy is available for liberation in the tissues, since a small proportion of the food is not absorbed from the intestine. Moreover, of the absorbed material, all may not be immediately utilised, but some may be stored, perhaps as fat. If, however, it were possible to determine just what amounts of *body*-protein, *body*-carbohydrate, and *body*-fat actually underwent combustion, and the calorie value of these materials were known, then it is obvious that the man's energy output could be computed from these data. The essential data for such a calculation can be obtained, and, as a matter of fact, the energy output is much more frequently estimated by this method of 'indirect calorimetry,' because the apparatus required is simpler to operate and much less costly than the respiration calorimeter. Even when a calorimeter is available, the direct estimation of the heat output is always accompanied by an indirect estimation, because a knowledge of the total heat output is of little value without a knowledge of how the calories are apportioned among proteins, fats, and carbohydrates.

For an estimation of the heat output by indirect calorimetry, the data required are (1) the nitrogen excretion in the urine, (2) the CO_2 excretion, and (3) the oxygen utilisation. The data obtained, the procedure of calculation is briefly as follows. The amount of protein metabolised can be found from the urinary nitrogen. From this, that part of the CO_2 excreted and oxygen utilised for which the protein metabolism has been responsible, may be assessed and deducted from the total CO_2 excretion and total O_2 utilisation. The remainder of the CO_2 output and the O_2 intake must be due to the metabolism of carbohydrate and fats. Further, the ratio $\dfrac{\text{non-protein } CO_2}{\text{non-protein } O_2}$, or the non-protein respiratory quotient, indicates in what proportions these two food-stuffs have contributed to the metabolism, since the fat molecule, being relatively poor in O_2, demands much more O_2 for its combustion than the carbohydrate molecule. This will be evident from the following formulæ for the oxidation of (1) a typical fat such as tripalmitin and (2) a carbohydrate like glucose:—

(1) $$2C_{51}H_{98}O_6 + 145O_2 = 102CO_2 + 98H_2O.$$

$$\text{Ratio } \frac{CO_2}{O_2} = \frac{102 \text{ mols.}}{145 \text{ mols.}},$$

which, since equal volumes of all gases contain the same number of molecules, may be written:

$$\frac{102 \text{ vols.}}{145 \text{ vols.}}, \text{ or approx. } 0.7.$$

(2) $$C_6H_{12}O_6 + 6O_2 = 6CO_2 + 6H_2O.$$

$$\text{Ratio } \frac{CO_2}{O_2} = \frac{6 \text{ mols.}}{6 \text{ mols.}} = \frac{6 \text{ vols.}}{6 \text{ vols.}} = 1.0.$$

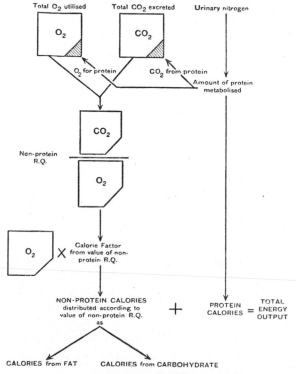

FIG. 49—Schema of indirect calorimetry

Thus the non-protein R.Q. in the theoretical case of a purely fat metabolism would be 0·7 approximately, and of a purely carbohydrate metabolism would be 1·0. The intermediate values actually found in normal metabolism mean a combined metabolism of both materials, the relative rôle that each is playing being indicated by the proximity of the non-protein R.Q. to either the pure fat value of 0·7 or the pure carbohydrate value of 1·0. The next step in the calculation is to obtain the total Calories due to the non-protein metabolism by multiplying the non-protein O_2 by a numerical factor whose derivation will be considered presently. These Calories may then be apportioned between carbohydrates and fats according to the value of the non-protein R.Q. Finally, the total heat output is obtained by adding to the non-protein Calories, the Calories derivable from the protein catabolism whose amount has already been determined. This somewhat complicated procedure may be presented in diagrammatic form (fig. 49).

We may now inquire how the various data and factors in the above calculation are obtained.

(1) *Measurement of the Oxygen Intake and Carbon Dioxide Output* – We have already seen that a respiration calorimeter includes the necessary apparatus for determining the CO_2 excretion and the O_2 utilisation. The first is given by weighing together the soda-lime container and No. 2 sulphuric acid bottle before and after the experiment. Since any water carried over in the air-current from the moist soda-lime is trapped in the second sulphuric acid bottle, the difference in weight is entirely due to the absorption of CO_2 by the soda-lime. The consumption of oxygen is measured by weighing the oxygen cylinder before and after the experiment, care being taken to have the spirometer at the same level at the end as at the beginning of the experimental period. An analysis of the air in the chamber has to be carried out at the beginning and end of the period, and any alterations in O_2 or CO_2 content allowed for. Corrections have also to be applied for any changes in the total volume of the air-circuit, which may be caused by temperature or barometric pressure alterations during the experimental period.

For the indirect determination alone, a similar but much smaller air-circulating and CO_2 absorbing system may be used, the subject being attached to the air-circuit by means of a face-piece or mouthpiece. Both of these are examples of the 'closed circuit' type of apparatus in which the same air, freed from CO_2 and with its deficiency in O_2 constantly being made good, is breathed over and over again.

In the 'open-circuit' type of apparatus the arrangement is different. The subject breathes ordinary atmospheric air, in which the percentages of CO_2 and O_2 are constant and known, and the excess and deficit of these gases in the expired air are determined. When the open-circuit method is applied to a chamber, atmospheric air is drawn into the chamber by a pump and thereafter passed through an absorbing system similar to that already described, the CO_2 being weighed. Gas analysis of frequent samples of the air-current as it leaves the chamber enables the O_2 deficit to be determined. Simple forms of the open-circuit method are much used for the indirect determination of the energy expenditure during short periods. The subject wears a mouthpiece or mask provided with valves such that only atmospheric air can be inspired, and all the expired air must pass out through a wide-bore tube into a spirometer bell or a collapsible bag (Douglas bag). The total volume of the expired air is known in the one case by the rise of the spirometer bell, and in the other, by squeezing the air out of the bag through a meter. In either case, an aliquot portion is taken and analysed for CO_2 and O_2. The CO_2 production and O_2 utilisation of the subject are then got by comparing these data with the atmospheric air.

(2) *Determination of the Gaseous Exchange due to the Protein Metabolism and its Calorie Value from the Nitrogen of the Urine* – The following computation (Loewy) is given as an example of how these data are obtained. An animal was fed with meat protein, the composition per 100 grm. of which was as follows:

Carbon.	Hydrogen.	Oxygen.	Nitrogen.	Sulphur
52·38	7·27	22·68	16·65	1·02

There were excreted in the urine the following amounts of these elements:—

9·41	2·66	14·10	16·28	1·02

and in the fæces:

1·47	0·21	0·89	0·37

leaving a remainder actually used by the body of:

41·5	4·4	7·69

These amounts of carbon and hydrogen would require for their oxidation 138·18 grm. of O_2 in addition to the 7·69 grm. already available, and as a result there would be produced 152·17 grm. CO_2. This amount of protein having led to the appearance of 16·28 grm. nitrogen in the urine, each gram of urinary nitrogen indicates an amount of protein metabolism associated with a utilisation of $\frac{138 \cdot 18}{16 \cdot 28} = 8 \cdot 49$ grm. oxygen and a production of $\frac{152 \cdot 17}{16 \cdot 28} = 9 \cdot 35$ grm. CO_2.

As a result of combustion within the bomb calorimeter, it was known that 100 grm. of the meat protein (fat and ash-free) produced 563·09 Cals. The energy loss in the urinary products was 113·70 Cals., and, in the fæces, 17·76 Cals., a total of 131·46 Cals. There were thus available to the body from 100 grm. of meat protein 563·09−131·46=431·63 Cals., or stating it per gram of nitrogen excreted in the urine, 26·51 Cals.

Summarising, 1 grm. of nitrogen in the urine indicates—

(1)   8·49 grm. O_2 used.

(2)   9·35 grm. CO_2 produced.

(3)   26·51 Cals. energy liberated.

(3) *The Calorie Value of Oxygen per litre at different Values of the Non-protein R.Q.* – A carbohydrate, *e.g.* starch, $(C_6H_{10}O_5)_n$, already contains sufficient intramolecular oxygen to oxidise all its hydrogen to water, and the oxygen necessary for its metabolism may be calculated as that required to oxidise the carbon. The molecular weight of the starch molecule being some multiple of 162, 162 grm. of starch will require 6 mols. of oxygen=192 grm. of oxygen for combustion. As a result, there are formed 6 mols.=264 grm. of CO_2. Hence 1 grm. of starch

requires for its combustion 1·185 grm.=0·828 litres O_2
and produces   1·63   grm.=0·828 litres CO_2,

the theoretical R.Q. of a pure carbohydrate diet, as already noted, being thus $\frac{0·828}{0·828}=1·0$.

By the bomb calorimeter, the heat of combustion of 1 grm. starch was found to be 4·1825 Cals., so that a utilisation of 0·828 litres O_2 in burning starch gives rise to a production of 4·1825 Cals., or 5·047 Cals. per litre of O_2. Thus, for each litre of O_2 used by the body for its carbohydrate metabolism, 5·047 Cals. of energy are liberated.

Fats vary slightly in their composition, but for an average fat it may be calculated by similar methods that 1 grm. of the fat

requires for its combustion 2·887 grm.=2·019 litres O_2
and produces   2·806 grm.=1·427 litres CO_2.

The respiratory quotient if this fat alone were metabolised would be $\frac{1\cdot427}{2\cdot019} = 0\cdot707$.

The heat of combustion of this fat, as measured by the bomb, was, per gram, 9·461 Cals., or $\frac{9\cdot461}{2\cdot019} = 4\cdot686$ Cals. per litre of O_2.

Thus we find that 1 litre of oxygen used in the body would theoretically produce the following results:—

Material Metabolised	Energy Liberation Cals.	R.Q.
100 per cent. carbohydrate, 0 per cent. fat.	5·047	1·000
100 per cent. fat, 0 per cent. carbohydrate.	4·686	0·707
Difference .	0·361	0·293

Now, the non-protein metabolism is, under normal conditions, never entirely one of fat alone or of carbohydrate alone, but since a rise of 0·293 units in the R.Q. is associated with a rise of 0·361 Cals. in the calorific value of each litre of oxygen, the significance of the intermediate R.Q. values that are actually encountered may be calculated by simple proportion. For convenience in metabolic work, tables have been prepared giving the values for each 0·01 grade of R.Q. from 0·707 to 1·000. The following is an example of such a table in abbreviated form:—

R.Q.	Percentage of Total Calories from		Calorie Value of 1 litre of Oxygen
	Carbohydrate	Fat	
0·707	0	100	4·686
0·75	15·6	84·4	4·739
0·80	33·4	66·6	4·801
0·85	50·7	49·3	4·862
0·90	67·5	32·5	4·924
0·95	84·0	16·0	4·985
1·00	100	0	5·047

As a concrete illustration of the application of all these arithmetical factors in an indirect calorimetric estimation, we may work out the following metabolic experiment of one hour's duration:—

Data $\begin{cases} \text{Total } CO_2 \text{ excretion, } 22 \cdot 16 \text{ grm.} \\ \text{Total } O_2 \text{ utilisation, } \quad 21 \cdot 31 \quad ,, \\ \text{Nitrogen in urine, } \quad 0 \cdot 321 \quad ,, \end{cases}$

Calories from protein $= 0 \cdot 321 \times 26 \cdot 51 = 8 \cdot 5$
CO_2 from protein $\quad = 0 \cdot 321 \times \quad 9 \cdot 35 = 3 \cdot 00$ grm.
O_2 for protein $\quad\quad = 0 \cdot 321 \times \quad 8 \cdot 49 = 2 \cdot 73 \quad ,,$

Non-protein $CO_2 = 22 \cdot 16 - 3 \cdot 00 = 19 \cdot 16$ grm.
Non-protein $O_2 \quad = 21 \cdot 31 - 2 \cdot 73 = 18 \cdot 58 \quad ,,$

Non-protein CO_2 in litres $= 19 \cdot 16 \times 0 \cdot 5089 = \quad 9 \cdot 75$
Non-protein O_2 in litres $\quad = 18 \cdot 58 \times 0 \cdot 6998 = 13 \cdot 0$

Non-protein R.Q. $= \dfrac{9 \cdot 75}{13 \cdot 0} = 0 \cdot 75$ (Calorie value of 1 litre $O_2 = 4 \cdot 739$)
Non-protein Calories $= 13 \cdot 0 \times 4 \cdot 739 = 61 \cdot 7$

Calories from fat $\quad\quad\quad = 84 \cdot 4$ per cent. of $61 \cdot 7 = 52 \cdot 1$
Calories from carbohydrate $= 15 \cdot 6$ per cent. of $61 \cdot 7 = \quad 9 \cdot 6$
Calories from protein $\quad\quad\quad\quad\quad\quad\quad\quad\quad = \quad 8 \cdot 5$

Total Calories . $\quad \underline{70 \cdot 2}$

In many metabolic estimations of short duration, and particularly in the determination of the basal metabolism, the protein metabolism is either neglected or allowed for in the calculation as 15 per cent. of the total energy output. Since a non-protein R.Q. cannot be obtained in the absence of a urinary nitrogen estimation, the calorie factor per litre of oxygen has to be assessed from the ordinary respiratory quotient, i.e. the ratio $\dfrac{\text{total } CO_2 \text{ excreted}}{\text{total } O_2 \text{ consumption}}$. A further simplification often introduced in basal metabolism estimations, especially for clinical work, is to assume an average value of $0 \cdot 82$ for the R.Q., which is its average value in the post-absorptive condition under which basal estimations are made. In these circumstances only the O_2 intake need be measured, and the calorie factor is a constant one of 4·8. This makes it possible to use a much simpler apparatus for the determination, as the only datum required is the O_2 intake of the subject. All that is then necessary is a simple closed circuit apparatus with soda-lime absorber to keep the rebreathed air free of CO_2, and a spirometer, which, by measuring the contraction in volume of the whole system, indicates directly the oxygen consumption of the subject. Such an apparatus is adequate for detecting the comparatively gross disturbances of the basal metabolism that are of clinical significance, but it is not much used in scientific work.

Energy Exchanges of Single Organs and Tissues – The principles just discussed are equally applicable to single organs and tissues. In animal experiments, the O_2 consumption and CO_2 output of individual organs *in situ* can be obtained by analysis of the arterial blood supplying the organ and the venous blood returning from it. It is by such methods that the O_2 consumption of the salivary glands and of the kidney, both of which are referred to elsewhere, are determined. In perfused isolated organs the gaseous exchange may be obtained in the same way from analyses made on the perfused solution before it enters and after it leaves the organ.

Estimations may be made on small organs, and even pieces of tissue, by enclosing them within a small glass vessel with a side-bulb containing KOH solution and connected to a delicate manometer. Since the CO_2 is absorbed by the KOH, the pressure changes in the manometer indicate the O_2 consumption of the tissue. A second experiment carried out without the KOH solution gives the difference between the CO_2 output and O_2 intake, and from this, taken in conjunction with the first result, the CO_2 output and the R.Q. may be obtained.

In all these methods for organs and tissues, however, the standard of accuracy is much lower than in determinations on the whole organism. The technique is usually difficult, the gaseous exchange to be measured is small, and, moreover, all organs and tissues contain considerable quantities of combined CO_2, part of which, on slight pH alteration, may be liberated and estimated as CO_2 of metabolic origin.

CHAPTER XVII
WORK AND EFFICIENCY

In industry the mechanical efficiency of an energy-transforming machine is of great importance. It is evaluated by stating the ratio between the output of mechanical work and the energy input of the machine, this ratio being usually expressed as a percentage. It is only natural that the physiologist should take an interest in the efficiency of the various energy transformations that occur in living organisms, and should attempt to find the relation between the physical work done and the expenditure of metabolic energy that this physical work entails. In this he meets the difficulty that the living organism, unlike inorganic machines, requires a certain input of energy for the mere maintenance of its integrity of structure. This maintenance quota must therefore be deducted in every case before the efficiency of a special activity can be assessed. In experiments on the efficiency of voluntary muscle this difficulty is comparatively small, because the difference between the metabolic activity of the muscles at rest and working can easily be obtained. But in other organs, the heart, for example, the maintenance quota is quite unobtainable, and the efficiency has to be stated as the relation between the external work of the heart and its total energy production. Even this is, of course, only possible in the excised heart.

In this chapter we shall consider the capacity for physical work and the efficiency of certain of the energy-transforming mechanisms of the body.

Work of Muscle – The work done by single muscles and their efficiency as energy transformers has already been dealt with. We saw that Hill's researches have shown that the total energy liberated by a stimulated muscle is twice the potential tension energy developed in the muscle. Thus, even if all the tension energy could be changed into external work, the maximum efficiency would never be more than 50 per cent. In the ordinary muscular movements of our bodies this efficiency is never reached for several reasons.   First, as Hill's experiments showed, some of the tension energy is lost in overcoming the viscous resistance of the muscle substance, this loss increasing with the rapidity of the muscle's contraction,. so that the full amount of the tension energy could only be turned into mechanical work if the muscle contracted with infinite slowness.   Secondly, this theoretical 50 per cent. efficiency and its decrement by the viscosity refers only to the muscle fibre, and not necessarily to the muscle as a whole. In most muscles the fibres do not run exactly in the direction along which the muscle acts.   The force exerted by the muscle along its line of action will thus be only a component of the force in the direction of the fibres.   Thirdly, there are losses due to friction in joints, in tendon sheaths, and in one muscle or part of a muscle moving relatively to another. Fourthly, the balance of the body requires the use of many muscles other than those which actually carry out the desired work.   Lastly, in any sort of muscular performance the muscles have to move not only an external load; they must also do a certain amount of internal work in moving themselves and the parts of the body that move with them.   These are five sources of loss of efficiency in ordinary muscular effort, and no doubt more could be brought out by pushing the analysis further.

What, then, is the combined effect of all these sources of loss in reducing the theoretical 50 per cent. efficiency; in other words, what is the *actual* efficiency, or relation between the useful external work and the extra liberation of metabolic energy in the body which the performance of that work entails ?   To obtain the actual efficiency of muscles working *in situ*, the external work done is measured by making the subject operate some type of ergometer, and the excess of the working metabolism over the resting metabolism is simultaneously determined by one of the methods detailed in the previous chapter.

There are many types of ergometer.   In most, the muscular movement under investigation is converted by suitable mechanical arrangements into a rotary motion of a heavy flywheel, to which some form of brake is applied.   The simplest is an ordinary brake-band held against the rim of the flywheel by the tension of a spring-balance. The load applied at the circumference of the wheel is directly indicated by the balance, and the work done per revolution of the wheel is the product of the load and the wheel's circumference. A more complex type uses as resistance the eddy currents induced by a magnetic field in a rotating copper disc. In this ergo-meter the rotating flywheel has a copper centre with a lead rim. A framework accurately balanced on the same axis carries a number of electro-magnets, energised from the supply mains, and with their pole-pieces placed close to the disc but not touching it. When the disc is rotated by the subject, the framework carrying the magnets tends to rotate with it. This tendency is prevented by loading a horizontal arm fixed to the framework. An automatic electrical control operated by the swinging frame itself keeps the magnetising current so adjusted that the loaded arm is always held horizontal whatever the speed of rotation of the disc. In these circumstances the load on the rotating disc is the weight applied to the arm. As a convenience, the point of application of the load is so fixed as to be $\frac{1}{\pi}$ metre distant from the axis; the work in kilogram-metres done per revolution of the wheel is then readily cal-culated, being given by load (in kilos) $\times 2\pi \times \frac{1}{\pi}$; that is, it is numerically equivalent to twice the applied weight.

The efficiencies obtained by these methods, provided that the movement investigated is one to which the subject is well accustomed, are usually from 20 to 30 per cent. The table on opposite page gives the results of some of the best known workers in these investigations.

When the muscular movement is an unpractised one, so that the subject's co-ordination is imperfect, the efficiencies are much lower owing to the needless use of many muscles that play little or no part in producing external work.

The five sources of loss of efficiency referred to account, therefore, for a reduction of a theoretical 50 per cent. efficiency to a practical one under the best conditions, of about 25 per cent. Atzler has shown that, to a certain extent, it is

Authority	Net Efficiency (per cent.)
Katzenstein (1891) . . .	25·4
Sonden and Tigerstedt (1895) .	27·4
Zuntz (1909)	28·0
Benedict and Carpenter (1909) .	20·6
Amar (1910)	32·5
Benedict and Cathcart (1913) .	21–33
Lindhard (1913) . . .	·25
Douglas (1920)	23–26

(Cathcart, in Burns's *An Introduction to Biophysics*)

possible to apportion the loss among the different sources, and that the loss is distributed differently in different types of work.

As in isolated muscles, so in muscle groups, the speed with which a defined amount of external work is done has a very great effect on the efficiency of performance (first source of loss). This is well illustrated by the observations of Benedict and Cathcart on a professional cyclist riding a bicycle ergometer (see p. 256). In each of the five experiments the external work per unit of time was kept as nearly as possible constant, but the load on the ergometer wheel was varied so that a greater or less number of pedal revolutions were required to produce the fixed amount of work.

The highest efficiencies were obtained with speeds of about 70 revs. per minute, and the efficiencies fell off markedly at higher speeds. As 70 revs. per minute was the subject's natural speed in actual cycling, a speed which he had no doubt found by experience to produce the best results, it is almost certain that, if observations had been made at speeds lower than this, the efficiency would again have been found to be below the optimal. The speed for optimal efficiency is always a compromise between rapidity of muscular action, which lessens the energy loss in maintaining the muscle in a contracted condition, and slowness of contraction, which lessens the energy loss in overcoming the muscle's viscosity (*cf.* Hill's experiments on biceps muscle, p. 226).

Revolutions per minute	External Work per minute (kg.-mt.)	Net Efficiency (per cent.)
90	825	22·6
124	833	15·7
80	752	22·1
105	778	17·7
71	667	24·5
108	671	15·6
71	570	23·1
94	548	20·4
105	574	17·0
72	510	21·5
88	535	19·5

Work of the Heart – Much of our knowledge of the physical work, energy liberation, and efficiency of the heart has been derived from the investigations of Lovatt Evans and his fellow-workers on the Starling heart-lung preparation. As the student will remember, this preparation has many advantages for the determination of the heart's mechanical work, since the arterial resistance and outflow may be controlled and accurately measured. Moreover, Lovatt Evans, by devising an ingenious closed-circuit respiration apparatus for use with the heart-lung preparation, was able to combine, with the calculation of the mechanical work, the determination of the metabolic changes, and thus to estimate the efficiency of the heart under varying conditions of outflow and arterial resistance. Of course, as Lovatt Evans points out, it must be remembered that the preparation is an excised and denervated heart, and the results obtained with it must be referred with caution to the heart beating naturally in the body. In particular, the absence of nervous control causes the heart to beat at a fast rate even when the output is relatively small, and the slower pulse rate that is found with low outputs in the heart of an intact animal would mean a lower oxygen utilisation and consequently efficiencies, at low outputs, higher than those obtained in the experimental preparation.

The mechanical work of the heart is arrived at in the following way. At each beat of the ventricles a certain volume of blood is driven with a certain velocity through the aortic (or pulmonary) orifice against the aortic (or pulmonary) arterial pressure. The work produced by the heart is thus expended partly, and, as we shall see, mainly, in overcoming the resistance of the arterial pressure, and partly in giving velocity to the blood-stream.

If the arterial pressure were constant and equivalent to a column of blood R metres in height, the work done in overcoming this resistance, when a volume Q litres of blood is expelled from the ventricle, would be QR kilogrammetres. In actual fact, however, the pressure in the aorta and pulmonary artery during expulsion is not constant; neither is the volume of blood expelled at a uniform rate throughout each systole. To be accurate, the work of overcoming the arterial resistance ought to be obtained by integration of the products of ejection-volume and arterial pressure for each infinitesimal period of time from the opening to the closure of the semi-lunar valves. Such calculations have been made, but the accuracy of the experimental data at present available hardly warrants them, and the work involved in overcoming arterial resistance is usually taken simply as QR, where Q is the total volume of blood expelled, and R is the mean arterial resistance.

The work which the heart does in imparting velocity to the blood may be expressed by the familiar formula $\frac{1}{2}mv^2$, where m is the mass of blood ejected and v is its velocity. Expressing mass in terms of weight (w), this becomes $\frac{wv^2}{2g}$, where g is the acceleration due to gravity. It is a difficult matter to obtain an accurate experimental value for v in this formula. The velocity of blood during expulsion fluctuates just as the arterial pressure and the volume of blood ejected fluctuate, and its accurate measurement would require a continuous record of the flow from the ventricle and mathematical integration of the data. An approximately accurate value for the mean

17

expulsion velocity may, however, be obtained from the average
rate of the heart's output of blood if we assume that

Velocity during ejection : average velocity of output : :
　　　　　Total duration of cardiac cycle : ejection period.

On this basis, if the ejection period occupies three-eighths of
the time of a whole cardiac cycle, the velocity during expulsion
will be $\frac{8}{3}$ times the mean velocity in the large vessels, as calculated
from the heart's output.　In general, if the velocity calculated
from the heart's output is V and the ejection velocity is v,
the duration of expulsion E and the duration of a whole
cardiac cycle C, then

$$\frac{v}{V}=\frac{C}{E} \quad \text{or} \quad v=\frac{VC}{E}.$$

Substituting this value in the previous formula, the work
expended in imparting velocity to the blood $=\frac{w(VC)^2}{2gE^2}$, and,
adding to this the work of overcoming arterial resistance, the
work done by each ventricle is

$$QR+\frac{w(VC)^2}{2gE^2}.$$

Lovatt Evans has amplified this formula so as to give the total
work of both ventricles.　Since the pulmonary arterial pressure
is one-sixth that of the aortic pressure, the value of the first
part of the expression for the right ventricle will be one-sixth
of its value for the left.　The value of the velocity factor in
the expression, in the absence of any precise data, is taken to
be the same for both sides of the heart.　The combined
output of work (W) by both ventricles is then

$$W=QR+\frac{QR}{6}+2\left\{\frac{w(VC)^2}{2gE^2}\right\}$$

or

$$W=\frac{7QR}{6}+\frac{w(VC)^2}{gE^2}.$$

Where the duration of the expulsion period E is three-eighths
of the total duration of the cardiac cycle C, as it is under

normal conditions of output and arterial resistance in the heart-lung preparation, the value of $\dfrac{C^2}{E^2}$ is $\dfrac{64}{9}$, or approximately 7. Using this approximation, the formula simplifies to

$$W = 7\left(\frac{QR}{6} + \frac{wV^2}{g}\right).$$

The share which the velocity factor takes in the whole work of the heart varies from a negligible value at low heart outputs to one of great magnitude at the higher outputs. This is clear from the formula, since a tenfold increase in Q (and hence also in w) results in a tenfold increase in QR, but, since the velocity will also be approximately ten times greater, in a thousandfold increase in the factor wV^2. The graph (fig. 50) shows how, assuming that the time-relations between systole and whole cardiac cycle remain constant, the value of the velocity factor rises from being a negligible fraction of the total work at low outputs until, when the output exceeds 104 litres per hour, it surpasses the QR factor.

These relations are of some clinical interest, for in aortic stenosis, where the exit from the left ventricle is narrowed, the blood must be ejected with greater velocity. This increase in velocity is not so great as might be supposed on first thought, because in aortic stenosis the systolic stage is prolonged relative to the whole cardiac cycle; this diminishes the velocity during actual ejection and tends to compensate for the stenosis. Even so, calculation from the formulæ will show that, if we suppose the aortic orifice to be narrowed from a normal diameter of 2·5 cm. to 1·0 cm., and systole to be prolonged until it occupies one-half of the whole cycle, the velocity factor for the left ventricle would rise from a negligible fraction to 8 or 9 per cent. of the total work in a resting patient whose output was 3·6 litres per minute and arterial pressure was 100 mm. The increase in the velocity component adds, of course, to the total work of the heart; the effect of this increased work is seen in the cardiac hypertrophy that is so prominent a feature in these cases.

As an illustration of the use of the heart-work formula, the

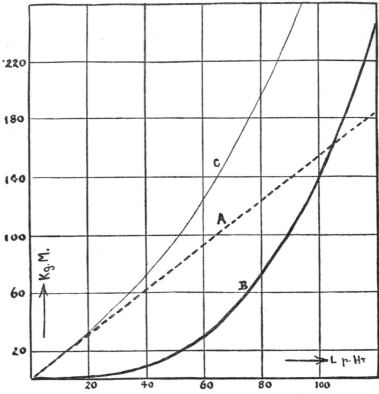

FIG. 50—Curves showing relative importance of the kinetic and static factors when the arterial pressure is 120 mm.

A=values of QR.　　　B=values of $\dfrac{7w\mathrm{V}^2}{g}$.　　　C=A+B.

(Lovatt Evans, *Journ. Physiol.*, 1918)

calculation of one of Lovatt Evans's experiments may be given:

Experimental data—

Arterial resistance=80 mm. Hg. =0·080 × 13[1]=1·04 metres of blood.

Heart output=81 litres per hour.

Velocity (calculated from output)=1·15 metres per second.

---

[1] Ratio $\dfrac{\text{Sp.gr. Hg}}{\text{Sp.gr. Blood}}$.

Calculation—

$$W \text{ (in kg.-mt. per hour)} = 7 \left\{ \frac{81 \times 1.04}{6} + \frac{81 \times (1.15)^2}{9.8} \right\}$$
$$= 175 \text{ kg.-mt.}$$

The oxygen utilisation of the heart in the above experiment, determined by Evans with his respiration apparatus, was 299 c.c. per hour. Using the factors that 1 litre of oxygen $= 4.88$ Cals., and that 1 Cal. $= 425$ kg.-mt.,[1] the energy liberated by the cardiac muscle was

$$0.299 \times 4.88 \times 425 = 620 \text{ kg.-mt.}$$

The efficiency with which the work was performed was thus $\frac{175}{620}$, or 28·2 per cent.

From a large number of such experiments, carried out under various conditions of arterial resistance and heart output, Evans and Matsuoka find that the efficiency of the heart varies considerably with alteration of these two factors. High arterial pressures increase the cost of work very steeply, so that the efficiency, after rising to a maximum at about 100 mm. Hg., declines rapidly. With increase of the output alone the efficiency rises rapidly at first, and in most cases continues to rise, up to the highest outputs obtainable. Evidently, therefore, the conditions of a moderate arterial pressure and a large output would give a maximum efficiency. It is interesting that these are just the conditions under which the heart is working during severe muscular exercise, when maximal cardiac efficiency is of the first importance to the organism. In the experiment quoted above, the conditions for optimal efficiency were presumably nearly realised, as the figure of 28·2 per cent. is the highest obtained in any of these heart-lung experiments. This figure corresponds very closely with the maximal efficiency obtained under the best conditions for the contraction of skeletal muscle.

A further analogy between skeletal and cardiac muscle is found in the factors controlling the optimal output of external work. In the chapter on Muscle we have already seen that the maximal work output is a matter of correct loading. The

---

[1] The factors used by Lovatt Evans.

best outputs are obtained when the initial load on the muscle is as large as it can overcome, and when this load progressively diminishes as the muscle shortens and its contractile tension diminishes.

Now Starling, in his 'law of the heart,' expressed his finding that the tension developed by the cardiac muscle fibres was a function of the length to which they had been stretched by the diastolic filling up of the ventricle. The heart thus increases its liberation of contractile tension energy when its diastolic volume is increased. Increased diastolic volume, however, may be the result either of increased inflow from the veins (which results in increased output from the heart), or of increased arterial resistance, and the use that the heart muscle can make of the extra tension which it develops is different in the two cases. If the arterial resistance is high, then the heart is subjected to a prolonged overload, and useful energy is lost because the contraction is an incomplete one; thus we find that the efficiency falls off rapidly at high arterial pressures. On the other hand, the heart responds well to demands for increased output, provided that the arterial resistance is not too high. In these circumstances, the increased diastolic filling results in the liberation of more tension energy, which is more fully made use of, as the load on the heart, at first large, diminishes progressively as the ventricles drive out the blood against the moderate arterial resistance. Hence it is found that, with constant arterial resistance, the efficiency increases with increased outputs, and the best efficiencies are obtained with an arterial resistance that optimally times the load-release of a ventricle working at its full capacity.

Work of the Human Heart – When we try to employ the formulæ just discussed to the determination of the work of the human heart, we are at once met with the difficulty of obtaining the necessary data. The velocity of output, for example, is determinable with fair accuracy in the heart-lung preparation, where a measured amount of blood is driven out through a cannula whose diameter is accurately known; but in the human subject we have no knowledge of the diameter of the aortic or pulmonary orifices in the living condition, and in spite of many methods and their extensive use, we are still far from general agreement as to the amount of blood discharged with each systole at rest and during effort of various degrees. The discovery of a reliable method for the determination of the systolic discharge would be of great value, not only to the physiologist, but to the clinician.

Most of the methods that have been so far devised depend on the following principle. If a gas which the blood can take up is present in the lungs, and if we measure (1) the total volume of gas absorbed by the blood per minute, and (2) the percentage amount of that gas taken up by the blood in its passage through the lungs, then the volume of blood travelling through the lungs will be given by

$$\frac{\text{total volume of gas absorbed per minute}}{\text{amount of gas absorbed by each 100 c.c. of blood}} \times 100.$$

Thus, in the diagram below (fig. 51), if 250 c.c. of gas are absorbed from the lungs by the blood per minute, and if each

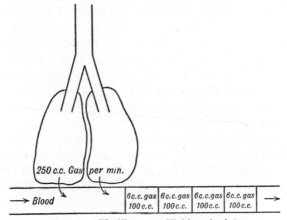

FIG. 51—To illustrate Fick's principle

100 c.c. of blood carries away 6 c.c. of it, the blood flowing through the lungs $=\dfrac{250 \times 100}{6}=4166$ c.c. per minute. This is therefore the amount of blood which is returned per minute to the left heart and pumped out by it. The pulse-rate being known, simple division gives the systolic output per beat.

The principle of this method was originally enunciated by Fick in 1870 for the ordinary respiratory gas, oxygen, and it is equally applicable to CO_2. If either of these gases is used for the determination, the total O_2 absorption or CO_2 output per minute in the lungs is readily estimated by the Douglas bag method. The percentage uptake (O_2) or release (CO_2) from the blood has to be found, however, from the difference of two estimations—one of the venous concentration, and the other of the arterial concentration—because the gases are present in both arterial and venous blood. In animals, values for the venous and arterial blood concentrations can be obtained by direct analysis of blood from the right heart and from an artery. In man, although direct examination of the arterial blood is possible by arterial puncture, the venous blood concentration must be determined indirectly, and in practice both are usually determined by indirect methods.

To obtain the arterial concentration of CO_2, an ordinary sample of alveolar air is taken and analysed to determine its partial pressure of CO_2. This partial pressure is identical with the CO_2 tension in the arterial blood, and by reference to a CO_2 dissociation curve we can find how many volumes of CO_2 per 100 volumes of blood will be present at this tension. Determination of the venous concentration is more difficult. Suppose that we could stop breathing for a time, and that during that time none of the blood leaving the lungs had made a complete circuit and returned to the lungs, the CO_2 would continue to come off from the blood until the partial pressure of the CO_2 in the air held in the lungs was equal to the CO_2 tension in the venous blood. Then by analysing the lung air the venous CO_2 tension could be obtained, and by reference to the dissociation curve this tension could be translated into volumes CO_2 per cent. of blood. Such an experimental procedure is impossible, but something similar can be done. The subject can periodically rebreathe his own expired air from a bag, always returning the expired air to the bag. In the intervals he breathes atmospheric air. The air in the bag is analysed from time to time, and its CO_2 content will be found to rise, and then to remain at a constant value. This value is identical with the CO_2 tension in the venous blood, and from this tension the volumes CO_2 per cent. may be got from the dissociation curve.

The following data were obtained from an experiment of this kind:—

CO_2 expired per minute ('Douglas bag estimation), 1057 c.c.
Percentage CO_2 in ordinary alveolar sample, 4·8 per cent.

This equals 48·8 vols. CO_2 per 100 c.c. blood (from dissociation curve).

Percentage CO_2 in rebreathing bag, 7·5 per cent.

This equals 57·4 vols. CO_2 per 100 c.c. blood (from dissociation curve).

Therefore

Every 100 c.c. blood gave up $57\cdot4 - 48\cdot8 = 8\cdot6$ vols. CO_2.
Blood circulating per minute $= \frac{1057}{8\cdot6} \times 100 = 12,290$ c.c.
Pulse-rate 136.
Systolic discharge $\frac{12,290}{136} = 90$ c.c.

Instead of using the rebreathing bag, a series of Douglas bags may be filled with mixtures of CO_2, O_2, and N_2, in which the CO_2 partial pressures vary in value round about the expected venous CO_2 tension. After taking a maximum breath of one of these mixtures, the subject holds his breath for four seconds, expires about half of the air in his lungs, holds his breath again for a further six seconds, and then expires the remainder. A sample of each expiration is analysed. If the CO_2 content of the two samples agree, then no gaseous interchange with the blood has occurred, and the partial pressure of CO_2 in the sample and its tension in the venous blood must be identical.

Again, instead of using the respiratory gases CO_2 and O_2, we may estimate the circulation rate and systolic discharge by introducing into the lungs a foreign gas which only dissolves in the blood. From the amount of the gas which has been absorbed into the blood from the lungs and its coefficient of solubility in the blood, the amount of blood passing through the lungs may be calculated. This is the principle of the method of Krogh, who used N_2O, and of the more recent method of Yandell Henderson, who used ethyl iodide. In these methods we have only to deal with a question of solubility, and the necessity for using dissociation curves is avoided. In the Krogh method, the duration of the period during which the nitrous oxide is held in the lungs must be less than the time for a complete circuit of the blood (about half a minute). If this period is exceeded, some N_2O will return to the lungs in the venous blood and vitiate the calculation. In Yandell Henderson's method this precaution was considered unnecessary, as the ethyl iodide inhaled and absorbed into the blood is very rapidly decomposed in the tissues to sodium iodide and alcohol, and it was believed that there was no return by the venous blood. The experiment might therefore extend over several minutes. The method is relatively simple in its technique, but unfortunately its reliability has of late been seriously questioned.

The results obtained by these different methods for the systolic discharge of a man at rest do not show any very great agreement, and among different persons examined by the same method there is also considerable variation. In round figures, the systolic output at rest, as determined by the N_2O method, varies from 40 to 100 c.c.; by one of the CO_2 methods, from 70 to 120 c.c.; and by the ethyl iodide method even higher figures are obtained. During muscular exercise the systolic output increases, in some subjects only slightly, in others to more than twice its resting value. Generally speaking, the athlete has a large systolic output even at rest, and during work he obtains his extra requirement of oxygen mainly by increased pulse-rate and greater deoxygenation of the blood in its passage through the tissues, the systolic output altering only slightly. The sedentary man has a pulse-rate and oxygen utilisation already relatively large at rest, so that there is less possibility of obtaining extra oxygen by altering them, and the increased demand has to be met in much greater part by increase of the systolic output.

Owing to lack of data, therefore, any estimates of the work done by the human heart must be regarded as only approximately correct at the best. Nevertheless, using what data are available, it is interesting to apply Evans's formula to the following three cases, assuming, for the purpose of calculating the mean velocity of output, that the aortic orifice has in life its post-mortem diameter of 2·5 cm. :—

(1) Man resting—
Arterial pressure 100 mm. = 1·3 metres of blood.
Output = 4 litres per minute (about 60 c.c. per beat at usual pulse-rate).
Calculated mean velocity of output = 0·136 metres per second.
Expulsion period : total cardiac cycle : : 3 : 8.
Work (in kg.-mt. per minute)

$$= \frac{7}{6} \times 4 \times 1 \cdot 3 + \frac{4(0 \cdot 136 \times 8)^2}{9 \cdot 8 \times 3^2}$$
$$= 6 \cdot 06 + 0 \cdot 05$$
$$= 6 \cdot 11.$$

The velocity component is less than 1 per cent. of the total work done.

(2) Man doing hard muscular work—
Arterial pressure 120 mm. = 1·56 metres of blood.
Output 20 litres per minute.
Calculated mean velocity of output = 0·68 metres per second.
Expulsion period : total cardiac cycle : : 3 : 8.
Work (in kg.-mt. per minute)

$$= \frac{7}{6} \times 20 \times 1 \cdot 56 + \frac{20(0 \cdot 68 \times 8)^2}{9 \cdot 8 \times 3^2}$$
$$= 36 \cdot 4 + 6 \cdot 7$$
$$= 43 \cdot 1.$$

The percentage work involved in imparting velocity to the blood is now raised to 16 per cent. of the total. Both the total work and the share attributed to the velocity component are by this calculation too high, because during muscular exertion the heart-rate increases and the duration of each cardiac cycle is shortened. The shortening falls mainly on the diastolic period, so that the expulsion period comes to occupy a relatively large portion of the whole cycle. This has quite a marked effect in reducing the value of the velocity component and also in slightly diminishing the total work, as may be seen from the following:—

(3) Same data as in (2), except that (expulsion period : total cycle) is now taken as 1 : 2.

Work (in kg.-mt. per minute)

$$=\frac{7}{6}\times 20 \times 1\cdot56 + \frac{20(0\cdot68\times 2)^2}{9\cdot8\times 1^2}$$
$$=36\cdot4+3\cdot8$$
$$=40\cdot2.$$

The velocity factor has been reduced to 9·5 per cent. of the total work and the total work to 40·2 kg.-mt. per minute.

This amount of work is approximately the equivalent of 0·1 Cal., and, if we assume that the heart is working at 25 per cent. efficiency, the liberation of energy in the cardiac muscle required to produce this amount of external work is 0·4 Cal. per minute, or approximately one-third of the basal energy requirement of the whole body.

Work done by Secreting Cells – The metabolic energy of the secreting cell is required for three functions: (1) The maintenance of the cell itself as a living unit; (2) the elaboration of its specific secretory products; and (3) if we accept the osmotic theory of the discharge of its secretion, the raising, and maintenance at a high value, of the osmotic concentration within the cell during the actual liberation of its secretion. So far there is no method of ascertaining what part of the work done by a secreting cell is devoted to each of these separate activities, the only estimate possible being that of the difference during rest and activity of the oxygen consumption of the glandular tissue in mass.

A number of such observations have been made by Barcroft and his associates on the salivary glands. They found that the oxygen consumption of the gland was increased by activity, and roughly in proportion to the degree of activity. What was of greater interest was the time-relation between the flow of the secretion and the extra oxygen consumption. The maximum extra oxygen consumption always occurred later than the maximum discharge of saliva, and this extra oxygen consumption might continue for several minutes after the flow of saliva had ceased. This suggests that, in a gland, as in muscle, the extra oxygen demanded during activity is not directly necessary for the immediate functioning of the tissue, but is required to restore and maintain the conditions in the cell which make its activity possible.

The observations of Asher and Karaulov on the glucose content of the blood flowing through the gland also support this view. It was only in the period immediately following the flow of secretion that they found the blood-sugar lower in the venous than the arterial blood of the gland, when presumably it was being oxidised to provide energy; during the actual flow of secretion, the concentration of sugar in the venous blood was certainly not less and might even exceed that in the arterial, probably owing to passage of fluid from the blood into the secretion, with consequent general increase in concentration of all the blood constituents. The immediate source of the energy for secretion would thus appear to come from the breakdown of some preformed substance. This substance is then restored during a recovery phase, the energy for its restoration being obtained at the expense of oxidation processes in which glucose itself or some derivative of it is involved.

Work of the Kidney – Although the function of the kidney is often called secretion, the process that goes on in the kidney cells is simply one of transference of substances from blood to urine. The kidney cells have no part in the preparation of the solids of the urine, if one excepts the single unimportant instance of hippuric acid. Their function is that of excreting a fluid containing the waste materials of the blood, and this fluid, the urine, is almost always more concentrated and hence of higher osmotic pressure than the blood. The formation of urine therefore seems to demand only the performance of osmotic work by the kidney cells, and the calculation of the physical work and its correlation with the physiological work should be simpler than in the true secreting cell, where the secretory substances have to be elaborated.

The student will remember that, according to Cushny's

theory, the concentration of the urine is a function of the tubules, the rôle of the glomerulus being to provide a filtrate from which the tubules absorb water and 'threshold' substances. As far as concerns the computation of the osmotic work of the kidney, however, it is immaterial how the kidney produces the urine. The essential fact is that the kidney produces a relatively concentrated urine from a relatively dilute blood, and all that the calculation of the osmotic work gives is the minimum theoretical amount of work necessary to effect this change of concentration.

The calculation of the osmotic work of the kidney may be made from a modification of the formula,

$$W = 2 \cdot 303RT \log \frac{c_1}{c_2} \quad \text{(p. 96)},$$

which expresses the work done when a solution changes in concentration from a value c_1 to a value c_2. The case of the blood-urine concentration is complicated by the fact that all the urinary constituents are not concentrated to the same extent. For example, while the ratio of the concentrations of NaCl in blood and urine is only as 1 : 2, the ratio of the urea concentrations of the two fluids may be as high as 1 : 60. To arrive at a proper estimate of the osmotic work, the calculation must be made for each constituent separately, and the total osmotic work obtained from the sum of these separate calculations.

For any one constituent the following formula is applicable:

$$W = nRT2 \cdot 303 \log \frac{c_1}{c_2} - c_2 nRT\left(\frac{1}{c_2} - \frac{1}{c_1}\right),$$

where

n = number of moles of the substance concentrated,
c_1 = molar concentration of substance in urine,
c_2 = ,,   ,,   ,,   ,, blood.

The resemblance of this formula to the one given above is evident. Without going into details of its development, it may be said that the second term $c_2 nRT\left(\dfrac{1}{c_2} - \dfrac{1}{c_1}\right)$ is introduced because the urine is concentrated from a fluid (blood) in which the concentration c_2 of the substance considered does not essentially alter during the process. If for the moment we accept the modern view and consider the process as being due to water reabsorption, it is evident that the osmotic effect of this concentration c_2 remaining in the blood will assist the reabsorption of water from the glomerular filtrate.

If our calculations are referred to 1 litre of urine, since n and c_1 are equal, the formula may be written:

$$W = RT \left\{ c_1 2 \cdot 303 \log \frac{c_1}{c_2} - (c_1 - c_2) \right\}.$$

von Rhorer, using such a formula, calculated the osmotic work done by the kidney in concentrating two of the urinary constituents, viz. urea and NaCl, when these substances were present in the urine in concentrations of 2·4 per cent. and 1·2 per cent. respectively, being thus forty times and twice their blood concentrations. The result obtained was 308 kg.-mt. per litre of urine. Cushny estimates that, if all constituents were taken account of, 500 kg.-mt. would not be an over-estimate of the osmotic work involved in producing 1 litre of urine of average composition.

To determine the metabolic energy associated with the work of urinary excretion, we must as usual have recourse to the oxygen consumption. Observations of this kind have been made by Barcroft and his fellow-workers. In dogs' kidneys they found an oxygen consumption of from 0·008 to 0·075 c.c. per gram of kidney per minute, and in rabbits' an average of 0·082 c.c. per gram per minute. If we take 0·04 c.c. per gram per minute as an average figure and apply this to man, assuming that the weight of the human kidneys is 280 grams, we obtain a daily consumption of approximately 15 litres of oxygen by the kidneys alone. Taking the average daily excretion of urine as 1500 c.c., this indicates a consumption of 10 litres of oxygen per litre of urine. If each litre of oxygen has a calorie value of 5·0, then, using Cushny's estimate of 500 kg.-mt. for the osmotic work, this means an efficiency of approximately 2 per cent. Even allowing for considerable error in the figures both for oxygen consumption and for osmotic work, this efficiency is very low compared with the efficiency of other biological processes. Moreover, Barcroft and Brodie, in their experiments on urea and sulphate diuresis, in which both the oxygen consumption of the kidney and the Δ's of the blood and urine were simultaneously measured, could find no parallelism between energy liberation as calculated from the oxygen consumption and the osmotic work. These observations and calculations serve to impress us with our fundamental ignorance of the whole mechanism of urinary excretion.

CHAPTER XVIII

LIGHT AND VISION

THE visible radiation which we call light is part of a series of electro-magnetic wave disturbances in the ether, the wavelengths which produce visual stimuli being limited within the comparatively short band of approximately 4000 to 8000 Ångström units.[1] Taking round figures, the shortest visible wave-lengths, from 4000 to 4500, when acting alone, give the sensation which we call violet; those from 4500 to 5000, a sensation of blue; from 5000 to 5750, green; 5750 to 5900, yellow; 5900 to 6500, orange; and waves longer than this, red sensations. When all the wave-lengths are combined together a sensation of white light is received.

Radiations both above and below these visible limits are known. On the shorter side there are the chemically active ultra-violet waves, which merge into the still shorter X-rays, the wave-lengths of the latter ranging from about 100 to 0·1 Å. units. On the longer side are the infra-red waves, which produce marked heating effects, and the now familiar Hertzian (wireless) waves, which may be several thousands of metres in length.

Polarised Light – The vibratory movements in the ether which constitute a ray of ordinary light occur in every direction at right angles to the direction of its propagation. If we think of a paddle-wheel and consider the axle of the wheel to represent the direction in which the light is travelling, then the planes of vibration of the light waves would be represented by the planes of the paddles. Under certain conditions it is possible, however, to obtain light in a form in which the vibratory motion is of a more restricted type. When the vibration occurs in one plane only, the light is said to be plane polarised. In our wheel analogy the light is now vibrating in only the plane of two exactly opposite paddles. As this type of light is employed for identifying and estimating various

[1] 1 Ångström unit $= \frac{1}{10,000,000}$ mm. or $\frac{1}{10,000} \mu$.

18

substances of biochemical importance, it is useful to know in a very elementary way how plane-polarised light may be produced, and how the plane of its vibration may be detected.

If a ray of light (R) is passed through a crystal of Iceland spar in any direction other than its axis of symmetry, the ray undergoes double refraction (fig. 52, A) and emerges as two rays, the ordinary (O) and the extraordinary (E) ray, the latter being so-called because it does not obey the laws of ordinary refraction (see below). Both emerging rays are polarised, but in planes at right angles to each other.

Now, Nicol found that if the two end-faces of a rhomb of Iceland spar are cut down until their acute angles are reduced from

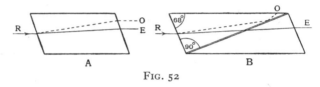

FIG. 52

their natural value of 71° to 68°, the crystal sliced diagonally and symmetrically through its blunt corners, the cut surfaces polished and the two halves cemented together again with canada balsam (fig. 52, B), the incident ray R is still doubly refracted, but the ordinary ray is reflected laterally by the balsam, and the extraordinary ray alone emerges from the opposite face of the crystal. By this arrangement, which is known as a Nicol prism, a beam of light can be obtained whose waves are vibrating in only one plane. If two Nicol prisms are placed in the path of a ray of ordinary light so that the light has to pass successively through them, we should expect that the light polarised by its passage through the first prism would only pass through the second if its orientation was similar to that of the first. Experiment proves this to be the case; the light only passes when the principal planes of the two prisms are parallel. Any axial rotation of the second prism from this position will result in a lessening of the intensity of the transmitted light, until when the principal planes of the two are at right angles to one another no light will pass through at all. If rotation is continued through a further 90°, the principal planes will again be parallel and the full intensity of light will be transmitted. Thus the changes in illumination caused by rotating the second prism may be used to detect the position of the plane in which the light is polarised by the first prism. Such an arrangement constitutes the basis of the polarimeter, the first Nicol prism being the polariser (P) and the second the analyser (A) (fig. 53).

The complete instrument includes certain other features, viz. C, a condenser to concentrate the light on the polarising prism; T, a telescope through which the transmitted light is viewed; S, a scale calibrated in degrees for reading the rotation of the analyser; and lastly, some means, often a quartz plate

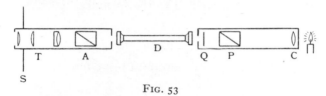

FIG. 53

situated at Q, for enabling the position of the analyser A relative to the polariser P to be set with great accuracy. The detailed action of the last is too complicated to discuss here.

To us the importance of this instrument is that the solutions of certain substances, especially of the carbon compounds, rotate the plane of polarisation either to the left (lævorotatory) or to the right (dextrorotatory). Such substances are said to be optically active. Suppose that an optically active solution has been introduced into tube D, the analyser A having been previously set to correspond with the polariser P. The polarised light has now to traverse the length of the solution before reaching the analyser, and it will be found that the analyser has to be rotated either to the right or left, according to whether the substance is dextrorotatory or lævorotatory, before correspondence is again obtained. The amount of this rotation observed on the scale depends on the length of the tube and the strength of the solution. If, therefore, we know the rotation given by a certain length of a standard solution of an optically active substance, e.g. dextrose, we can find the strength of any other solution of dextrose from the rotation produced by an exactly equal column of it. This method of estimation, which is particularly useful in solutions of the sugars, is polarimetry. The standard, or the *specific rotation* of any substance, $[a]_D$,[1] with which other solutions of the same substance are compared is the rotation given by a column, 1 decimetre long, of a solution containing 1 grm. of substance per cubic centimetre of solvent. For example, the $[a]_D$ of dextrose is $+52 \cdot 6°$, the positive sign indicating a rotation towards the right.

As an instance of the use of the instrument we may take the following. A solution of dextrose, placed in a 2-decimetre tube, gave an angular rotation of 5°. The concentration and rotation are related according to the formula,

$$P = \frac{100a}{s \times l},$$

where   P = percentage concentration to be found,
   a = observed rotation,
   $s = [a]_D$,
   l = length of tube in decimetres.

In the example quoted, therefore,

$$P = \frac{100 \times 5}{52 \cdot 6 \times 2} = 4 \cdot 75 \text{ per cent.}$$

Optical activity is believed to be due to an asymmetric arrangement of the atoms within the molecule. For instance, lactic acid exists in two forms identical except in their action on polarised light. The structural formula of lactic acid may be represented either as

$$\begin{array}{ccc} CH_3 & & CH_3 \\ | & & | \\ HO—C—H & \text{or} & H—C—OH, \\ | & & | \\ COOH & & COOH \end{array}$$

the difference between these formulæ lying in the spatial arrangement of the hydrogen and hydroxyl groups, and it is

[1] [a] signifies specific rotation ; the subscript D, by sodium light.

assumed that the one arrangement corresponds to the dextrorotatory and the other to the lævorotatory form. Two such
forms of the same substance are known as optical isomers, and
the phenomenon as stereoisomerism.

We may now revise some elementary principles of optics,
familiarity with which is essential to a proper comprehension
of the functioning of the eye. They are chiefly concerned
with the phenomena of reflection from concave and convex
spherical surfaces, and with refraction.

Reflection – When a ray of light strikes a reflecting surface
normally (perpendicularly) to that surface, it is reflected back
along its original path. If it strikes the surface otherwise than
normally, then it is reflected at such an angle to its original
path that the angle between
incident ray and normal is equal
to the angle between reflected
ray and normal. If XY (fig.
54) is the section of a concave
spherical mirror, the parallel
rays S, T, and Z, being reflected according to this law, will
be found, if the arc of the mirror
be small, all to pass through one

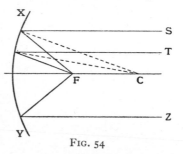

FIG. 54

point F. This point at which parallel rays are brought to
a focus is known as the principal focus of the mirror. Also
if C is the centre of curvature of the surface, any ray travelling
along a radius from C to the mirror will be reflected back along
the same path, since all radii are normal to the spherical surface
at their point of contact with it. By using these two types of
rays we may graphically determine the position and size of
the reflected image *ab* of an object AB, as shown in fig. 55. It
will be observed that in a concave mirror the image is an
inverted one. Also a little consideration will show that, for
constant distance between AB and mirror, the less curved the
surface XY, the larger the image will be.

Take now a convex mirror with its centre of curvature at

C and a virtual [1] focus at F (fig. 56).   Using the same method of construction, we find that the image of an object AB is a virtual one and upright.   Again, the less the curvature of the

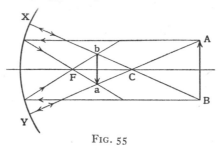

FIG. 55

surface XY, the larger the image.   The use of these relation-ships of size and orientation of image as indicators of the curva-ture of certain surfaces in the eye will be referred to shortly.

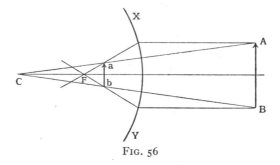

FIG. 56

Refraction – When an oblique ray of light passes from a rarer to a denser medium it is bent towards the normal. Passage from a denser to a rarer medium causes a bending away from the normal.   This phenomenon of refraction is due to the fact that the velocity of light is slower in a denser medium.   Why this change of velocity should result in a change of direction will be made clear from the following diagram (fig. 57).   Let AB be the front of a series of light-waves advancing through air to strike the surface of the denser

[1] A point to which light-rays actually converge or from which they actually diverge is called a real focus.   A point on which they *appear* to converge or from which they *appear* to diverge is called a virtual focus.

medium, XY, obliquely. The part of the wave-front at B
will meet the denser medium before that at A. This side of
the wave-front will therefore be slowed down while A is still
continuing at its original velocity, and the whole wave-front
will execute a wheeling motion until the A side of the wave-
front also meets the denser medium, when both sides will
again move at the same rate. The wave-front, which we may
represent by CD, is now, owing to what we have called the
wheeling motion, advancing at an angle to its previous direction.
If XY, in addition to being as a whole denser than air, is

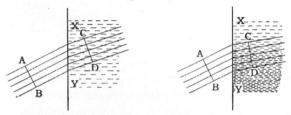

FIG. 57—Refraction by a uniformly dense medium (left) ; and by a
medium of which one part is denser than the other (right)
(After Hartridge, in Starling's *Principles of Human Physiology*)

especially dense in the Y region, the wave-front at the B side
will be even more slowed down and the amount of refraction
be even greater. This condition is found in the human eye,
where the central part of the lens is denser than the periphery.

When light undergoes refraction by passing from one
medium to another of different density, it is found that, no
matter at what angle the light strikes the boundary surface, the
sine of the angle (i, fig. 58) which the incident ray makes with
the normal bears a constant ratio to the sine of the angle (r)
between the normal and the refracted ray. This ratio, which
varies with different media and is used to measure their refractive power, is known as the refractive index.

The refractive index of a medium is not the same for all
visible wave-lengths; hence, if we take a glass prism and
allow a beam of white light to fall upon one of its faces, the
unequal refraction will cause the white light to be separated out
into its components and a spectrum will be produced (fig. 58).
The red rays are least refracted and the violet rays most
refracted. This separation of the colours is called dispersion,

and different media have different powers of dispersion. A
medium may have a high R.I. and a low dispersive power,
and *vice versa*. We may note in passing that disproportion
between R.I. and dispersive power in different glasses is utilised
for making compound prisms for deviating the direction of
light with minimal dispersion or, *vice versa*, for creating the

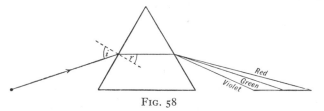

FIG. 58

maximum dispersion into a spectrum with no change in
direction. An example of the latter is a direct vision spectro-
scope, the use of which in examining the hæmoglobin deriva-
tives is familiar to the student. In this instrument the prism
is a combination of two crown-glass prisms and one of flint
glass. The mean deviation is nil, but the dispersion of the
combination is sufficient to produce a short spectrum.

Lenses – A lens is a portion of a refracting medium bounded
by spherical surfaces. The refracting media of the eye as a

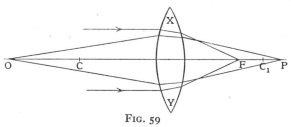

FIG. 59

whole may be regarded as a convex lens, so we may confine
ourselves to a discussion of that type of lens alone. Fig. 59
shows a simple biconvex lens. The centres of curvature of
its two spherical surfaces are C and C_1. The line joining
these centres of curvature is known as the principal axis. Rays
diverging from a source at O will be refracted by the lens
and brought to a focus at P. Similarly, rays originating at
P will be brought to a focus at O. Two such points are there-

fore known as 'conjugate foci.' Now, if the distance of O
from the lens is u and the distance from the lens to P is v, it
can be shown that

$$\frac{1}{u}+\frac{1}{v}=\text{a constant, denoted }\frac{1}{f}.$$

If u is infinity, in other words, if the rays from the source are
parallel, then $\frac{1}{u}=0$ and $\frac{1}{v}=\frac{1}{f}$, or $v=f$. f is known as the focal
length of the lens, and is therefore the distance from the lens
at which *parallel* rays are brought to a focus (F in diagram).
In clinical work the focal lengths of lenses are measured in
dioptres, the dioptre being the reciprocal of the focal length
measured in metres. For example, a 1-dioptre lens has a
focal length of 1 metre, a 5-dioptre lens has a focal length of
$\frac{1}{5}$ of a metre, and so on. A plus sign before the dioptre figure
indicates that a convex lens is meant, a minus sign a concave
lens.

In every lens there is a point on the principal axis called the
optical centre, through which rays pass without any deviation
in direction. All ray paths which pass through this point are
called secondary axes. In a thin lens, the centre of the lens
and the optical centre may usually be regarded as coincident.
By using the secondary axes, and the fact that parallel rays
after refraction pass through the principal focus, the position of
the image ab of an object AB may be found graphically as shown
in fig. 60. Note that the image is inverted and diminishes in
size the further the object is from the lens.

Now although, in the diagram (fig. 60), the ray Aa passing

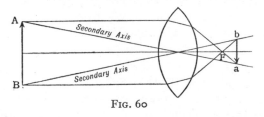

FIG. 60

through the optical centre has been depicted as one straight
line from A to a, this is only true for an infinitely thin lens.

In actual fact, when the lens has some thickness, although there is no change in direction of the ray, it always suffers more or less displacement, as shown exaggerated in fig. 61. If AA_1 is prolonged until it meets the principal axis at N, and aa_1 till it meets the axis in N_1, these two points N and N_1 are known as the nodal points of the lens. In any refracting

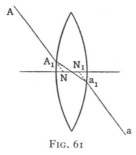

FIG. 61

system the nodal points have the property which we have just noted, namely, that if an incident ray has a direction such as to pass through the first nodal point, the corresponding emergent ray will appear to come from the second nodal point in a direction parallel to that of the incident ray. A biconvex lens, to which we have been restricting our discussion for the moment, has thus two nodal points. It will also have two principal foci, one on either side of the lens, the one formed by the refraction of parallel rays striking the lens from the left, and the other by parallel rays striking it from the right. These two principal foci, along with the two nodal points, form four of the six cardinal points which characterise not only single biconvex lenses, but any centred [1] system of spherical optical surfaces. The remaining two are the 'principal points' at which the 'principal planes' of the system intersect the principal axis. These principal planes have the property that an object in one principal plane forms an upright image of exactly the same size in the second principal plane.

A knowledge of the position of the cardinal points in any system enables one easily to define the path along which any incident ray will emerge, and hence to determine the positions of object and image and their relative sizes.

Now, if we consider refraction by a relatively dense medium with only a single convex surface, it is evident that such a surface will have only three cardinal points: (1) the principal focus F; (2) one nodal point N, which can be shown to be coincident with the centre of curvature C of the surface; and (3) one principal point P, which can be shown to lie in a plane

[1] With a common principal axis.

approximately in the position of the curved surface (fig. 62).
As we shall see presently, the refracting system of the eye

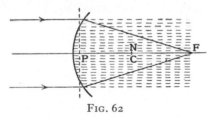

FIG. 62

can be reduced with only slight error to such a single convex
surface.

Depth of Field and Depth of Focus – Consider a point
source of light S being brought to a point focus F on a screen
AB (fig. 63). Now imagine the source moved to S_1, the
position of the screen remaining as before. The image of S_1
will be a small circle of light, and not a point. If, however,
the circle is a very small one, our eyes will not be able to

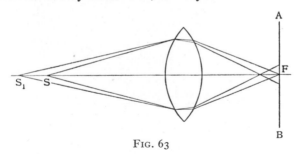

FIG. 63

appreciate it as other than a point. Hence objects at S_1 will
also be apparently sharply focussed on the screen AB. The
same is true of a point slightly nearer the lens than S. An
object which is theoretically only in perfect focus at S can
therefore be moved through a slight distance on either side
of S and still be *apparently* in perfect focus. The distance
between the extremes of this allowable movement is known as
the depth of field. Similarly, if the position of the object
remained fixed, the screen could be moved through a small
distance without apparently affecting the sharpness of the
image. The permissible movement of the screen is known as

the depth of focus. The latter term is also frequently used where actually the depth of field is meant.

Optical Defects – In all that has been hitherto said it has been implied that a simple convex lens can form a perfect inverted image of an object, provided that object is not brought too close to it. This is not so; the image is defective in several ways, some of which we must discuss, because the same defects are found to greater or less extent in the human eye. The defects of glass lenses may, however, be more interesting to the student if presented along with the parallel defects in the living lens. We will therefore first consider the optical system of the eye.

The Refracting System of the Eye – The refracting media of the eye are the cornea, the aqueous, the lens, and the vitreous. To determine what part each plays in the refraction of rays entering the eye, we must know the radii of curvature of each of the surfaces and their refractive indices. The radii of curvature may be obtained either by actual measurement in an excised eye, or, in the living eye, by using the

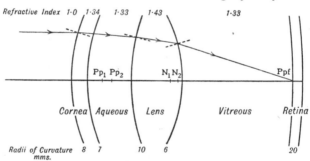

FIG. 64—Diagram of optical system of eye
(Modified from Hartridge, in Starling's *Principles of Human Physiology*)

surfaces as mirrors and measuring the apparent size of the images reflected from them. The refractive indices are determined on the excised eye by a refractometer. These data are incorporated in fig. 64. In this diagram it will be observed that the R.I.'s of cornea and aqueous are very similar—in fact so similar that refraction at their junction may be disregarded. Neglecting the refraction at this point, note that a ray parallel to the axis, though refracted *away from the normal* at the junction between lens and vitreous, is nevertheless progressively bent towards the optical axis by refraction at (1) the surface between air and cornea, (2) the surface between aqueous and lens, and (3) the surface between lens and vitreous. Of these three the greatest by far is at the corneal surface. This is brought out in another way by comparing the focal lengths of the cornea and lens, each acting separately.

		Dioptres.
Focal length of the cornea . . .		42
,, ,, ,, lens		23
,, ,, ,, whole eye . . .		65

In the disease called cataract the lens becomes so opaque that it has to be surgically removed; its absence has then to be compensated by the wearing of a convex spectacle lens, but the power of this lens does not need to be +23 dioptres. About +10 dioptres is sufficient for distant, and +14 dioptres for near vision, because the refracting power of the glass lens in air is so much greater than that of the natural lens in contact with the aqueous and vitreous, which have an R.I. one-third greater than that of air.

The refraction caused by the lens deserves special mention, because of its structural peculiarity. The lenticular fibres are so arranged as to be much denser at the centre than at the periphery. The R.I.'s of the two portions are therefore not the same, being 1·37 for the peripheral and 1·41 for the central zone. We have noticed that such a distribution of densities in a medium increases the refractive power of the medium, and a little consideration will show that it increases the refractive power of the lens beyond what it would be if it were entirely composed of material of the higher R.I. of 1·41. The equivalent R.I. of the lens as a whole is, in fact, 1·43, as indicated in the diagram. A further advantage of this form of construction in the lens is the diminution of spherical aberration (p. 291).

If in addition to the R.I.'s and the radii of curvature the distances between each of the refracting surfaces are known, then it is possible to find the positions of the six cardinal

points of the optical system of the eye. They are shown in
fig. 64, and their distances, referred to the anterior surface of
the cornea as zero position, are given in the following table :—

Anterior principal focus   .   . 13·6 mm. in front of cornea.
Posterior principal focus (Ppf) . 22·6 ,,   behind the cornea (on
                                            retina).
First principal point (Pp₁)   . 1·7 ,,   behind the cornea.
Second principal point (Pp₂) . 2·0 ,,   ,,   ,,   ,,   ,,
First nodal point (N₁)   .   . 7·0 ,,   ,,   ,,   ,,   ,,
Second nodal point (N₂) .   . 7·3 ,,   ,,   ,,   ,,   ,,

In this table notice that the two principal points lie very close
together, and so do the two nodal points.   If the reader will
now refer to p. 282 he will see that it would be possible, with
only slight error, to consider the refracting system of the eye
as one curved surface located at a position between the two
principal points, and with its centre of curvature between the

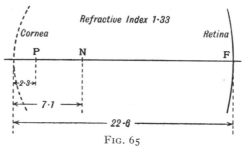

Fig. 65

two nodal points.   Such a system, which is known as the
'reduced' eye, is shown in diagrammatic form in fig. 65.   The
position of its three cardinal points in relation to the cornea,
the necessary radius of curvature of the refracting surface, and
R.I. are given in the following table :—

Principal point (P) .   .   .   .   . 2·3 mm. from cornea.
Nodal point (N)   .   .   .   .   . 7·1 ,,   ,,   ,,
Principal focus (F) .   .   .   .   . 22·6 ,,   ,,   ,,
Radius of curvature of imaginary refracting
    surface   .   .   .   .   .   . 5·0 ,,   ,,   ,,
Refractive index   .   .   .   .   . 1·33 ,,   ,,   ,,

Problems in ocular refraction are much simplified by the use
of this 'reduced' eye.   As a simple example we may take the

calculation of the size of the retinal image of some object, say a letter 1 mm. high printed on a sheet held 300 mm. from the eye. A little consideration will show that, by the proposition of similar triangles, the size of an object : size of its retinal image : : distance of the object from the nodal point : distance of image (retina) from the nodal point. Our object is 300 mm. from the cornea and therefore 300+7·1 mm. from the nodal point, and the nodal point is 15·5 mm. distant from the retina. Hence, if x be the size of the image,

$$\frac{1}{x} = \frac{300+7\cdot1}{15\cdot5} \quad \text{and} \quad x = 0\cdot05 \text{ mm.}$$

Accommodation – The refractive media of the eye are adjusted to bring parallel rays to a focus on the retina, *i.e.* the eye is focussed for objects at infinite distance. If the optical system remained as described and an object was brought from infinity towards the eye, the image would become blurred at a point a few metres distant, the blurring being due to the fact that the object is now so poorly focussed on the retina that the images of adjacent parts of it are overlapping and stimulating the same cones. The point at which this occurs is known as the 'far point,' and the distance from infinity to this point is obviously the depth of field (frequently called the depth of focus) for the eye as we have so far described it. Now just as the depth of field in a camera can be increased by 'stopping-down' with a diaphragm, thus shutting off the light-rays from the more peripheral parts of the lens, so is the depth of field for the eye dependent on the size of the pupil. This is shown in the following table :—

Pupil Diameter	Depth of Field
1 mm.	∞ to 8 metres.
2 ,,	∞ ,, 16 ,,
3 ,,	∞ ,, 24 ,,
4 ,,	∞ ,, 32 ,,

(Hartridge, in Starling's *Principles of Physiology*)

As we can see objects much closer than the nearest far point of 8 metres given in the above table, it is evident that the eye must have some means of focussing these nearer objects.   In the camera this is done, of course, by altering the distance between lens and focussing screen; in the eye it is done by altering the curvature of the lens, particularly its anterior surface, by the process known as accommodation. That it is mainly the anterior surface of the lens which alters may be proved by observing what are known as the Sanson-Purkinje images.   In the passage of light across the various refracting surfaces of the eye a certain part of the light is reflected.   The anterior surfaces of cornea and lens therefore act as convex mirrors, the cornea having the greater curvature, while the posterior surface of the lens acts as a concave mirror. If a candle is held close to the eye of a subject who is looking into distance three reflected images will be seen—two upright from the convex surfaces and one inverted from the concave surface.   Of the two upright ones, that from the cornea will be smaller than that from the anterior lens surface, as the cornea has the more curved surface (p. 278).   If the subject is then asked to fix his gaze on a near object, the larger of the two upright images will be observed to diminish in size, while the other two remain unaltered.   Accommodation consists, therefore, mainly in an increase in convexity of the anterior surface of the lens.   A very slight increase of curvature occurs also in the posterior surface.

The mechanism by which this alteration in shape of the lens is produced is as follows.   The lens is normally held in its capsule under tension, a tension produced by the intraocular pressure forcing the choroid and its ciliary processes outwards and backwards.   During accommodation the ciliary muscles contract, drawing each ciliary process forward and at the same time constricting them as a whole into a smaller ring.   The tension on the suspensory ligament is thereby relaxed, and the lens bulges forward into a more spherical shape.   The actual magnitude of these changes may be gathered from the following table (p. 289).

The figures, taken from a young adult, show an increase in the power of the lens of 10 dioptres during maximum

	Distant Vision	Accommodation for Near Vision
Radius of anterior surface .	10 mm.	6 mm.
Radius of posterior surface .	6 ,,	5·5 ,,
Focus of lens in dioptres .	23	33
Range of accommodation .	10	

(Hartridge, in Starling's *Principles of Physiology*)

accommodation. Such an increase is sufficient to enable objects
at a distance of about 10 cm. from the eye to be clearly
focussed. The eye is unable to form clear images of objects
nearer than this limit, which is known as the 'near point.'

As one grows older there is a loss of elasticity in the lens,
so that the capacity for accommodation diminishes and the
near point recedes farther and farther from the eye, as shown
in the following table :—

Age	Range of Accommodation in Dioptres	Distance of Near Point from Eye (Cm.)
10	13·8	7
20	11·5	10
30	8·9	14
40	5·8	22
50	2·0	40
60	1·1	100

(Hartridge, in Starling's *Principles of Physiology*)

This alteration in the range of accommodation is usually
unnoticed until about forty years of age, when the near point
has receded so far that one finds difficulty in reading unless the
book is held unnaturally far from the eyes. When this stage
is reached the condition is known clinically as presbyopia,
and is remedied by using, for close work, spectacle lenses of
the necessary degree of convexity to compensate for the loss
of accommodation.

The Iris acts as a diaphragm of variable aperture. The action of the sphincter and dilator pupillæ muscles can vary the diameter of the pupil from about 8 mm. to less than 1 mm. The functions of this variable diaphragm are three. First, it protects the retina against too intense illumination; a strong light causes its immediate constriction, and it partially dilates again when the retina has had time to adapt itself to the strong light. Secondly, it limits the bad effects of spherical aberration by cutting off the peripheral rays (p. 291) ; spherical aberration is most pronounced when the lens is accommodated for near vision, and to correct this as far as possible the accommodation reflex is accompanied by a simultaneous constriction of the pupil. Thirdly, its simultaneous action during accommodation increases very greatly the depth of field, as shown by the following figures:—

Eye Focussed for Objects at 25 cm. Distance	
Pupil Diameter	Depth of Field
4 mm.	0·8 cm.
3 ,,	1·1 ,,
2 ,,	1·6 ,,
1 ,,	3·2 ,,

(Hartridge, in Starling's *Principles of Physiology*)

Defects of the Eye as an Optical System – We have mentioned that the image given by a simple convex lens is subject to certain defects, and that the eye, like any other optical system, has similar imperfections. Now, when any part of the retina is stimulated by an image which excites the attention, automatic reflex movements of the six muscles of the eyeballs instantly bring the image on to the most sensitive part of the retina. We are therefore chiefly concerned with the influence of optical defects on the sharpness of the image at this point, the fovea centralis. It is interesting that though the fovea does not lie on the optic axis, but is displaced about half a millimetre to the temporal side, this displacement does not detract from the definition of the images projected on it, but actually improves it. The following are the more important optical defects.

Spherical Aberration – This defect is due to the fact that rays passing through the peripheral part of a lens are more refracted than those passing through the centre. They are therefore brought to a focus at a point F_2 nearer the lens than the focus F_1 of the more central rays (fig. 66). This defect may be corrected in glass lenses either by cutting off the peri-

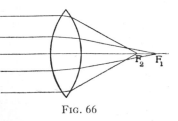

FIG. 66

pheral rays with a diaphragm, or by making the edges of the lens of lesser refractive power, through having its curvatures in these parts flatter. We may note that the same effect would be achieved if the R.I. of the material of the lens varied progressively from a high value at the centre to a low one at the periphery.

In the Eye – Not only for foveal vision, but for the whole retina, spherical aberration is almost completely corrected by all these methods: the 'stopping-down' by the iris, the fact that the curvature of the cornea is flatter at its periphery than in its centre, and the heterogeneous structure of the lens.

Chromatic Aberration – We have seen that refraction is accompanied by a dispersion, the red rays being refracted to

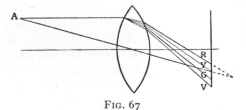

FIG. 67

a less extent than the violet. The focus for the red rays will therefore be at a greater distance from the lens than that for the violet, the foci for the other wave-lengths lying at intermediate points. If a screen is placed at Y (fig. 67), the yellow rays from point A will be sharply focussed to a point, but this image will be surrounded by a ring of superimposed red and green, and outside that again a ring of violet, and the image as a whole will be blurred. Chromatic aberration in glass lenses (*e.g.* camera lenses) can be partially corrected by combining convex and concave lenses of different dispersive power in such a way that the final composite lens produces convergence of the rays with very little dispersion.

In the Eye – Chromatic aberration is reduced by the cutting off of peripheral rays by the pupil, and the more contracted the pupil the less will be the chromatic aberration (*cf.* Diffraction).

Chromatic Difference of Magnification – The different wavelengths of light are not only brought to a different focus, but consideration of fig. 67 will show that the images formed by each of them separately are of different sizes. This defect is known as chromatic difference of magnification.

In the Eye – At the slightly eccentric position occupied by the fovea, the effects of chromatic difference of magnification and chromatic aberration largely neutralise one another.

Diffraction – This is a property of light itself which limits the perfection of image obtainable with any optical system. The nature of diffraction may be sufficiently gathered from the following illustration. Imagine light from a distant source impinging on an opaque screen with a small hole in it. The light transmitted through the hole does not proceed as an advancing wave-front of the same width as the diameter of the hole, but spreads out on either side of the original wave-front, so that, when projected on a screen, the illuminated patch directly opposite the hole merges gradually and not abruptly into the shadow of the margins of the aperture. In this area of spread, interference effects occur which give rise to the formation of diffraction patterns. Moreover, the spreading affects the different wave-lengths of light to a varying extent, so that in the area surrounding the bright patch narrow spectra are formed. It is evident, therefore, that in any optical instrument where we have to deal with narrow beams of light the sharpness of the image will be interfered with, both by diffraction of the light as a whole, and also by the differential diffraction of the component colours of white light.

In the Eye – Diffraction must interfere to some extent with
the perfection of the retinal images formed in the eye, and the
narrower the pupil the more marked it will be.   Diffraction
effects are therefore worst when chromatic aberration is least,
and *vice versa*.   In the normal eye, the most accurately focussed
images on the fovea are those produced by the yellow rays, and
it can be shown that, by the combined effect of chromatic
aberration, chromatic difference of magnification, and diffraction, this yellow image is overlapped by ill-defined images of
the red and green rays, and further outside, by a still more
ill-defined blue image.   Since, under ordinary conditions of
illumination, the retina is most strongly stimulated by the
yellow rays and only slightly sensitive to blue, the confusion
effect of the red, green, and blue images is almost negligible.

Curvature of Field and Distortion – The usual optical diagrams suggest that a plane object gives a plane image.   In
actual fact, with a simple lens the image is not plane.   The
focal length of a lens for rays striking it with varying degrees
of obliquity is not the same; as the obliquity increases the

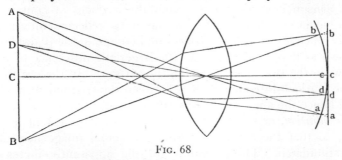

FIG. 68

focal length decreases.   If we consider a plane object AB
(fig. 68) at right angles to the principal axis, the rays from the
point C will be focussed at *c*, and the rays from A and B at
points *a* and *b*, which are nearer the lens.   The focal points,
therefore, lie on a curved surface.   Further, if this image is
projected on a flat surface, not only will portions of it be out
of perfect focus, but the relative sizes of parts of the image will
not be the same as the relative sizes of the corresponding parts
of the object.   The distances *cd* and *ca* of the plane surface
image will not bear the same relation to one another as the

corresponding distances CD and CA of the object. The image will therefore be a distorted representation of the object. Both of these defects can be avoided by giving the projection screen a suitable curvature.

In the Eye – The relatively unimportant peripheral images are alone affected, and in any case, this defect is practically non-existent because of the curvature of the retinal surface which corresponds almost exactly with the curvature of the focal surface.

As well as these adaptations, the eyeball shows a number of others which assist in the formation of sharp images.

Halation, which is troublesome in photographic plates, is due to light which has once traversed the sensitive emulsion being reflected back on to different parts of the emulsion by the glass support. In the retina, any reflection there may be takes place so close to the sensitive layer that the reflected light falls on the same cones and rods as were stimulated by it before reflection. Halation is therefore absent.

Flare – Just as light may be reflected externally to form the Sanson-Purkinje images from the surfaces of contact of two media of different R.I., so may it be reflected internally. This reflection from the surfaces of a compound lens system is known as flare, and is greater the larger the difference of R.I. between the two media forming the surface. In the eye there is no marked difference in R.I. between the component media, and hence the amount of flare will be small.

Irradiation, or spread of light, occurs to some extent in the eye, so that the cones bordering the actual image may also be stimulated. This accounts for the apparently increased size of an object brightly illuminated; a familiar example is the destination screen of a tramcar illuminated by a single central bulb. It appears as ⌐UNIVERSITY¬ by day, and by night ⌐UNIVERSITY¬.

Internal Reflection – The pigmented layer of the retina prevents to a large extent the reflection of light from one part of the eyeball to another. Moreover, light passing into the back of the eye from a source directly in front of it would, owing to the shape of the eyeball, be reflected mostly on to the insensitive portions in front of the ora serrata. Conversely, of course, light entering the eye obliquely and striking these anterior portions would be reflected posteriorly towards the sensitive retina; but little of such oblique light ever enters the eye, mainly owing to the shielding effect of eyebrows, cheeks, nose, and eyelids.

Errors of Refraction – The eye that we have so far described, perfectly normal in its optical system, is called emmetropic. Abnormalities of refraction (ametropia) are frequent. As these are described in some detail in every textbook, they will only be very briefly outlined and summarised in diagrammatic form (fig. 69).

Hypermetropia – In this condition of long sight the eyeball is too short, and in the unaccommodated eye parallel rays come to a focus behind the retina. By using some accommodation the subject may be able to focus distant objects, but the remaining range of accommodation is then smaller, and the near point is therefore farther away from the eye than normally. The remedy is to use a convex spectacle lens of such power as to converge the parallel rays so that the unaccommodated eye focusses them on the retina, and has still the normal range of accommodation for nearer objects.

Myopia – This is the opposite condition (short sight); the eyeball is too long, and parallel rays are focussed in front of the retina. Images of distant objects are therefore blurred, and the object has to be brought near the eye before a defined image is obtained. Accommodation is not used at all until this point is reached, and by full accommodation, therefore, objects much closer than the normal near point may be focussed. The remedy is to use a concave lens of sufficient diverging power to cause parallel rays to focus on the retina.

Presbyopia – This condition has been already dealt with on p. 289.

Astigmatism – There are two varieties of this condition, the regular and the irregular. In regular astigmatism the curvatures of the refracting surfaces (usually the cornea) are not the same in all meridians, the meridians of greatest and least curvature being at right angles to one another, with a

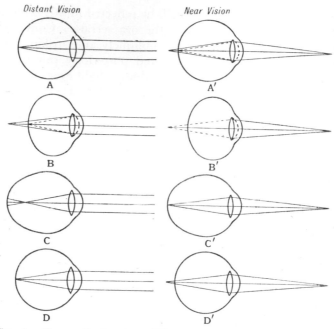

FIG. 69—Errors of refraction.   The dotted lines represent the change
in the lens and the paths of the rays during accommodation

A, emmetropic eye focusses distant objects without, and A', near objects with, accommodation.
B, hypermetropic eye cannot focus distant objects without, but may be able to do so with, some
    accommodation.   B', remaining extent of accommodation insufficient to focus near objects.
C, myopic eye cannot focus distant objects at all.   C', can focus near objects without
    accommodation, and, by full accommodation, could focus objects closer than the normal
    near-point.
D, presbyopic eye can focus distant objects normally, but D', owing to lack of power of
    accommodation, cannot focus near objects.

continuous gradation between them.   Rays transmitted through
the meridian of greater curvature are thus brought to a focus
in front of those from the same source passing through the
meridians of lesser curvature.   If a subject suffering from
astigmatism looks at a spoked wheel and sees certain spokes
in sharp focus, those at right angles will be out of focus.   The
defect is corrected by a cylindrical lens of such power, and so
set in relation to the eye, that the curvature of the glass lens
compensates for the deficiency in the meridian of least curvature in the eye's refracting system.   If this makes the eye
ametropic, the other side of the lens is spherically ground to
provide the necessary correction.

In irregular astigmatism due to lesions, *e.g.* a healed ulcer, in the cornea or the lens, the focal length of the optical system differs quite irregularly in the different meridians.   No correction is possible, but the retinal image may often be sharpened by wearing a pin-hole diaphragm in front of the eye.

Physical Basis of Colour Sensation – We have seen how white light can be resolved into its component wave-lengths by dispersion, so forming a continuous band of varying colour. In fig. 70 is given a diagram showing roughly the relation of the spectral colours to wave-length.   If all the wave-lengths of the spectrum be recombined by allowing the spectrum to fall on

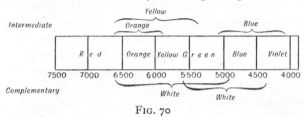

FIG. 70

a second prism set oppositely to the first, white light is again produced.   A sensation of white light may also be produced by mixing certain pairs of wave-length groups.   For instance, a certain band of wave-lengths in the red region superimposed on a certain band from the blue-green region gives a sensation of white.   This is indicated diagrammatically in the lower portion of the figure.   On the other hand, if we take the same red portion of the spectrum and combine it with yellow, the intermediate colour, orange, results (upper portion of diagram). Similarly, combination of red light with pure green light produces the intermediate yellow.   What then happens when the combination is between red and some zone intermediate between the green that gives yellow and the blue-green that gives white?   A combined effect is obtained, *i.e.* a yellow diluted with more or less white.

Similar results are obtained at the opposite end of the spectrum. Violet and yellow give white, but violet and green give blue, and violet and greenish yellow produce various diluted shades of blue.   Such diluted colours are said to be unsaturated, *e.g.* pink is unsaturated red, cream is unsaturated yellow, etc.

Colours such as red and blue-green, or yellow and violet, which combined together give white, are called complementary colours, and when one of a pair of complementary colours is removed from white light, the other member of that pair is the predominant colour of the remaining light. While various red wave-lengths are complementary to their appropriate blue-green wave-lengths, and various zones of the yellow are complementary to their appropriate violet zones, it will be seen on reference to the diagram that this leaves a portion of the spectrum in the green region for which there is no complementary colour. A complementary colour for green is found, however, in purple, which is not a spectral colour, but can be formed by mixing red and violet. With the three primary colours of red, green, and violet it is thus possible to produce not only every colour of the spectrum, but by using in addition the capacity of complementary colours to produce white, to match every shade of unsaturated colour.

Apart from differences in hue and in saturation, colours differ in intensity, which is a matter of the amplitude of the light-wave, and in luminosity or brightness, the most luminous part of the spectrum to the eye being yellow. The latter quality is physiological or, perhaps, psychological, and has no physical counterpart.

The natural colour of opaque objects is due in general to absorption of certain wave-lengths and scattering of others. Thus a blue object appears blue because it absorbs from the white light which falls on it the red, orange, and yellow wave-lengths, and scatters only the blue and, perhaps, some of the green. A red object absorbs all but the red and part of the yellow. The narrower the band of wave-lengths scattered, the purer the colour. Similarly with transparent materials: a blue glass, when white light passes through it, appears blue, because all but the blue wave-lengths are absorbed by the glass.

Now it was said above that certain pairs of colours are complementary, and when mixed give white. It must be remembered that this applies to the superimposing of spectral colours only and not to the mixing of pigments. The colour of pigments is, as we have seen, due to absorption, and the mixing of two pigments increases this absorption. A mixture of yellow and blue pigments would give green, since the yellow absorbs all the blue end of the spectrum and the blue all the red end, leaving only the intermediate green to be scattered.

Natural colours being in general due to absorption, it follows that the colour of an object will vary with the colour of the light illuminating it. Thus a blue object will appear black if illuminated by red, orange, or yellow light, since all these are completely absorbed. In green light it would look greenish, as most blues absorb green incompletely. In blue light, of course, it appears blue. For the same reason colours often appear different in sunlight and artificial light. This is particularly noticeable with blues. Most artificial lights are very deficient in wave-lengths of the blue region, and consequently blue objects viewed in artificial light appear much darker than in daylight.

Retinal Changes and the Production of Visual Sensations – Proof that it is the layer of rods and cones, and no other layer of the complicated retinal structure, which is sensitive to light is easily obtained as follows. A beam of strong light (a, fig. 71) is thrown through the sclerotic, causing shadows of the retinal vessels (b) to be projected on to a portion of the retina (c) not normally shadowed by them. The subject perceives these shadows as a series of branching figures (Purkinje figures) projected on his visual field (d). If the light is moved laterally to a_1, the projected figures will appear to move in the same direction. From a knowledge of the dimensions of the eyeball, and the relation between movement

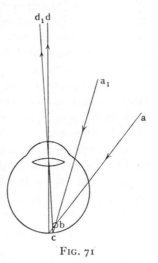

FIG. 71

of source and displacement of projected image, it is possible to calculate the position of the sensitive area, and by these calculations the sensitive area is located in the layer of rods and cones.

When light falls on the eye, the following are the more important changes which occur in the retina and its connections:—

(1) The rhodopsin or visual purple is bleached.

(2) The retina as a whole becomes more acid in reaction.

(3) Electrical changes are produced somewhat similar to those occurring when a muscle or nerve is stimulated. The maximum of this electric response occurs coincidently with the maximum sensation. Moreover, with constant intensity the maximum response is obtained with yellow light in an eye which has become accustomed to bright illumination, and with green rays on the dark-adapted eye.

(4) A series of rhythmic electrical changes occur in the optic nerve, as in other sensory nerves, the frequency of these impulses depending on the intensity of the light stimulus, and the area of retina stimulated.

It will be recalled that the visual purple is associated with the rods, and that the distribution of the rods and cones in the retina is such that there are only cones at the fovea, about equal numbers of rods and cones in the area immediately surrounding this, and a gradually diminishing ratio of cones to rods as we proceed towards the periphery. Histological examination shows also that while each cone has a separate neural connection in the optic nerve, at the periphery one optic nerve fibre may serve many rods.

The difference in function suggested by this histological arrangement is confirmed by the findings that (1) the peripheral part of the retina is colour blind; (2) visual acuity is greatest in the foveal region in a good light, though (3) in a poor light the fovea is blind, and the part of the retina most easily stimulated is the peripheral part; e.g. a faint star is most readily perceived when it occupies a peripheral position in the field of vision.

These facts lead to the conclusion that the central part of the retina, and therefore presumably the cones, are responsible for colour sensations and for the perception of minute detail, while the rods are insensitive to colour, and are specially adapted for stimulation by light of feeble intensity.

Now, since the visual purple is associated only with the rods and becomes bleached by light, it seems justifiable to conclude that it is the photochemical change in the visual purple that excites the rods. Confirmation both of this and of the division of function between rods and cones is afforded by the study of the sensations produced by a spectrum under different conditions of illumination.

On looking at a spectrum produced by dispersion of an intense light, one appreciates all the component hues and finds maximum brightness in the yellow. If the intensity of the light is progressively lessened, the colours gradually fade until one no longer perceives the spectrum as a band of varying colour, but as a band of varying shades of grey. Along with this loss of colour sensation there is a shifting of the zone of maximum brightness from the yellow to the green, the red end becoming relatively much darker and the blue end relatively lighter (Purkinje's phenomenon). If the intensity is further lessened, the spectrum disappears altogether. A gradual increase in intensity produces exactly the reverse series of changes.

Owing to this shift in the most luminous part of the spectrum with varying intensity of illumination, what is called the 'photochromatic interval' is not the same for all colours. By photochromatic interval we mean the interval between the appearance of a zone of the spectrum as a light sensation and its perception as a definite colour. Thus, on gradual increase of intensity, the relative brightness of the green and blue makes them early visible as shades of grey, but a long interval elapses before they become definitely coloured. The red zone, on the contrary, remains quite dark until the intensity approaches close to that necessary for colour appreciation, and hence its photochromatic interval is short. Red is either red or nothing at all.

Now, if the bleaching of the visual purple is the essential change in what has been aptly called 'twilight vision,' we should expect its reaction to be adapted to the non-coloured twilight spectrum just described, and to be maximal, therefore, towards its brightest, i.e. its blue end. This has been experimentally proved; the maximum bleaching of visual purple is obtained by green light. Moreover, it is the green light which is maximally absorbed by the visual purple, so that the pigment conforms to Draper's Law, that photochemical change is produced in a substance only by light which it absorbs. It has further been shown that the time-course of the bleaching of the visual purple indicates a monomolecular reaction (p. 69), while the rate of recovery of the eye from light stimulation (during which period the visual purple is being re-formed) indicates a bimolecular reaction. It would appear, therefore, that the bleaching consists in a breakdown of the visual purple molecule into two components, which recombine during the recovery phase.

A complete explanation of twilight vision thus seems to be available in the stimulation of the rods by the photochemical action of light on the visual purple. Nevertheless, Edridge-Green holds that the rods are not sensory end-organs at all. He considers that they are purely for the purpose of secreting the visual purple, which spreads to the cones, and that the photochemical changes in the pigment affect the cones and not the rods. Except for this hypothesis, which has not received any general acceptance, we have no explanation at all of the functioning of the cones, though they, as the sole occupants of the foveal area and as the colour receptors, are of far more importance in ordinary vision than the rods. While it is true that certain pigments exist in the cones of some animals, there is no evidence that these pigments are light-sensitive, and their distribution among different animals is too irregular for much functional importance to be attached to their presence. The fucsin of the pigmented layer, while it may play some part in the regeneration of the visual purple, has apparently no direct visual function.

It is usually assumed, however, that the cones also function by photochemical action, and various theories have been advanced to explain their ability to differentiate colours and their visual function generally. None of these theories is really satisfactory, for none has any experimental backing, and only a brief mention will be made of two of them.

According to the Young-Helmholtz theory there are in the retina, presumably in the cones, three different light-sensitive substances, each of which responds to one of the three primary colour sensations of red, green, and violet. The sensation of white is aroused by simultaneous stimulation of all three. The intermediate colours, and all their various unsaturated tints, are perceived by stimulation of the three primary substances in different degree. Thus the sensation of orange would be aroused by a stimulation of the red and, to a lesser extent, of the green substance. A slight stimulation of the red substance combined with marked stimulation of the green substance would produce a sensation of yellow, and so on.

Another theory, that of Hering, also supposes the existence of three substances, each one of which produces a different colour sensation according to whether it is undergoing anabolic or catabolic change. There is a red-green substance which, when catabolism is predominant, gives a red sensation, and when undergoing anabolism a green sensation. Similarly, there is a yellow-blue and a white-black substance. Red light falling on the eye produces catabolic change in the red-green material, green rays anabolic change in the same substance. A sensation of orange would arise when catabolic changes occurred simultaneously in both red-green and yellow-blue substances, and so on. Both these theories, like the resonance theory of hearing, attribute a considerable amount of analysis to the receptor organ. Other theories, such as that of Edridge-Green, lay all the burden of colour analysis on the cortical centre.

After-Images – The sensations produced by light stimuli have the peculiar property of recurring in a diminished degree a short time after the cessation of the stimulus. This is the cause of after-images, and indirectly the cause of the phenomena of contrast. During a short period after a light stimulus has ceased to fall on the retina, the part affected transmits a very much fainter secondary image similar to the primary image transmitted during the stimulation period. For example, if the eyes are closed after looking at a bright white light, a secondary image of the light will be seen for a short time. This is the positive after-image.

Further, the part of the retina transmitting the positive

after-image appears temporarily to lose its sensitivity to a second stimulus of the same type as the original one, so that if the source is looked at a second time the sensation is much less intense.   Now, if during the reception of a positive after-image of a patch of white light, a larger white patch is so looked at that its image overlies the same zone of the retina, the resulting sensation is of a dark patch corresponding in area to the first stimulus, on a surrounding white ground.   This of course is because the retinal area first stimulated is in a less sensitive condition than the area surrounding it.   Such pheno-mena are known as negative after-images.   Similarly, a coloured stimulus acting alone will produce a positive after-image of the same colour; e.g. the after-image of a red stimulus is red.   If there is a second red stimulus affecting a wider area during the period of this red after-image, the sensation will be a negative after-image of a dark patch on a red ground. If, now, the second stimulus, in place of red, is one of white light, the after-image area being refractory to red will only feebly react to the red component of white light, but its reaction to the other components will produce the sensation of the complementary colour.   The negative after-image in this case will be one of a bluish-green tint on a red ground.

During the after-image period, not only does the retina show a diminished sensitivity to stimuli of the same colour (including for the present black, white, and grey) as produced the after-image, but it seems to respond with hypernormal intensity to a stimulus of an opposite colour.   In this lies the explanation of contrast.   A red object looked at twice within a short interval looks comparatively dull the second time.   If a green (complementary) surface is looked at shortly after looking at a red surface, the green appears more intense. These are examples of successive contrast.   Moreover, this hypernormal sensitivity to opposite stimuli extends to an area of the retina somewhat beyond the boundaries of the area initially stimulated.   A grey patch on a white ground looks darker than the same grey patch on a black ground.   In the first case the refractory condition of the retina under the white stimulus extends into the grey area and diminishes the sensi-tivity of that area to white light; so the grey looks darker.

Similarly, a grey patch on blue appears to be tinted with the complementary yellow, a grey patch on green to be tinted with red. Such are examples of simultaneous contrast.

If after-images are so frequent a product of retinal action, the question arises why they do not interfere more with ordinary vision, and why, during a continued stimulation of the same part of the retina, the image obtained does not fade. No definite explanation of the first can be given; it can only be stated that the reception of a different stimulus on the retina appears to banish the after-image of a previous one. As for the second question, the absence of fading may be more apparent than real, as it is in practice very difficult to maintain constant fixation of the eyes on one point, and any movement of the eyes or body will alter the position of the retinal image, and so remove the after-images. Apart from this, however, there is perhaps a suppression of the after-images formed during a long stimulus, these suppressed after-images being accumulated until the cessation of the stimulus, when they are perceived with unusual intensity.

The Ophthalmoscope – The ophthalmoscope is an instrument for examining the condition of the retina in the living subject. We have seen that the eyeball is well protected against internal reflections, but nevertheless it is possible, by projecting a beam into it, to get sufficient light reflected from the retina to produce an image in an observer's eye. To receive this image the observer's eye must be in line with the illuminating beam, as the latter is reflected along the path by which it entered the eye. This was achieved in the original form of the instrument, invented by Helmholtz in 1856, by using a bundle of glass plates set at an angle to the visual axis, as in fig. 72, A, light from the illuminating source being partially transmitted through the plates and partially reflected into the observed eye. The reflected beam from the retina was then again partially reflected from the plates, but was also in part transmitted through the plates to enter the observer's eye.

In the modern form of the instrument, a mirror with a hole in its centre through which the observer can view the reflected beam is used in place of the glass plates of Helmholtz. The instrument may be used in either of two ways, the 'direct'

20

or 'indirect' method. In both cases a bright source of light is placed behind and slightly to the side of the subject's head. In the direct method the mirror, with the observer's eye immediately behind its aperture, is held close to the subject's eye. The path of the rays is shown in fig. 72, B. (To avoid

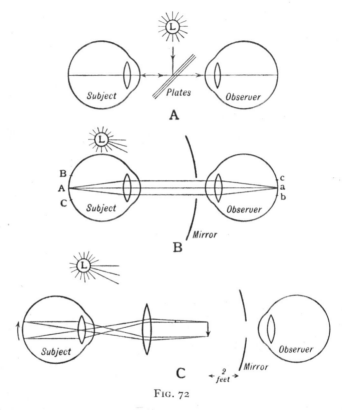

Fig. 72

confusion in this and the subsequent diagram, the illuminating rays from the source to mirror and mirror to retina are omitted.) Both subject's and observer's eyes are unaccommodated; *i.e.* they are in the condition in which parallel rays are focussed on the retina. Rays from any point A on the subject's retina will therefore emerge from his eye parallel, and again converge to a focus at *a* on the observer's retina. Similarly, rays from B and C will be focussed at *b* and *c*. The observer thus has, on his retina, an inverted image *cab* of the subject's retina, and he interprets this as being the image of an erect object placed at infinite distance. Now, if the subject's eye is not emmetropic, the rays will not emerge from it parallel as described above. They may be made so, however, and at the same time his type and degree of ametropia estimated, by placing a lens of appropriate corrective power in front of his eye. Ophthalmoscopes are therefore provided with a series of convex and concave lenses mounted on a disc on the observer's side of the mirror, and by rotating the disc any one of these lenses can be interposed in the path of the reflected beam.

The indirect method is diagrammatically illustrated in fig. 72, C. In this method a biconvex lens is placed two or three inches in front of the subject's eye, and the observer with his reflecting mirror stands about two feet away. As the diagram shows, in this case an inverted image of the subject's retina is focussed by the lens, and it is this image which is viewed by the observer. The retina is therefore seen inverted.

The direct method gives an erect image magnified about twelve times, but a small field of view; the indirect an inverted image of smaller magnification (about three), but a larger field. This instrument has proved invaluable to clinicians not only for estimating errors of refraction and detecting lesions in the retina and optic nerve, but also for judging the state of the vascular system generally from the appearance of the readily visible retinal vessels.

Monocular and Binocular Vision – So far we have been concerned with the reception of images and their interpretation in a single eye, but ordinarily our visual sensations arise from both eyes simultaneously. Binocular vision has many advantages apart from the obvious one, that the duplication of so essential an organ renders injury to one less disastrous. In the first place, the combined visual field of the two eyes is much larger than that of one eye. In the second, binocular vision adds considerably to the precision with which we can estimate distance, and hence also size, for these two are intimately related. The visual judgment of size is based primarily on the size of the retinal image, but since a line 4 in. long at 10 ft.

from the eye produces the same size of retinal image as a 2-inch line at 5 ft. distance, it is evident that visual perceptions gathered from the size of the image must be correlated with some estimate of the object's distance, before any judgment of the true size of the object can be formed. The following are the most important factors influencing our judgments of distance when only one eye is used.

When objects are near enough to require accommodation, the impressions derived through our muscle-sense of the degree to which the ciliary muscles are contracted, tell us the amount of accommodation necessary to focus the object on the retina, and, by experience, we learn to associate certain degrees of accommodation with certain distances. With more distant objects we have to depend, in monocular vision, on aerial and mathematical perspective, parallax, and the apparent size of familiar objects whose actual size is known.

(a) *Aerial Perspective* – The air contains minute particles in suspension, and is not entirely transparent. The smaller details of a distant scene are therefore obscured, the contrast between lights and shades is diminished, and the variety of colour is lost in a bluish haze. Because this is our general experience, we judge objects seen through a fog to be at greater distance than they really are, and they often look excessively large simply because our retinal images of them are mentally projected to a distance much greater than their actual distance. On the other hand, when the air is particularly clear, as after a shower of rain, distant objects appear to us unnaturally close.

(b) *Mathematical Perspective* – Lines which are actually parallel (*e.g.* railway lines) seem to converge as they recede from us, because the angle subtended by them at the eye diminishes with distance. Lines above the eye-level appear to slope down in the distance, lines below the eye-level to slope up, and all parallel lines appear to meet (or, if extended, would appear to meet) in a point on the eye-level. These appearances also help us in our judgments of distances. In fact, we are so accustomed to associate them with distance, that a drawing in correct perspective suggests solidity and depth, while a drawing with imperfect perspective, or none, looks flat.

(c) *Parallax* – When we change our position, the apparent movement of one object behind another often helps us in our judgment of the distance between them. For example, we look at a flagpole with a background of buildings, and note the particular part of the building obscured by the pole. If we move sideways, the pole appears to move across the building behind it. The amount of this apparent movement will be small if the pole is close in front of the building, and larger in proportion to its distance from the building.

(d) When we look at a scene which contains objects whose actual size is known to us, we can estimate by comparison the size of other less familiar objects in close proximity to them.

(e) We are aware, generally without explicitly recognising it, of the direction of the light; and the lights and shades upon objects, and the shadows they cast, help us to judge their relative positions and distances.

When we use both eyes, we add to all these methods one which is more precise than any of them, namely, the degree of convergence of the eyes. In order that the right and left retinal images may fall on corresponding points of the two retinæ, it is necessary to converge the eyes to a greater extent for a near than for a distant object. As with the ciliary muscles in accommodation, sensations from the muscles which move the eyeball give information as to the degree of convergence, and these degrees we associate with various distances of object. An attempt to perform some movement requiring accurate estimate of distance, *e.g.* threading a needle, first with both eyes open and then with one eye shut, will prove how much sense of convergence adds to our accuracy of judgment.

Above all, binocular vision gives us impressions of depth and solidity. The pictures of external objects on the two retinæ are not identical, because the right and left eyes see the object from slightly different points of view. Thus, on looking at a truncated cone with both eyes open, we see it as in fig. 73, B; with the left eye alone we see more of its left side, as in fig. 73, L; with the right eye alone more of its right side, as in fig. 73, R. The simultaneous occurrence of two such pictures on the retinæ we associate with solidity.

Stereoscopic pictures demonstrate very clearly that our appreciation of solidity arises in this way. They are obtained by photographing the same scene from two points slightly apart (by the width between the human eyes or sometimes more), so

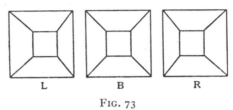

L   B   R

FIG. 73

as to get a right-eyed and a left-eyed picture. The pictures are viewed through a stereoscope, a device in which the right-eyed and left-eyed pictures can be seen only by the corresponding eyes. In one of the commonest types, the

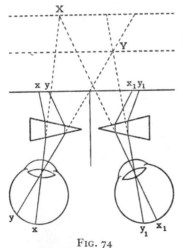

FIG. 74

Brewster stereoscope, this is achieved by looking at the pictures through prisms separated by an opaque partition (fig. 74). The prisms produce a convergence of the eyes, and the partition prevents each eye from seeing the other's picture. The rays of light from each picture, refracted by the prism, produce an image on the retina of the corresponding eye, and the images of corresponding points in the two pictures are mentally projected to a plane behind the pictures. The particular plane that they appear to occupy depends on the relative differences in separation between the pairs of corresponding points in the two pictures. Thus, in the diagram, if x and x_1 and y and y_1 are corresponding points, and the distance xx_1 is greater than yy_1, the combined image (X) of x and x_1 would appear to occupy a plane behind that of the combined image (Y) of y and y_1. If we reversed the picture so that the left eye viewed the right eye's picture (x_1y_1), and *vice versa*, then the distance xx_1 would be less than yy_1, and the combined image X would appear to be in front of Y. If such a reversal is carried out with ordinary stereoscopic pictures, the parts of the picture that normally stand out in relief now appear hollow, and *vice versa*.

Stereoscopic vision is also intimately connected with our estimates of distance of objects within the convergence range, because the nearer an object is to the eye, the more do we see of its right- and left-hand sides. An interesting demonstration of this is given by Helmholtz's telestereoscope. In this instrument the line of vision of each of the converged eyes is displaced, by means of mirrors, farther from the median line of the body. By this device our eyes are virtually farther separated from one another, and we see more of the sides of objects than we usually do. Everything consequently appears correspondingly nearer and in greater relief.

CHAPTER XIX

SOUND AND HEARING

SOUND-WAVES in air consist of longitudinal vibrations of the gaseous molecules, by which alternate phases of condensation and rarefaction are produced. They may be graphically represented as A (fig. 75), where the relative proximity of the air particles to one another, and therefore the air-pressures, are represented by the closeness of the vertical lines. The

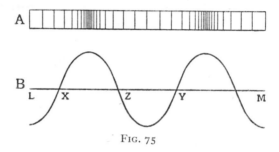

FIG. 75

waves are more usually represented as an air-pressure curve, B (fig. 75), rising above and falling below a median straight line, LM, which represents the average air-pressure. Ordinates above this line represent increases of pressure, and those below diminution of pressure. This wave-like motion is propagated through the atmosphere at a velocity of approximately 340 metres per second at ordinary air temperatures.

If the recurrence of these phases of condensation and rarefaction takes place with a regular periodicity, a musical sound is produced, and if the regularity is such that the wave-form is 'simple harmonic,' that is, if the cycle XY in the diagram is repeated over and over again, the sound is a pure tone. If the recurrence of the phases is quite irregular, we experience the sensation we call noise.

Musical sounds differ from one another in three essential factors—pitch, loudness, and quality. The pitch of a sound, *i.e.* whether it is high or low, is a matter of the frequency with which the alternations of condensation and rarefaction recur—the more rapid the alternations the higher the note. Loudness depends on the amplitude of the wave, *i.e.* on the extent to which the air is compressed and rarefied in each cycle. The quality of a musical sound depends on the number and relative intensity of the overtones which accompany the fundamental note of any sound-producing instrument. When the overtones are of frequencies 2, 3, etc. times the frequency of the fundamental, they are called harmonics. Take, for example, a stretched wire (fig. 76). This wire when set into vibration will produce a note of frequency *n* when vibrating as a whole (1), at the same time it vibrates to a lesser extent

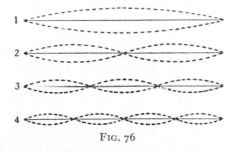

FIG. 76

in two halves (2), three thirds (3), and four quarters (4), and so on. In addition to producing its fundamental note of frequency *n* vibrations per second, the string will therefore be sounding, with much feebler intensity, the following harmonics: a note an octave higher (frequency 2*n*), one an octave and a fifth above the fundamental (3*n*), and one two octaves higher than the fundamental (4*n*), and so on. The same is true of all musical instruments whether the air is set into vibration by bowing a string, or by vibrating a reed, or by any other method. The differences of quality or timbre between one instrument and another are due to the number and relative emphasis of the overtones produced. The horn, especially when sounding a low fundamental, produces a large variety of overtones. The flute is very poor in overtones, and for this reason is good for accompanying other instruments, including the human voice; its relative freedom from overtones prevents the formation of dissonant intervals with the overtones of the other instrument.

Interval, Consonance, and Dissonance – Two musical sounds differing in pitch are said to be separated by a certain interval. When two tones are simultaneously sounded, those

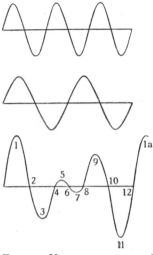

differing by certain intervals are consonant, *i.e.* are pleasing to the ear, others are dissonant. It is a matter of experience that the most consonant intervals are those in which the frequencies of the two notes bear the simplest numerical relationship to one another. The order of consonance of two tones is therefore (1) unison, where the frequency ratio is $1:1$; (2) the octave, where the ratio is $1:2$; (3) the perfect fifth, ratio $2:3$; (4) the perfect fourth, ratio $3:4$; and so on. When two such tones are sounding together, the condensation and rarefaction phases of each will not always correspond, and the wave-form of the resulting disturbance will be a composite one. The diagram (fig. 77) gives

Fig. 77—Upper curve, wave of frequency $3n$; middle curve, wave of frequency $2n$; lower curve, compound wave of both (for phase relation depicted)

the form of the compound wave for an interval of a perfect fifth.

Difference Tones and Beats – It may be observed in the diagram that once during the cycle of the compound wave the crests and troughs of the component waves almost coincide, and by reinforcing one another cause a specially marked air disturbance in the compound wave (10, 11, 12, 1a in diagram). If the two component notes had frequencies of 256 and 384 respectively, this marked disturbance in the compound wave would recur with a frequency of 128, *i.e.* the difference between 384 and 256, and this gives rise to a third tone, known as the difference tone, which in this case would be an octave below the component of lesser frequency. Such difference tones, though very faint, can be detected by a trained ear.

If the two component frequencies are numerically close together, it is evident that the difference frequency will be very low, and may be below the limit of about 20 cycles, at which air disturbances begin to form musical tones. When this is the case, the effect of the difference frequency is to produce rhythmic waxings and wanings of the compound sound which are known as beats. The closer the frequencies of two simultaneously sounding tones, the slower the beats, until with perfect unison beats disappear together. This phenomenon is used by tuners to bring two sound-producing instruments to exactly the same pitch.

Resonance – If a tone of a certain frequency is produced close to a stationary stretched string (or any other form of sound-producer) of the same fundamental frequency, the string or other sound-producer will be set into vibration by the sound-waves impingeing upon it. Similarly, the sound produced by a tuning-fork or other source may be intensified by the proximity of a hollow vessel containing an air-column whose natural period of vibration corresponds with that of the source of sound. This phenomenon of resonance or homorhythmia requires for its complete exhibition an exact correspondence in frequency between the sound-producer and resonator. A certain much smaller sympathetic vibrational effect is obtained with a resonator whose natural frequency is a harmonic of the sounding body, but none at all where there is no relation between the frequencies. This phenomenon of resonance is, of course, not limited to sound-waves, but is to be found in all types of oscillatory motion.

Damping – This is a term applied to any method of hastening the rate at which a vibrating body normally loses its vibrating movement, *e.g.* the application of the finger to a 'ringing' glass.

The human ear is an apparatus which has a wide range of capabilities in the differentiation of various kinds of air disturbances.

(1) It distinguishes between a musical sound and a noise.

(2) It differentiates, as loudness, between varying amplitude of air-waves. The limiting amplitude detectable is amazingly small—Rayleigh, in estimating the variation in air-pressure in a just audible sound-wave to be 6×10^{-9} atmospheres, says : "The result shows that the ear is able to recognise the addition and subtraction of densities far less than those to be found in our highest vacua."

(3) It appreciates as musical tones air disturbances of frequencies between about 20 cycles and 30,000 cycles, these limits varying somewhat in different individuals. The number of separately distinguished tones within the range has been estimated at 1500 to 2000, the best discrimination being found within the range 500 to 4000 cycles. The trained ear of a musician is said to be able to detect a difference in frequency of only $\frac{1}{64}$ of a semitone. In the neighbourhood of C'' (512 cycles), this means a difference of only half a cycle per second. Most individuals can detect a difference of 2 cycles at this pitch.

(4) When a single musical note is produced, the trained ear can pick out several of the overtones and place these overtones with respect to their intervals from the fundamental. The untrained ear recognises the presence or absence of overtones as differences in the quality of the sound.

(5) In a combination of two or more tones sounding simultaneously, the trained ear can not only detect the individual components, but also certain difference tones.

Let us see now what explanations have been offered of the working of such a wonderfully discriminating mechanism.

Anatomically, the ear consists of three parts. The external ear comprises the pinna and external auditory meatus, and at the internal end of the meatus is the tympanic membrane dividing the external from the middle ear. The middle ear consists of a cavity hollowed out of the petrous part of the temporal bone. This cavity is in communication with the pharynx through the Eustachian tube and contains the ossicles (malleus, incus, and stapes), along with two small muscles, the tensor tympani and the stapedius. The line along which each of these muscles acts is shown in the diagram (fig. 78).

The internal ear consists of a tubular cavity, also in the petrous part of the temporal bone. The cavity makes two and a half turns in a spiral direction around a central pillar of bone, called the modiolus. (For clearness, the cochlea has been represented in the figure as if almost completely uncoiled.) Within this bony cavity lies a membranous tube, the duct of the cochlea or scala media. The cochlear duct by no means fills the cross-section of the bony tube, but, closely applied to the

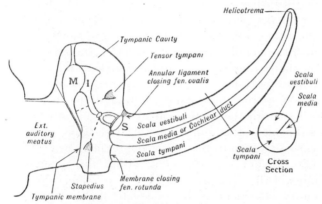

FIG. 78—Schematic diagram of ear with cochlea uncoiled

M, malleus; I, incus; S, stapes. The dotted lines show the direction of action of the ossicular muscles. Inset, cross-section of cochlea

outer wall of the tube, it stretches about half-way across and is met by a bony shelf, the spiral lamina, which projects outwards from the central modiolus. In this way the cross-section of the bony tube is divided into three portions, as shown in the inset of the diagram, the cochlear duct being one, and the other two the scala vestibuli and scala tympani. At the base of the spiral, both these scalæ would open into the tympanic cavity were it not that the openings are occupied, in the vestibular scala by the foot-plate of the stapes and its annular ligament, and in the scala tympani by the membrane of the fenestra rotunda. At the base of the spiral, the cochlear duct is continuous through the saccule and utricle with the semicircular canals. At the upper end of the spiral it ends blindly just short of the ending of the bony tube, so that at this point there is a small communication, known as the helicotrema, between the scala vestibuli and scala tympani. The whole of the internal ear is filled with fluid—the vestibular and tympanic scalæ by perilymph, and the scala media by endolymph. Further consideration of the structure of the cochlea will be left until we come to deal with its function. Meantime we will deal with the functioning of the outer and of the middle ear.

Briefly, these constitute a transmitting mechanism whereby the air disturbances are converted into alterations of the pressure of the perilymph at the base of the scala vestibuli. The alternate condensations and rarefactions of the air which constitute the sound-wave impinge on the tympanic membrane. This is thereby given a to-and-fro movement, a movement which must be followed by the malleus, because its handle is attached to the membrane. Through the articulation of the malleus with the incus, and of the incus with the stapes, the movement is transmitted to this last bone, which, by its ligamentous fixation to the rim of the foramen ovale, is allowed a certain amount of movement within that opening. The vibrations of the tympanic membrane are thus converted into a vibratory movement of the foot-plate of the stapes, which in turn sets up fluid pulsations in the perilymph of the scala vestibuli.

Each component part of this transmitting chain exhibits a number of adaptations to its particular function.

The External Ear – The pinna in many animals is trumpet-shaped, and capable of a considerable amount of muscular movement. By altering the direction of the pinna until the sound is heard at maximum intensity, the animal may not only obtain a more efficient collection of the sound-waves, but may localise the source of the sound. In man the pinna is practically immovable, and the trumpet flattened until it appears only as irregularities of surface. It can be shown, however, that these irregularities still play some part in aiding the collection of sound-waves, for, if the hollows are filled up with wax, leaving only the entrance to the meatus free, both the intensity and quality of sounds are impaired. The external auditory meatus conducts the sound-waves by repeated re-flection from its walls, in such a manner that they impinge

almost perpendicularly on the tympanic membrane, although
the latter is set obliquely to the axis of the canal.

The tympanic membrane consists of a layer of fibrous
tissue covered, on its external side, by a continuation of the
epithelial lining of the external auditory meatus, and on its
internal surface by the mucous membrane of the tympanic
cavity.   The fibrous layer is composed of fibres running
radially from the umbo to the region where the membrane
is attached to the bony wall of the meatus.   There are also
concentrically arranged circular fibres more marked at some
parts of the membrane than others.   Helmholtz first drew
attention to the fact that, while the membrane shows a general
concavity towards the external auditory meatus, there is also
a slight convexity in the same direction near the periphery.
If this convexity were absent, the inward travel of the membrane in response to a phase of increased air-pressure in the
sound-wave could only occur by the stretching of the radial
fibres.   The provision of this convexity allows the inward displacement of the membrane to take place by a straightening
out of this curvature, and thus the membrane is made more
sensitive to waves of small amplitude.   But the double curvature probably serves a further purpose.   One of the troubles
with all diaphragms for sound-recording or sound-producing
instruments is that they have a natural period of vibration of
their own, and if this natural frequency lies within the range of
audible tones, the diaphragm will tend to record or produce to
excess those tones which have a frequency at or near its own.
Such resonance peaks are avoided in the tympanic membrane
by the presence of this double curvature of its surface and by
the irregular distribution of tension in its component fibres, so
that different parts of the membrane have different natural
frequencies of vibration.   The reader may recall the attempts
in some cone loud-speakers to avoid resonance peaks by
making one part of the cone stiffer than the remainder.   Aperio-
dicity in the tympanic membrane is further helped by the
damping produced by its being loaded with the malleus and,
through the malleus, with the other components of the
transmitting chain.

The Middle Ear – Of especial interest in the middle ear are the malleo-incal articulation, the arrangement of the ossicles as a system of levers, the method of fixation of the stapes in the fenestra ovalis, and the two ossicular muscles, the tensor tympani and the stapedius. The malleus and incus are so attached by ligaments to the tympanic cavity that they can only rotate around a horizontal axis (fig. 79) passing through (1) the anterior ligament of the malleus, (2) the lower part of the head of the malleus, (3) the body of the incus, and (4) the short process of the incus. When the handle of the malleus moves inward with inward movement of the tympanic membrane, the parts of the malleus and incus above this axis must move outward. The long process of the incus, which extends below the axis, will follow the direction of the handle of the malleus and move inwards, carrying with it the stapes, to which it is articulated. The outward movement of the tympanic membrane will be followed by the reverse series of changes. At the malleo-incal articulation the malleus is provided with a small tooth-like process which engages with the body of the incus. The presence of this tooth is believed to prevent the incus and stapes from following a sudden excessive outward movement of the tympanic membrane, such as might occur from inflation of the tympanic cavity through the Eustachian tube. While in an *inward* movement of the tympanic membrane the incus is locked to the malleus head by this tooth-like process, in an *outward* movement of the membrane the malleus and the incus may separate from one another and a certain amount of relative motion between the two be permitted.

The stapes is fixed into the fenestra ovalis by an annular ligament. This ligament, though very narrow all round, is, according to the measurements of Guibe and Eysell, six and a half times broader anteriorly than posteriorly. The result of this eccentric placing of the foot-plate of the stapes in the oval foramen is that its movement is not a direct inward and outward movement, but rather a rotation around the narrower part of the ligament which acts as a hinge (fig. 79). To-and-fro movements of the tympanic membrane are thus converted through malleus and incus into a movement of the stapes that may be compared to the slight opening and closing of a hinged door. It will be observed from fig. 78 that the line

of action of the stapedius muscle is such as to pull the stapes
out of the foramen by a similar movement of rotation.

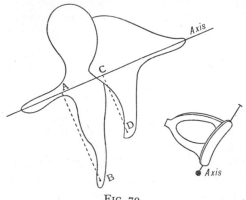

FIG. 79

It is apparent that this transmission of motion from the
tympanic membrane to stapes involves a number of lever-
like actions, resulting in a diminution of the amplitude of the
movement with a corresponding increase in force.   Fig. 79
shows the axis of rotation of malleus and incus, and the relative
distances from the axis to (1) the tip of the handle of the malleus,
and (2) the tip of the long process of the incus.   The relation
between these two lengths AB : CD is as 3 : 2, so that the
movement of D will only be two-thirds of the movement of
B.   Further, the movement of D is transmitted to the stapes
in a line which is not perpendicular to the plane of the foot-
plate, and this, combined with the fact that the stapedial movement is a rotary one, reduces still more the movement of the
foot-plate, and hence also the displacement of perilymph.   The
amount of the reduction has been estimated at 2 to 1, so that
altogether the effective movement of the stapedial foot-plate is
$\frac{2}{3} \times \frac{1}{2}$, or $\frac{1}{3}$ that of the tympanic membrane.   The force with
which the stapedial foot-plate is moved will, correspondingly,
be three times the force of displacement of the tympanic membrane.   Another factor has still to be considered.   The transmission system of the ear is essentially a mechanism for trans-
forming changes of air-pressure to changes of fluid-pressure in
the perilymph.   The area of the tympanic membrane is about

21

twenty times that of the foot-plate of the stapes, so that the pressure per unit of area in the perilymph, from this cause alone, will be twenty times the pressure per unit of area on the tympanic membrane. This, added to the mechanical advantage obtained through the system of levers will, if we neglect frictional losses at the various articulations, therefore give a total increase of effective pressure from membrane to foot-plate of 60 to 1.

It might be supposed from the above description that the movement of the ossicular chain is of a visible order, but this is far from being the case. The actual movements of the transmitting mechanism in the reception of sound-waves are extraordinarily small. Observations of the maximum movement of the handle of the malleus, when movements of the tympanic membrane are artificially produced by inflation of the tympanic cavity, indicate that the maximum displacement of the stapes under these conditions is of the order of 0·06 mm. The movement in response to sounds of ordinary intensity must be very much smaller, and with weak tones the stapedial movements are probably ultramicroscopic.

There remain for consideration the two ossicular muscles. The tensor tympani, arising from a groove just above the Eustachian tube, is inserted into the neck of the malleus just below the axis of rotation. Its contraction (fig. 78) will draw the tympanic membrane inwards. The stapedius, arising from the wall of the tympanic cavity, is inserted into the neck of the stapes. Its action, as we have already seen, is to rotate the stapes so as to draw the foot-plate out of the fenestra ovalis. Since the tensor tympani, by drawing the handle of the malleus inwards, will, through the incus, tend to force the stapes further into the fenestra, and the action of the stapedius is to rotate the stapes outwards, it is evident that these two muscles are antagonistic to one another. Considerable speculation and controversy has been aroused as to the exact function of these little muscles. The most probable view seems to be that they form a sort of adjustable spring-loading to the whole transmitting mechanism. Their supposed action may perhaps be best appreciated from a consideration of the following simple model. AB (fig. 80) is a rod running easily on the pulleys *d* and *e*, and carrying at A a large disc representing the tympanic membrane, and at B a smaller disc representing the stapes. From a fixed point C extend springs under tension to each disc, that on the left representing the tensor tympani, that on the right the stapedius. In such a model the rod when at rest will be held in a certain zero position by the antagonistic actions of the springs. In the same way the normal tone of the ossicular muscles will hold the tympanic membrane, ossicles, and stapes in their zero position, and will tend to return them to this position when they have been displaced from it by either the condensation or rarefaction phase of the sound-wave. Returning to the model, we see that a movement of

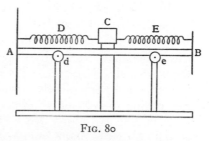

FIG. 80

the rod to the right, while hindered by spring E, will be assisted by the tension of D, and a movement of the rod in the reverse direction will be aided by E and hindered by D. A to-and-fro movement of the rod, such as could be produced by sound-waves falling on the disc at A, will occur most readily when the vibration periods of the springs are made to correspond with the frequency of the sound-waves impingeing on the disc. An analogous action is quite possible in the ear muscles. The tone of these muscles is under reflex control, and by the appropriate adjustment of their tone, the transmitting system of membrane and ossicles could be adjusted so as to respond most sensitively to vibrations of the particular frequency being received at the time. Hensen has, in fact, observed that the tensor tympani does reflexly contract in response to sound vibrations, and the higher the pitch of the sound falling on the ear, the greater its contraction. The mechanism may act in the reverse direction as well, for the rejection of unwanted sounds or for diminishing the effectiveness of transmission of over-loud sounds, by throwing the natural period of the transmitting mechanism out of resonance with the received sound. The muscles then would have a damping effect on the vibratory movements of the ossicles, just as, in the model, the presence

of two springs of hetero-rhythmic period would tend to prevent
the oscillatory motion of the rod.

The cavity of the middle ear is connected with the pharynx
by means of the Eustachian tube.   This connection maintains
the pressures within the tympanic cavity at atmospheric value.
The pressures on the two sides of the tympanic membrane are
thus equalised, and no hindrance is offered to the free vibrations of the tympanic membrane.   Moreover, when the
membrane is pushed in or withdrawn by the alternate pressure
changes in a sound-wave, the presence of atmospheric pressure
within the tympanic cavity aids in returning the membrane to
its zero position.   The pharyngeal opening of the Eustachian
tube is normally closed, but opens during the act of swallowing.
If it remained permanently open, the vibrations of one's own
voice during speech and singing would probably be conducted
to the middle ear and heard with unpleasant intensity.   The
necessity for its periodic opening as a means of equalising the
pressures on the two sides of the tympanic membrane is
illustrated by the impairment of hearing that results when the
Eustachian tube is blocked by an extension of a nasal catarrh.
Also, rapid changes in external air-pressure, such as are experienced in aeroplane ascents, or on entering a caisson where the
pressure is higher than atmospheric, cause deafness and unpleasant sensations in the ear, which are immediately relieved
by the equalisation of pressure produced by swallowing.

The Internal Ear – Such is the mechanism by which the
disturbances of air-pressure which constitute sound-waves are
converted into fluid-pressure disturbances of similar wave-form
in the perilymph of the scala vestibuli.   Before we pursue their
further course we must take up some points in the minute
anatomy of the cochlea.   Fig. 81 shows a cross-section of the
internal ear similar to the inset of fig. 78, but on a larger scale.
The section is diagrammatic, but indicates sufficiently well the
important functional features.

An osseous shelf known as the spiral lamina projects into
the bony tube.   The cochlear duct, as shown in the diagram,
is triangular in section, and has one of its sides closely applied
to a portion of the outer wall of the bony tube.   The other
two sides are formed respectively by Reissner's membrane

and by the basilar membrane. Both of these meet, and are affixed to, the edge of the spiral lamina, thus completing the division of the bony tube into the three compartments, the perilymph-filled vestibular and tympanic scalæ, and the endolymph-filled cochlear duct.

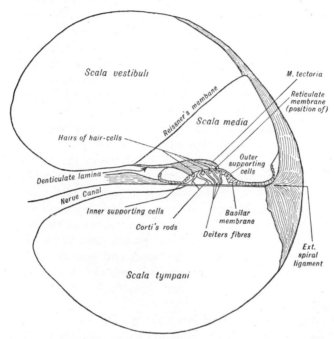

FIG. 81—Section across one of the coils of the cochlea (semi-diagrammatic)

The basilar membrane is a fibrous elastic structure carrying on its upper surface the organ of Corti, which consists, from the spiral lamina outwards, of a series of (1) inner supporting cells; (2) an inner hair cell; (3) the two rods of Corti enclosing between them the arch of Corti; (4) three to five more hair cells with a supporting structure between each pair—these structures are known as Deiter's fibres, and resemble Corti's rods; (5) a mass of outer supporting cells. There are rows and rows of such structures set on the basilar membrane throughout its whole length from base to apex of the spiral.

On top of these structures there extends a very thin membrane, the membrana reticularis, which is pierced with holes through which the cilia of the hair cells protrude. Extending from the denticulate lamina of the spiral shelf is a thick gelatinous membrane, the membrana tectoria, which, though unattached to Corti's organ in the ordinary dehydrated specimen, is, in the fresh condition, closely applied to the upper surface of the organ of Corti, with the cilia of the hair cells embedded in it. The branches of the auditory nerve, which enters the cochlea through the central modiolus, are carried in the spiral lamina to be distributed to both inner and outer hair cells.

One other structure remains to be mentioned, the external spiral ligament. This is a fan-shaped ridge of fibres which forms the outer attachment of the basilar membrane. Both basilar membrane and this external spiral ligament show a progressive change in size from the base to the apex of the cochlea. At the base the basilar membrane is relatively narrow and the external spiral ligament well developed. Successive sections toward the apex show a gradual broadening of the basilar membrane and a gradual diminution in the thickness of the external ligament. If the basilar membrane could be removed from the cochlea, unwound, and spread out in a flat sheet, it would form a trapezoidal area about $\frac{1}{6}$ mm. broad at the narrow (basal) end and $\frac{1}{2}$ mm. broad at the wider (apical) end.

We are now in a position to consider one or two of the theories that have been formulated to account for the capacity of sound analysis. That which has probably been most generally accepted and seems to have most to commend it is the resonance theory. That resonance might be the basis of tone perception was suggested by Cotugno as early as 1761, but the resonance theory is usually identified with the name of Helmholtz, who, in his *Sensations of Tone* (1861), first propounded a connected theory on this basis. It has been modified and further developed by Wilkinson and Gray.

According to the resonance theory, the fibres of the basilar membrane form a series of stretched strings, each one of which responds by sympathetic vibration to those tones that correspond exactly or very nearly in frequency with its own natural period of vibration. The air-waves, turned into fluid vibrations in the perilymph, thus set into vibration the area of basilar membrane made up of those fibres which correspond in frequency most nearly to the frequency of the air-waves. Low tones would cause the fibres at the apex to vibrate, and high tones those at the base.

Perception that certain of the fibres of the basilar membrane have been set into vibration is then brought about in the following way. That portion of the organ of Corti, attached to the vibrating basilar fibres, will also undergo a vibratory up-and-down movement, pulling the membrana tectoria with it. The hinge on which the organ of Corti executes this movement is placed just at the foot of the inner rod of Corti, where the basilar membrane joins the lamina spiralis. The hinge on which the tectorial membrane rotates is placed, however, at the edge of the denticulate lamina. The centres of the arcs of movement of these two adherent portions are not the same, the radius of the arc through which the tectorial membrane moves being the larger. During vibration, in addition to movement of the organ as a whole, relative movement will therefore occur between the upper surface of the organ of Corti and the tectorial membrane, and this will result in the bending of the hairs of the hair cells. The stimulation of the hair cells then gives rise to a nervous impulse in the auditory nerve fibres connected to them. Vibration in any one part of the basilar membrane will thus stimulate only one set of auditory nerve fibres, and, through them, only that portion of the cerebral cortex connected thereto. The stimulation of a definite cortical area will by experience be associated with the reception of a note of a particular pitch.

The objection may be raised at this point that since even a pure tone stimulates not one single fibre of the basilar membrane but sets a localised area of several fibres into vibration, how is it that the cortical interpretation of such a sensory disturbance is that of a pure tone? Gray points out, however, that a similar effect is produced in skin sensations. If light pressure is applied to a certain point of the skin, we localise it to that point. Increase the pressure even

to the extent of visibly depressing the surrounding area of
skin, and we still localise the pressure to the point of maximum pressure.   Similarly in the ear, the perceived frequency
of vibration would be identified with the point of maximum
vibration of the basilar membrane.

One of the difficulties that has always been felt in accepting the resonance theory is the extremely minute size of the
resonating structures, the fibres of the basilar membrane.   At
the broadest part of the membrane they are only $\frac{1}{2}$ mm. long,
and at the narrowest about $\frac{1}{6}$ mm.   In comparison with
any similar mechanism of human manufacture, it seems
impossible to conceive of such minute fibres reacting by
sympathetic vibration to a range as large as the ten or eleven
octaves that are comprised within the limits of human audi-
bility.   It is mainly towards the removal of this difficulty that
the efforts of Wilkinson and Gray have been directed.

The formula for the frequency of vibration of a string is

$$n=\frac{1}{2l}\sqrt{\frac{t}{m}},$$

where n=frequency, l=length of string, t=tension, and
m=mass per unit length.   In words, the frequency varies
inversely as the length, directly as the square root of the tension,
and inversely as the square root of the mass per unit length.
Let us apply this formula to the fibres of the basilar membrane.
The fibres vary in length in the ratio of one to three, but
this would account only for a pitch variation of one and a
half octaves.   Wilkinson and Gray point out, however, that
there is also certainly a differentiation in mass of the vibrating structure, and probably also a differentiation in tension, and
that these differentiations are in the same sense as the obvious
length differentiation;   that is, the resonators of lowest frequency are at the apex of the cochlea, and those of highest
frequency at the base.   The difference in mass arises from
the fact that the resonating element is composed not of fibre
alone, but of fibre *plus* its attached organ of Corti, and *plus*
the sectional column of fluid existing between it and the
fenestra ovalis on the one hand, and the fenestra rotunda
on the other.   The length of this vibrating fluid column will

be small when the vibrating section is at the foot of the cochlea, where the two foramina are close together, and longest at the apical end, from which both foramina are most distant. The shortest strings are thus most lightly loaded and the longest strings most heavily loaded. Taking the distance between the two foramina as 2 mm. at the base of the cochlea and 40 mm. as the shortest distance from the foramen ovalis to the helicotrema and back to the foramen rotunda, there would be a relative difference in loading at base and at apex of cochlea of 1 : 20. The variation in frequency accounted for by this variation in mass alone would be $1 : \sqrt{20}$, or approximately a little more than two octaves. Adding the variation due to the difference in length of the fibres of the membrane, the total variation allowed by the two factors of mass and length would account for about three and a half octaves. The remaining seven octaves must be accounted for by variations in tension, and, as the agent of this tension variation, Wilkinson and Gray put forward the external spiral ligament. Certainly this body does diminish in bulk progressively from base to apex, and therefore is presumably graded in tensional strength so as to favour resonance to high frequencies at the base and low at the apex; but, from the formula, it may be calculated that the required gradation for seven octaves is from 1 to 16,384, and it is difficult to conceive of a fibrous structure of such small dimensions being differentiated in tension to such a degree.

At the same time, the resonance theory has a certain amount of experimental and clinical evidence to support it. The former consists of experiments first done by Witmaack and repeated since by other workers, in which animals were subjected to long-continued sounds of different pitch, and the cochlea was examined post-mortem for degenerative changes. Continued stimulation by high-pitched notes was found to be associated with degenerations in the lower whorl of the cochlea, while the lower tones produced degenerative changes at the apex.

The following is some of the clinical evidence. Deafness to sounds over a certain frequency-range often occurs in boiler-makers and others whose occupations subject them to continued loud noises; in such conditions, the defective part of the range corresponds more or less closely to the frequencies of the noises in which they work.   The sensitivity of the ear is not equal for different frequencies in normal individuals, there being maxima and minima quite irregularly placed throughout the whole audible range; this is quite explicable on the resonance theory.   It also offers a possible explanation of the curious condition of 'double disharmonious hearing,' sometimes met with as a congenital condition, and sometimes as a transient phenomenon in inflammatory conditions resulting in the blockage of the Eustachian tube.   In this condition, the same tone has a different pitch when heard by each ear separately. When congenital, it might be due to an asymmetrical arrangement of the basilar fibres of the two ears as regards any of the factors that determine their resonance frequencies.

From the point of view of comparative anatomy, the resonance theory is not altogether satisfactory.   The mammalian cochlea which has been described consists of a comparatively long basilar membrane with many Corti organ units containing four hair cells per unit.   In the birds, the basilar membrane is short, containing relatively few units, each of which possesses some thirty or forty hair cells.   On anatomical grounds, therefore, birds should have a shorter audible range of frequencies and a greater acuity of hearing than a mammal.   Evidence that this holds as a general rule is lacking.

An objection raised to the resonance theory is that the basilar fibres are not free strings fixed only at their ends, but are also attached laterally to one another, so that their individual vibration would be impossible.   Individual vibration is not, however, postulated, but a vibration of a section of membrane which is at a maximum in the region of one particular fibre and diminishes on either side of this maximum —a vibration of this type would not be made impossible by the lateral attachment of the fibres, provided the longitudinal tension of the membrane as a whole were small, as compared with the tension on each fibre from spiral lamina to external spiral ligament.

Another theory of hearing that has received considerable attention is the so-called 'telephone' theory originated by

Rutherford in 1886, and more recently elaborated by Sir Thomas Wrightson and supported by Sir Arthur Keith. In Wrightson's theory, the vibratory motion is not limited to a localised area of the basilar membrane and to the segments of fluid between that area and the two scalar foramina, but, no matter what the frequency of the impingeing note, the perilymph, endolymph, and basilar membrane throughout the whole extent of the cochlea are set into motion by the stapes, and execute a movement which in wave-form is the exact counterpart of that of the air-wave acting on the membrana tympani. The hair cells are stimulated in a manner similar to that already described, but all the hair cells are stimulated simultaneously. The analysis of the sound received is then performed entirely by the cerebral auditory centre from the frequency and character of the nerve impulses transmitted by the flexing of the hairs of the hair cells. How severe an imposition on the cortex this implies will be apparent from the following. According to Wrightson, a nerve impulse is transmitted each time a hair is (1) bent to the left, (2) reaches its zero position, (3) bent to the right, and (4) again reaches the zero position, these points corresponding in the air-pressure curve (fig. 75) with the maxima of positive and negative pressure and the points of crossing the mean pressure line. Now, if the reader will refer to fig. 77 he will find that this will mean for the transmission of a pure tone of 256 cycles, 1024 nerve impulses per second; for a pure tone of 384 cycles, 1536 impulses per second; and for the compound tone of the two frequencies sounding together, also a recording of 1536 impulses per second. But, in the last case, in order that we may appreciate these 1536 impulses as the product of a compound tone, they must be differentiated both according to the time-interval between them, and according to the amplitude of hair movement which produced them. This example is a comparatively simple case involving low frequencies. A more complex combination of higher frequencies would lay a much heavier burden of analysis on the cortex. Apart from the difficulty of conceiving how analysis is effected at all, Adrian's recent findings that the frequency of sensory nerve impulses in general is, at the most, of the order of a hundred per second or so, seems conclusive evidence against the Wrightson view.

The theory of Ewald may also be briefly mentioned.   Ewald constructed an 'acoustic camera,' consisting of a box filled with water and divided into two by a slotted brass plate.   A very thin rubber membrane was stretched over the slot and illuminated through a glass window in the box.   Each apartment of the box was provided with a membrane-covered opening, representing respectively the oval and round windows. On placing a vibrating tuning-fork close to the oval window, and observing the surface of the membrane through a microscope, one can see that the vibrations transmitted through the fluid produce a series of 'standing waves' on the membrane surface.   The action is analogous to the patterns that may be produced on a vibrating plate covered with a light powder; the powder is driven off the vibrating parts and accumulates at the nodes, thus producing a patterned figure.   The pattern of standing waves in Ewald's experiment was found to vary according to the pitch of the fork used.   Ewald believes that similar patterns of standing waves are produced in the basilar membrane by the vibrations transmitted through the perilymph and endolymph, and that only the hair cells corresponding to these points of surface disturbance are stimulated.   With different frequencies, different sound patterns will be produced and different sets of auditory nerve fibres stimulated.   There is not much anatomical basis for this speculation, for Ewald's rubber membrane equally stretched in all directions is fundamentally unlike the basilar membrane with its fibres graduated in length, load, and probably tension.

Localisation of Sound – Many animals localise sound by moving the pinna about until the sound is heard with maximum intensity.   In human beings localisation depends partly on the relative intensities of the sound in the two ears, but perhaps more on the phase difference in the air disturbances reaching each ear.   If the source of sound is directly in front of the head, the distance from source to each ear is equal, and the air disturbances will be 'in phase,' *i.e.* the incidence of 'crest' and 'trough' in the sound-waves will be synchronous on the two tympanic membranes.   If the source be to one side of the head, the sound has farther to travel to one ear than to the other, and the air disturbances incident on each tympanum, and consequently the movements of each ear's transmitting mechanism, will be out of phase. The effect may be demonstrated by conveying the sound of a tuning-fork to each ear separately through two rubber tubes. If the tubes are of equal length the sound is localised in front of the head, but if they are unequal, it seems to come from the side of the shorter tube.

Bone Conduction – It is not essential for the reception of sensations of sound that the transmitting system of the ear should be functioning, for sound vibrations may be conducted directly to the cochlea by means of the bones of the skull. When hearing is defective, this bone conduction can be used as a diagnostic measure to discover in what part of the ear the defect lies. If a vibrating tuning-fork is applied to one of the cranial bones and the note is heard distinctly, it may be assumed that the internal ear is in order, and that the defect is to be found in the transmitting apparatus. If the defective condition is such as to produce an immobility of the stapes, bone-conducted sounds are heard with even greater intensity than in a normal ear. An individual so affected in one ear only, will hear a tuning-fork placed on the mid-line of the skull louder in the affected ear than in the normal ear. A similar phenomenon may be observed in a normal individual when one ear is plugged with cotton-wool. The explanation of this result is that, when the stapes is rigid, the vibrations transmitted from the skull bones to the perilymph are forced to travel across the basilar membrane, while when the stapes is free, it also will be set in motion, and a portion of the energy of the vibrations in the perilymph is dissipated.

REFERENCES

A BOOK of this kind hardly warrants a detailed list of references, but to the reader who wishes to pursue the subject of any chapter, the following short list of books and papers may be a convenience.

(A) PHYSICAL CHEMISTRY

General

FINDLAY, *Physical Chemistry for Students of Medicine*, Longmans, Green & Co.

KERRIDGE, *Principles of Physical Chemistry for Medical Students*, Oxford University Press.

STEEL, *Physical Chemistry and Biophysics for Students of Biology and Medicine*, Wiley & Sons.

Structure of Matter

ANDRADE, *The Mechanism of Nature*, Bell & Sons.

THOMSON, G. P., *The Atom*, Thornton Butterworth.

Surface Action

BAYLISS, *Interfacial Forces and Phenomena in Physiology*, Methuen.

ADAM, *The Physics and Chemistry of Surfaces*, Clarendon Press.

Osmotic Pressure

FINDLAY, *Osmotic Pressure*, Longmans, Green & Co.

Hydrogen-ion Concentration

CLARK, *The Determination of Hydrogen Ions*, Baillière, Tindal & Cox.

MICHAELIS, *Die Wasserstoffionenkonzentration*, Berlin.

Colloids

HATSCHEK, *An Introduction to the Physics and Chemistry of Colloids*, Churchill.

FREUNDLICH, *The Elements of Colloidal Chemistry*, Methuen.

OSTWALD, *A Handbook of Colloid Chemistry*, Churchill.

(B) PHYSIOLOGY

General

BAYLISS, *Principles of General Physiology*, Longmans, Green & Co.

BURNS, *An Introduction to Biophysics*, Churchill.

McCLENDON and MEDES, *Physical Chemistry in Biology and Medicine*, Saunders.

334

(B) PHYSIOLOGY—*continued*

Enzymes

BAYLISS, *The Nature of Enzyme Action*, Longmans, Green & Co.

HALDANE, J. B. S., *Enzymes*, Longmans, Green & Co.

OPPENHEIMER, *Die Fermente*, Leipzig.

EULER, *Allgemeine Chemie der Enzyme*, Wiesbaden.

Cell and Cell-Membrane

McCLENDON and MEDES, *Physical Chemistry in Biology and Medicine*, Saunders.

BAYLISS, *Principles of General Physiology*, Longmans, Green & Co.

LEATHES, " The Rôle of Fats in Vital Phenomena " (Croonian Lectures), *Lancet*, 1925, 1.

Secretion

VINCENT, SWALE, *An Introduction to the Study of Secretion*, Arnold.

BAYLISS, *Principles of General Physiology*, Longmans, Green & Co.

Blood

BARCROFT, *The Respiratory Function of the Blood*, Cambridge University Press.

HALDANE, *Respiration*, Oxford University Press.

HENDERSON, L. J., *Blood*, Lippincott.

Excitability

EVANS, LOVATT, *Recent Advances in Physiology*, Churchill.

ADRIAN, *The Basis of Sensation*, Christophers.

LAPICQUE, *L'Excitabilité en fonction du temps*, Les Presses Universitaires de France (for chronaxie).

LEWIS, *The Mechanism and Graphic Registration of the Heart-beat*, Shaw & Son (for electrocardiograph).

Muscle

EVANS, LOVATT, *Recent Advances in Physiology*, Churchill.

HILL, A. V., *Muscular Movement in Man : The Factors Governing Speed and Recovery from Fatigue*, McGraw-Hill Book Co.

—— *Lectures on Certain Aspects of Biochemistry*, University of London Press.

MEYERHOF, *ChemicalDynamics of Life Phenomena*, Lippincott.

HILL, A. V., *Journ. of Physiol.*, 1922, lvi, 19.

HILL, A. V., HARTREE, LEVIN and WYMAN, LONG, LUPTON, FURUSAWA, GARNER, and others. Papers in *Proc. Roy. Soc.*, 1924, B, 96 onwards.

(B) PHYSIOLOGY—*continued*

Energy Exchange

Lusk, *The Science of Nutrition*, Saunders.

Benedict and Carpenter, *Carnegie Institution of Washington*, Publication No. 123, 1910.

Loewy, in Oppenheimer's *Handbuch der Biochemie*, Jena.

Work and Efficiency

(a) *Muscle*

Benedict and Cathcart, *Carnegie Institution of Washington*, Publication No. 187, 1913.

(b) *Heart*

Evans, Lovatt, *Recent Advances in Physiology*, Churchill, 1st ed.

—— *Journ. of Physiol.*, 1912, xlv, 213 ; 1918, lii, 6.

—— and Matsuoka, *Journ. of Physiol.*, 1915, xlix, 378.

(c) *Glands*

Barcroft, *The Respiratory Function of the Blood*, 1st ed., Cambridge University Press.

Bayliss, *Principles of General Physiology*, Longmans, Green & Co.

Cushny, *The Secretion of Urine*, Longmans, Green & Co.

Eye

Hartridge, in Starling's *Principles of Physiology*, Churchill.

Ear

Wilkinson and Gray, *The Mechanism of the Cochlea*, Macmillan.

Wrightson, *The Analytical Mechanism of the Internal Ear*, Macmillan.

INDEX

α-RAYS, 4.
Abderhalden, 146.
Aberration, chromatic, 291.
   spherical, 291.
Absolute zero, 13, 25.
Accommodation, 287.
Acid, effect on oxyhæmoglobin
   dissociation curve, 165.
   lactic and muscle, 217.
Acidosis, 185.
   compensated and uncompen-
     sated, 186.
Activator, 137.
Adair, 169.
Adam, 42.
Adrian, 204, 205, 331.
Adsorption, 38.
   and enzymes, 131, 133, 138.
   and osmosis, 113, 142.
   electrical, 39.
   quantitative aspect of, 40.
After-image, 303.
Agar-bridge, 102.
Aggregation, 56.
   of hæmoglobin, 168.
Alignment chart, 181.
Alkali-tolerance, 189.
Alkaline reserve, 184.
Alkalosis, 185.
' All or nothing ' law, 192.
Amagat, 28.
Amicron, 109.
Amphoteric electrolytes, 77.
Anelectrotonus, 191.
Angle of capillarity, 36.
Ångström unit, 273.
Anisotropic, 216, 217.
Anrep, 160.
Anti-enzyme, 138.
Aortic stenosis, 259.
Armstrong, 133.
Arrhenius, 49, 56, 58, 61.
Arthus, 130.
Asher, 269.
Astigmatism, 295.
Atom, structure of, 8.

Atomic number, 8.
Atwater, 241.
Atzler, 254.
Autocatalysis, 129.
Avogadro's law, 26.
   number, 61, 111.

β-RAYS, 5.
Barcroft, 165, 268, 271, 272.
Basilar membrane, 325, 326, 328.
Bayliss, 138, 159.
Beats, 314.
Bechhold, 110.
Beckmann, 49.
Becquerel, 4.
Benedict, 255.
Berkeley, 53.
Bernouilli, 22.
Bert, 164.
Bethe, 147, 152.
Biltz, 145.
Bimolecular reaction, 69.
Binocular vision, 307.
Blood, 162.
   pH of, 88, 104, 105, 179.
     calculation of, 188.
     direct determination of, 188.
     pathological variation of, 185.
Bohr, 164.
Boiling-point, 32.
Bomb calorimeter, 238.
Bone conduction, 333.
Boyle's law, 25.
Bradford, 159.
Bragg, 44.
Brodie, 272.
Brownian movement, 111, 142.
Buffer mixtures, 87.
Buffers, 75.

CALOMEL half-cell, 101.
Calorie and calorie, 20.
   value of oxygen, 245, 248.
   values of proteins, carbohydrates,
     and fats, 239, 240.
Calorimeter, bomb, 238.
   respiration, 241.